A Short-title Catalogue
of Household and
Cookery Books published in
the English Tongue
1701-1800

Elizabeth Raffald.

Madam Johnson

Mr. JOHN FARLEY

EDW. KIDDER

These portraits of four eighteenth-century cookery writers are all taken from the books which they wrote.

A Short-title Catalogue of Household and Cookery Books published in the English Tongue 1701–1800

VIRGINIA MACLEAN

PROSPECT BOOKS · LONDON
1981

ISBN 0 907325 06 8

© Virginia Maclean 1981

Published by Prospect Books
45 Lamont Road, London SW10 0HU

Distributed in the USA by
The University Press of Virginia

Printed in Great Britain
at the University Press, Oxford
by Eric Buckley
Printer to the University

CONTENTS

LIST OF ILLUSTRATIONS

All the illustrations of title-pages are taken from the first editions of the books in question, unless otherwise indicated.

The publishers and the author wish to thank the following institutions for providing photographs of the material reproduced. In doing so, they draw attention to the fact that incidental blemishes, ephemeral markings, and the like have been removed from these photographs for the purposes of reproduction. To the Brotherton Library of the University of Leeds: for those on pages xi, 28, 41, 44, 45, 51, 53, 76, 80, 81, 83, 96, 98, 100, 110, 120, and 130; and for three of the portraits (not Mrs Raffald) on the frontispiece. To the National Library of Scotland, Edinburgh: for those on pages xii, 58, and 122. To the Glasgow University Library: for that on page xvi. To the Wellcome Institute for the History of Medicine Library, London: for that on page 126. And to Prospect Books for those on pages 12 and 148.

ACKNOWLEDGEMENTS

I WOULD like to record my thanks to the following people who have given freely of their time and expertise, during the two distinct stages of this work.

From 1974 to 1977 I have had the privilege of being supervised by Professor William Beattie, CBE, the Director of the Institute for Advanced Studies in the Humanities, and by Mr John M. Simpson of the Department of Scottish History, both in the University of Edinburgh. To both I am greatly indebted for their patience, guidance, and valuable suggestions. I must, however, add that any errors are mine alone.

To thank the many librarians, library assistants, cataloguers, and collectors in the British Isles and North America who made this catalogue possible would require a tome. With a few exceptions (all being libraries or institutions who did not even respond to my initial request for assistance, which was in the form of a questionnaire), the number of people concerned include at least one, and in many cases two or three, from every one of the bodies in the 'List of Abbreviations used for Libraries', which follows shortly. I fully acknowledge my indebtedness to all those kind but unnamed people. There remain other very helpful people whom I must not only thank, but also name, as they include those who gave me specific aid; most of them in the libraries I visited in order to carry out vital research.

Dr Edwin Clarke, the Director of The Wellcome Institute for the History of Medicine, London; Dr Marcus E. Crahan, a leading collector of rare household and cookery books, of Los Angeles, California; Miss Phyllis M. Downie, of Edinburgh, the former Reference Librarian in Edinburgh University Library; Miss Joan P. S. Ferguson, Librarian of the Royal College of Physicians of Edinburgh; Mrs Lucille Fillin, a leading collector of cookery books, of Rockville Center, New York; Eric G. Forbes, Professor in the History of Science at Edinburgh University; Miss Jean R. Guild, the present Reference Librarian in Edinburgh University Library; Miss Penny Heath-Eves, Library Assistant in the Woodward Biomedical Library, University of British Columbia, in Vancouver; Dr Alexander Law, OBE, of Edinburgh; Mrs Mary MacDonald, of the School of Scottish Studies at Edinburgh University; Mr D. J. McKitterick, Department of Rare Books, Cambridge University Library; Dr Ailfrid MacLochlainn, Director of the National Library of Ireland, Dublin; Dr Anne Matheson, of the National Library of Scotland, Edinburgh; Mr P. S. Morrish, Sub-Librarian, Brotherton Library, Leeds University; Dr Stephen T. Riley, Director of the Massachusetts Historical Society, Boston, Mass.; Dr Alastair H. T. Robb-Smith, a leading authority on Hannah Glasse, of Woodstock, Oxfordshire; Mr Richard J. Roberts, Keeper of Printed Books at the Bodleian Library, Oxford University; Mrs Jean S. A. Robertson, Reference Librarian in Glasgow University; Miss Elizabeth Shenton, the Assistant to the Director of the Arthur and Elizabeth Schlesinger Library on the History of Women in

America, at Radcliffe College, Cambridge, Massachusetts; Mrs Barbara Feret Schuman, the Librarian of the Culinary Institute of America, Hyde Park, New York; Mr Thomas W. Shaw, Keeper of Printed Books at Guildhall Library in the City of London; Miss Norah E. Smith, Assistant Librarian in Edinburgh University Library; Mr Evan W. Williams, Special Collections Librarian and University Archivist at Kansas State University, Manhattan, Kansas, who was especially kind and helpful; and Miss C. Anne Wilson, Assistant Librarian at the Brotherton Library in Leeds University for introducing me to the John F. Preston collection of English cookery books and the Blanche L. Leigh cookery collection.

I owe a special debt of gratitude to my late husband James, who gave me every encouragement and support, before his untimely death in January 1978.

*   *   *   *   *

It gives me pleasure to extend the above list, and to record my thanks to the following who have given much help and advice. To Mrs Dorothy M. Booma for her kind hospitality in Massachusetts; to Mr and Mrs Robert Platt of Fairfield, Connecticut, for their kindness; to Mr Hamish L. Davidson, Head of the Department of Catering and Hotel Studies, Napier College, Edinburgh; and my colleagues Mrs Elizabeth M. Wood and Miss Mary C. Wyllie; to Mrs Evelyn Bridgeford for so carefully preparing the typescript; to my publishers, Prospect Books; also Ms Caroline Davidson of Prospect Books for kindly arranging for research carried out in Washington, DC.

Finally, a special word of thanks to my brother Richard and sister-in-law Renate for all their encouragement.

Virginia Maclean

Edinburgh, *August 1980*

LIST OF SHORT TITLES
USED FOR FREQUENTLY
CITED SOURCES

Ann.Cat.   *The Annual Catalogue for the years 1736-1737* (with an introduction by David Fairweather Foxon), English Bibliographical Sources, Series 1, No. 5, republished by Gregg-Archive, 1965

Aresty   Esther B. Aresty, *The Delectable Past*, London, 1965. [Bibliographical section only]

BABCat.   A catalogue in a series published by Beeleigh Abbey Books (W. & G. Foyle Limited); being No. BA/20, 'Agriculture and Botany: Medicine: Science and Technology', Maldon, Essex [1975]

B.&G.Cat.   Two catalogues published by Birrell & Garnett Limited, 30 Gerrard Street, London, W.1, each cited with its catalogue number after the short title, as follows: No. 27, 'Domestic Books of All Ages' [c.1931]; and No. 37, 'A Catalogue of Cookery Books from the Collection of J. E. Hodgkin, Esq., Dr. A. W. Oxford and other sources' [c.1934]

Bib.Ann.   *Bibliotheca Annua: The Annual Catalogue for the year 1699; and for the years 1701-1703* (with an intro. by David Fairweather Foxon), English Bibliographical Sources, Series 1, No. 4, republished by Gregg-Archive in 2 vols. (1: 1699; 2: 1701-1703), 1964. The appropriate volume number is cited after short title

Bitting   Katherine Golden Bitting, *Gastronomic Bibliography*, San Francisco, 1939; reprinted Ann Arbor, 1971. The present compiler has used the original 1939 edition

BMCat.   *British Museum General Catalogue of Printed Books*, Photolithographic Edition to 1955, 263 vols., London, 1960-6.

Brit.Mag.   *The British Magazine: 1746-1750* (with an intro. by David Fairweather Foxon), English Bibliographical Sources, Series 1, No. 8, republished by Gregg-Archive, 1965

Christie's Cat.   Catalogues of books offered for sale, published by Messrs Christie's (Christie, Manson, & Woods, Auctioneers, London), various dates. The date of the catalogue referred to is cited after short title

Crahan   Marcus E. Crahan, *One Hundred Sixteen Uncommon Books on Food and Drink*, Berkeley, 1975

DNB   *Dictionary of National Biography*, Sir Leslie Stephen and Sir Sidney Lee (edd.), 21 vols., London, 1908-9

Drexel   Theodor Drexel, *Catalog der Kochbücher-Sammlung von Theodor Drexel*, 6 issues, Frankfurt a.M., 1885-7-8-91. This is the catalogue of Drexel's cookbook collection, of which there were six different issues between 1885 and 1891. The appropriate date is cited after short title

Evans   Charles Evans, *American Bibliography: A Chronological Dictionary of all Books, Pamphlets and Periodical Publications Printed in the United States of America, 1639-1800*, 14 vols., Chicago, 1903-34

Gents.Mag.   *The Gentleman's Magazine* (or *Monthly Intelligencer*), 'Sylvanus Urban' (ed.), Series 1, 103 vols., London, 1731-1833

Hazlitt   William Carew Hazlitt, *Old Cookery Books and Ancient Cuisine*, London, 1886, republished 1902. The present compiler has used the 1902 edition

Henrey   Blanche Henrey, *British Botanical and Horticultural Literature before 1800*, 3 vols., Oxford, 1975. The present compiler has used volume 3 only

Lewer   Henry William Lewer, *A Book of Simples*, London, 1908

Lincoln   Waldo Lincoln, *American Cookery Books, 1742–1860*, Worcester, Massachusetts, 1929, republished 1954. The present compiler has used the 1954 edition

Lond.Mag.   *The Monthly Catalogue from the London Magazine: 1732–1766* (with an intro. by David Fairweather Foxon), English Bibliographical Sources, Series 1, No. 7, republished by Gregg-Archive, 1966

Lowenstein   Eleanor Lowenstein, *Bibliography of American Cookery Books, 1742–1860*, Worcester, Massachusetts, 1972

Lyle Cat.   A catalogue in a series published by John Lyle, Bookseller (Lyle & Davidson Limited); being no. 3, Harpford, Sidmouth, Devon [1976]

Maggs Bros. Cat.   A catalogue in a series published by Maggs Bros. Ltd., 34/35 Conduit Street, London, W.1; being No. 645, 'Food and Drink through the Ages: 2500 B.C. to 1937 A.D., 1937

Mon.Cat./1   *The Monthly Catalogue: 1714–1717* (with an intro. by David Fairweather Foxon), English Bibliographical Sources, Series 1, No. 1, republished by Gregg-Archive, 1964

Mon.Cat./2   *The Monthly Catalogue: 1723–1726; and 1727–1730* (with an intro. by David Fairweather Foxon), English Bibliographical Sources, Series 1, No. 2, republished by Gregg-Archive in 2 vols. (1: 1723–6; 2: 1727–30), 1964. The appropriate volume number is cited after short title

Murphy   A catalogue published by the Anderson Galleries, Inc., 489 Park Avenue, New York City; being No. 2063, 'The Fine Collection of Cookery Books formed by Mrs. Claudia Quigley Murphy', 1926. Widely called 'Murphy'

NUCat.   *The National Union Catalog Pre-1956 Imprints*, 684 vols., London and Chicago. Publication commenced 1968, project not yet completed

Oxford   Arnold Whitaker Oxford, *English Cookery Books to the year 1850*, London, 1913, republished 1977. The present compiler has used the 1913 edition

Pennell   Elizabeth Robins Pennell, *My Cookery Books*, New York and Boston, 1903

Plomer/1   Henry R. Plomer, *A Dictionary of the Printers and Booksellers who were at Work in England, Scotland, and Ireland from 1668 to 1725*, Oxford, 1922

Plomer/2   Henry R. Plomer, *A Dictionary of the Printers and Booksellers who were at Work in England, Scotland, and Ireland from 1726 to 1775*, Oxford, 1932

Pub.Adv.   *The Public Advertiser*, London Daily Newspaper, owned by the Woodfall family, which commenced in 1734

RB   *A Register of Books: 1728–1732, extracted from the Monthly Chronicle* (with an intro. by David Fairweather Foxon), English Bibliographical Sources, Series 1, No. 3, republished by Gregg-Archive, 1964

Rudolph   G. A. Rudolph, *The Kansas State University Receipt Book and Household Manual*, Kansas State University Library Bibliography Series, No. 4, Manhattan, Kansas, 1968

Scots Mag.   *The Scots Magazine*, Series 1, 79 vols., Edinburgh, 1739–1817

Simon   André Simon, *Bibliotheca Gastronomica*, London, 1953. Reprinted 1978

Sotheby Cat.   Catalogues of books offered for sale, published by Messrs Sotheby's (formerly Sotheby & Co., now Sotheby Parke Bernet & Co., Auctioneers, London), various dates. The date of the catalogue referred to is cited after short title

Stark   Lewis M. Stark, 'The Whitney Cookery Collection', *Bulletin of the New York Public Library*, issue of February 1946, pp. 3–26 (with an index)

Vicaire   Georges Vicaire, *Bibliographie gastronomique*, 1st edn., Paris, 1890; 2nd edn., London, 1954. Reprinted 1978

Watt   Robert Watt, *Bibliotheca Britannica; or a General Index to British and Foreign Literature*, 4 vols., Edinburgh, 1824. [Authors: vols. 1 and 2; Subjects: vols. 3 and 4]

Wing *STC*   Donald Wing, *Short-Title Catalogue of Books Printed in England, Scotland, Ireland, Wales, and British America, and of English Books Printed in other Countries, 1641–1700*, 3 vols., New York, 1945–51

oſ   *The Cook's Pocket-Companion.*

How to Truſs a Pigeon.

Explanation.

When you draw a Pidgeon, leave in the Liver becauſe it has no Gall ; then puſh up the Breaſt from the Vent, and holding up the Leg, paſs a Skewer juſt between the Brown of the Leg, and the Bent of the Thigh, having firſt turned the Pinions under the Back ; and take Care that the lower Joint of the largeſt Pinions are paſſed with the Skewer in such a Manner that the Legs are between them, and the Body, as at 1, and then you are right.

Mrs Lydia Honeywood was one of the many eighteenth-century cookery writers who showed readers how to truss birds. Note the inverted page number.

A Dinner Novem.ᵣ 15.ᵗʰ

To Change.   To Change.

Aspa-ragus
Fish Mar. Ble-mange Jellys Stur-geon
Pome-toon

Aspa-ragus
Fish Mar. Ble-mange Jellys Stur-geon
Pome-toon

Atletts & Cockscombs Ragoust.

A Pottage of Cray Fish with Tenches la force

A Rockam Puff.

Brown Fowl of sorts.

A Pike Roft forct, larded, & Oysters in shells

A Fricaßy of Tenches

Almond Cream.

A Grand Pyramid of Sweet Meats, & Fruit.

Sagoe Cream.

Collard Pigg Italian way

A Haunch of Venison larded, rost, & Olaves of Veal Sheeps-Tongues

Sylla-bubs.

Sylla-bubs.

A Bisque of Fish fry'd of sorts

Pistachoi Cream.

Lemon Cream.

A Fricaßy of Chick-ens.

Collar'd Eels.

A Grand Pyramid of Sweet Meats, & Fruit.

White Fowl of sorts.

Carps Stewed brown.

Side Board.

A Patty of Pidgeons Royal.

A Bisque of Squabs, &c

Oyster Loaves.

Side Board

A Baron of Beef rost

A Venison Pasty.

A twenty four Dish Table

Many eighteenth-century cookery books included diagrams of elaborate table settings. This one, taken from Charles Carter's book of 1730, is among the most handsome.

LIST OF ABBREVIATIONS
USED FOR LIBRARIES

A. LIBRARIES IN THE BRITISH ISLES (BI)

The abbreviations in this section of the list have been devised by the present compiler, and they are based on the system used in the *National Union Catalog*. All copyright libraries are included.

ANLW	Aberystwyth, National Library of Wales
AUL	Aberdeen University Library
BPL	Birmingham Public Libraries, Social Sciences Department
BULA	Bristol University, Long Ashton Research Station
BaCE	Bath College of Higher Education
CUL	Cambridge University Library
DCL	Derbyshire County Library, Local Studies Department
DNLI	Dublin, National Library of Ireland
DTCL	Dublin University, Trinity College Library
DoCL	Dorset County Library, Bournemouth Reference Library
ESBL	East Sussex County Library, Brighton Area Library
ENLS	Edinburgh, National Library of Scotland
EPLC	Edinburgh Public Libraries, Central Branch
ERCP	Edinburgh, Royal College of Physicians
ERHAS	Edinburgh, Royal Highland Agricultural Society of Scotland
EUL	Edinburgh University Library
GPL(M)	Glasgow Public Libraries (Mitchell Library)
GSU(A)	Glasgow, Strathclyde University (Andersonian Library)
GSU(S)	Glasgow, Strathclyde University (Scottish Hotel School Library)
GUL	Glasgow University Library
LBL	London, The British Library
LGL	London, The Guildhall Library
LLL	London, The London Library
LRAS	London, Royal Agricultural Society of England
LRHS(L)	London, Royal Horticultural Society (Lindley Library)
LRSM	London, Royal Society of Medicine
LWML	London, The Wellcome Institute for the History of Medicine Library
LWS	London, The International Wine and Food Society
LePL	Leeds Public Library Services, Central Library
LeU(B)	Leeds University, Brotherton Library
MCL	Manchester, Chetham's Library
MPL	Manchester Public Libraries, Library of the Social Sciences
MU(JR)	The John Rylands University Library of Manchester
NPL	Newcastle upon Tyne Public Libraries
NUL	Newcastle upon Tyne University Library

OBL	Oxford University, The Bodleian Library
RAL	Roxburghshire, Abbotsford Library
RUL	Reading University Library
SFC(WF)	St. Fagan's, Cardiff, National Museum of Wales (Welsh Folk Museum)
SLCL	Sheffield City Libraries, Central Library

B. LIBRARIES IN NORTH AMERICA

The abbreviations in this section of the list have been, with few exceptions, copied from the symbols used in the *National Union Catalog*. The exceptions (which are marked with an asterisk) have been devised by the present compiler, and they are broadly based on the same system.

CLSU	California, Los Angeles, University of Southern California (USC)
CLU-C	California, Los Angeles, University of California at Los Angeles (UCLA), William Andrews Clark Library
CSmH	California, San Marino, Henry E. Huntington Library
CU	California, Berkeley, University of California at Berkeley (UCB)
CU-A	California, Berkeley, University of California at Davis
CU-B	California, Berkeley, University of California at Berkeley (UCB), Bancroft Library
*CaBVaUW	Canada, British Columbia, Vancouver, University of British Columbia, Woodward Biomedical Library
CaOLU	Canada, Ontario, London, University of Western Ontario
CaOTP	Canada, Ontario, Toronto Public Library, Metropolitan Bibliographic Center
*CaOTUTF	Canada, Ontario, University of Toronto, Thomas Fisher Rare Book Library
CoU	Colorado, Boulder, University of Colorado
CtY	Connecticut, New Haven, Yale University
CtY-M	Connecticut, New Haven, Yale University, Medical School Library
*CtZHS	Connecticut, Hartford, Connecticut Historical Society
*DCLC	District of Columbia, Washington, Library of Congress
DFo	District of Columbia, Washington, Folger Shakespeare Library
DNAL	District of Columbia, Washington, US National Agricultural Library
DNLM	District of Columbia, Washington, US National Library of Medicine
FTaSU	Florida, Tallahassee, Florida State University
FU	Florida, Gainesville, University of Florida
IC	Illinois, Chicago Public Library
ICJ	Illinois, Chicago, John Crerar Library
ICN	Illinois, Chicago, Newberry Library
ICRL	Illinois, Chicago, Center for Research Libraries
ICU	Illinois, Chicago, University of Chicago
IEN	Illinois, Evanston, North Western University
IU	Illinois, Urbana, University of Illinois
IaAS	Iowa, Ames, Iowa State University of Science and Technology
IaU	Iowa, Iowa City, University of Iowa
*InSL	Indiana, Indianapolis, Indiana State Library
InU	Indiana, Bloomington, Indiana University
KMK	Kansas, Manhattan, Kansas State University
KU	Kansas, Lawrence, University of Kansas
KyU	Kentucky, Lexington, University of Kentucky

LU	Louisiana, Baton Rouge, Louisiana State University
MB	Massachusetts, Boston Public Library
*MBSi	Massachusetts, Boston, Simmons College
MCR	Massachusetts, Cambridge, Radcliffe College
MH	Massachusetts, Cambridge, Harvard University
MH-A	Massachusetts, Cambridge, Harvard University, Arnold Arboretum
MH-BA	Massachusetts, Cambridge, Harvard University, Graduate School of Business
MHi	Massachusetts, Boston, Massachusetts Historical Society
*MOSV	Massachusetts, Old Sturbridge Village
MSaE	Massachusetts, Salem, Essex Institute
MWA	Massachusetts, Worcester, American Antiquarian Society
MWelC	Massachusetts, Wellesley, Wellesley College
MdBJ	Maryland, Baltimore, Johns Hopkins University
MiD	Michigan, Detroit Public Library
MiEM	Michigan, East Lansing, Michigan State University
MiU	Michigan, Ann Arbor, University of Michigan
MnU	Minnesota, Minneapolis, University of Minnesota
MoU	Missouri, Columbia, University of Missouri
NB	New York, Brooklyn, Brooklyn Public Library
NBu	New York, Buffalo, Buffalo and Erie County Public Library
NIC	New York, Ithaca, Cornell University
NNC	New York, New York City, Columbia University
NNNAM	New York, New York City, New York Academy of Medicine
NPV	New York, Poughkeepsie, Vassar College
NRU	New York, Rochester, University of Rochester
*NSL	New York, Albany, New York State Library
NSyU	New York, Syracuse, Syracuse University
NYPL	New York, New York City, New York Public Library
NcD	North Carolina, Durham, Duke University
NcU	North Carolina, Chapel Hill, University of North Carolina
*NhHS	New Hampshire, Durham, New Hampshire Historical Society
NjP	New Jersey, Princeton, Princeton University
NjR	New Jersey, New Brunswick, Rutgers University (New Jersey State University)
OCl	Ohio, Cleveland, Cleveland Public Library
OClW	Ohio, Cleveland, Case Western Reserve University
OHi	Ohio, Columbus, Ohio State Historical Society
OrU	Oregon, Eugene, University of Oregon
PBL	Pennsylvania, Bethlehem, Lehigh University
PHi	Pennsylvania, Philadelphia, Historical Society of Pennsylvania
PP	Pennsylvania, Philadelphia, Free Library of Philadelphia
PPC	Pennsylvania, Philadelphia, College of Physicians
PPJ	Pennsylvania, Philadelphia, Jefferson Medical College
PPL	Pennsylvania, Philadelphia, Library Company of Philadelphia
PPULC	Pennsylvania, Philadelphia, Union Library Catalog
PU	Pennsylvania, Philadelphia, University of Pennsylvania
PV	Pennsylvania, Villanova, Villanova College

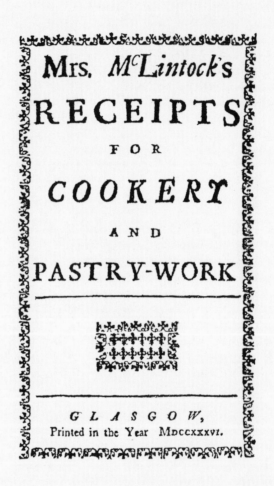

Mrs. McLintock's
RECEIPTS
FOR
COOKERY
AND
PASTRY-WORK

GLASGOW,
Printed in the Year MDCCXXXVI.

This rather crude title-page belongs to the first cookery book published in Scotland. Mrs McLintock's work is among the 'discoveries' made by the present compiler. It had not previously been mentioned in any bibliographical work, and only two copies are known to survive, both at the University of Glasgow.

INTRODUCTION

WITH the ever-increasing interest, both popular and academic, in the history of food, cookery, household management, and also gastronomy, especially among undergraduate and postgraduate students compiling major or minor dissertations on these subjects by topic or period, there is a parallel need for research tools, such as short-title catalogues or bibliographies, which can provide research-workers with essential information, including the whereabouts of books or special editions of books they wish to consult.

This work was suggested by the experience of the present compiler, who found, when carrying out research for a book on the eighteenth century,[1] that the four main bibliographies on cookery and household management were either inadequate or defective or both. Firstly, they are spoiled by factual errors (which have been perpetuated in recent 'reprints'), and secondly, and perhaps more importantly, they all omit the sort of practical information which all researchers require, such as locations of first editions and (where applicable) any or all subsequent editions. The four main bibliographies are:

1. BITTING, Katherine Golden, *Gastronomic Bibliography*, San Francisco, 1939; reprinted Ann Arbor, 1971
2. OXFORD, Arnold Whitaker, *English Cookery Books to the year 1850*, London, 1913; reprinted London, 1977
3. SIMON, André Louis, *Bibliotheca Gastronomica*, London, 1953; reprinted London, 1978
4. VICAIRE, Georges, *Bibliographie Gastronomique*, Paris, 1890, reprinted London, 1954 and 1978

It is too easy to criticize other works, especially pioneer works such as Vicaire, who made the first major attempt to give a full description of cookery books; but all of them blighted their fine efforts with careless mistakes, and not one made any real attempt to list the various editions of each book or, as a consequence, to state where all such editions were located. All four were mainly concerned to compile catalogues of their private collections, to which they added extra information, often in a haphazard fashion, and the result of this approach has been the publication of what appear to be reference works of a general character, which in fact are of a particular and narrower interest. This is also true of other bibliographers in the same field, who have published catalogues of private collections, or have extracted items from Bitting, Oxford, Simon, and Vicaire to produce what seem to be general reference works, but are no more than consolidations of selections from narrow publications with, in many cases, the errors of the originals left uncorrected. In defence of the four main bibliographers (and any others who were, or still are, concerned only with

---

[1] Virginia E. Maclean, *Much Entertainment: A Visual and Culinary Record of Johnson and Boswell's Tour of Scotland in 1773*, London and New York, 1973.

their private collections), the locations of their books were (or still are) their own homes, and there was no need to state the obvious. On the other hand, few books in the main four bibliographers' collections were first editions, and for the majority of their entries there was a need to say where uncollected first or other editions were to be found for consultation, because each of them gave his or her work a title which more than implied that the work's coverage was wide and comprehensive. The only way in which all four were comprehensive was in not limiting their interests to one century or (with the exception of Oxford) one language. Of the four, only two are frequently used by cataloguers as reference works for books that were published in the English tongue—Bitting and Oxford; and for the purpose of this work the practice is continued so that the reader has two bibliographies which are still in print and readily available in leading libraries for consultation.

Having encountered some of the ways in which existing bibliographies can mislead or fail to provide sufficient or accurate data for research workers, the present compiler decided to compile, to the best of her ability, a working 'tool' for others doing research in the field of food, cookery, household management and also gastronomy in the eighteenth century, and that the best way of attempting to achieve this main aim was to have several secondary aims. These are:

1. Giving works or subsequent editions which have never been listed before, by using sources, such as magazines and newspapers, which previous cataloguers have ignored.

2. Correcting or amending, wherever possible, the errors of previous cataloguers and bibliographers.

3. Giving locations for the earliest known editions of all eighteenth century works in the field and (where appropriate) locations for all discoverable later editions published in the eighteenth century.

4. Giving sources for the existence of works for which locations could not be found, and the same for later editions.

5. Including under entries, whenever appropriate, 'Notes' on sources or matters of interest, such as possible or actual plagiarism, or comments on authors.

6. Ensuring, as far as possible, that every cookery book and household work in the English tongue, wherever published, was listed in the short-title catalogue. However, one special exception has been made concerning the 'rule' about works being in the English tongue, and that is Dr Martin Lister's Latin edition of the classic book on cookery by the Roman cook Apicius. To have omitted such an influential work, which is still being reprinted, was unthinkable.

It is a cliché, but as soon as the matter of selection arose after the initial survey of other catalogues and checklists, the present compiler was faced with every bibliographer's and cataloguer's dilemma: what to put in, and what to leave out.

Compilers of cookery and household works in the eighteenth century maintained the practice of their predecessors and included in their books, either as an integral part or as a supplement or as an 'addition' in a later edition, one or more sections on medical self-help, under headings which were invariably entitled 'Every man his own doctor' or 'Every woman her own doctor' or very similar words. Where these medical receipts were an integral part of a cookery or household work there was no dilemma; all such works were selected for inclusion. As the century progressed, however, and as the disgusting 'old wives' cures' were displaced by the results of improved medical training, more and more books were produced which were devoted solely to home medication, and many of these were far too technical or specialized to be understood by ordinary housewives. Many of these works had titles which suggested that they were intended as lay guides for families who were isolated or could not readily gain the services of qualified physicians and surgeons, but their inclusion in this short-title catalogue could not be justified. There were others solely devoted to home medication, such as the work of Dr William Buchan, which had been carefully prepared for the ordinary housewife, and were household works, and these have been included.

The same dilemma applied to drink, which in this century is treated as a separate subject and is not thought of in relation to cookery or household matters. Many eighteenth-century cookery books, however, did contain one or more sections on brewing ale and making all kinds of wine. In a century when potable water, even in flat rural areas let alone towns, was a rarity, due to the pollution of slow-moving rivers by cattle and human beings and bad sanitation generally, the brewing of ale in homes and making stocks of wines as various fruits and flowers came into season were necessities, not luxuries, and housewives were just as interested in the quality of drink as they were in the quality of food. So, where drink-making was an integral part of a cookery or household work, there was no difficulty; it has been included. Where books were solely devoted to brewing or wine-making, a selection of the better-known (or rather, better-advertised) works was taken for inclusion in the catalogue, and those which were deliberately written as household books, such as the works of Samuel Child, appear in their own right. Border-line cases on drink concern those books and pamphlets which were mainly inspired by xenophobia in wartime, when the authors set out to persuade their readers that English-made wines could be just as good, if not better, than French, Spanish, Portuguese, and Italian products, and said as much on their title-pages. These publications probably had a good sale as special household works, and so a small selection of these has been included as well. Books on spirits presented a problem, but some of them can be classed as special household works which dealt with the acceptance or rejection of certain types of food and drink as a means of becoming or remaining healthy, or as a way of prolonging life. Books on the use and abuse of tea, coffee, cocoa, and white bread fall into the same broad classification of special household works— diet and regimen—and, again, a small selection of these (and vegetarian) works has been included. Bread, as the main staple, also had obvious and particular importance at times of scarcity or high prices or both, and during such times, especially in the last decade of the century, books and pamphlets appeared suggesting cheap meat dishes and soups as alternatives to bread for the hard-hit labouring classes. Moreover, these works contain some of the rare examples of receipts for large-scale cookery and catering, and their inclusion is justified for this reason alone.

Too little is known about large-scale cookery in the eighteenth century. Not one book, for instance, has been found which deals with cooking for the Army or Navy because, perhaps, food for both services was funded out of allowances made to regimental or ship's commanders, whose paymasters or pursers were keen to show a 'profit' out of those allowances, and did not wish to publicize the sort of economies in catering which made such profits possible. The Spithead Naval Mutiny of 1797 and, obviously, the Cardwell Army Reforms of 1868 to 1871 came too late for any eighteenth-century writer to investigate the victualling and catering deficiencies in the forces. Mention of the army proper is a reminder of another 'army'; the army of domestic servants, which greatly exceeded the total number of peacetime soldiers and sailors. It has been estimated by reliable sources, including Lord North, the Prime Minister, and Patrick Colquhoun, the famous London magistrate, that in London alone in the second half of the century there were between 80,000 and 100,000 male servants and almost the same number of female servants, or that one in eight of the city's population was in domestic service; with one in eleven of the population for England as a whole.[1] On these grounds, any work dealing with the training, control, or complaints of servants could be regarded as a household work, and a selection of them has been included in the catalogue. The best known, perhaps, is Dean Jonathan Swift's ironic *Directions to Servants*, which was intended to shame them out of bad habits.

Lastly, a very small number of works have been selected for inclusion which must be classed as miscellaneous, among them books devoted to one item of food (for example, herrings) and a few poems, mostly satires on food or cookery, and one on whisky.[2]

[1] J. Jean Hecht, *The Domestic Servant Class in Eighteenth-Century England*, London, 1965, pp. 33–4.

[2] William McVitie, *Whisky: a Poem*, Edinburgh, 1795. It seems odd that a Scot should publish such a scathing attack on whisky in this period, when distillers, using wartime anti-French feeling to denigrate brandy and claret as the household favourites of the upper and middling classes, were trying hard for the first time (with considerable advertising) to promote whisky as the spirit for the discerning Englishman, who had hitherto regarded it as the drink of the Scottish poor or, worse, as the beverage of the barbaric Highlanders.

ARRANGEMENT OF MATERIAL

1. *Headings*

THE arrangement of headings is strictly alphabetical by author's surnames or, in the case of anonymous works, by titles. Wherever the definite and indefinite articles occur as the first word of a title or descriptive name or pseudonym, they have been ignored, and the first letter of the next word has determined the alphabetical order. A work written by more than one author is listed according to the first-named author's surname. The second or other authors are listed under separate headings according to alphabetical order, with a cross-reference (or cross-references) to the first-named author. A work written under a descriptive name (e.g. A Lady) is listed as a heading (ignoring the definite or indefinite article, if present; e.g. LADY), with a cross-reference to the title. A work written under a pseudonym is listed as a heading, with a cross-reference to the title; and the same applies to a work written under initials only. A work that has been translated into English is listed as a heading under the translator's surname, with a cross-reference to the author or, if anonymous, to the title. Any work originally written anonymously, under a descriptive name, under initials or pseudonymously, but where the author's identity has been later discovered, is listed under the author's surname, and the former description is listed as a separate heading, with a cross-reference to the author. Where the Christian name of an author is not known, the surname is followed by a dash in square brackets, but where the sex is known the brackets are followed by an apt description, also in square brackets, e.g. [Mrs]. An author with a title of nobility is listed under the family surname, followed by the Christian name(s), followed by the title. The dipthongs 'æ' and 'œ' are treated as 'e' whenever they begin a word; and 'Mc' is treated as 'Mac', because the 'c' in 'Mc' was originally an inverted apostrophe which stood for two letters 'ac'.

2. *Title-page entries*

In all cases the short title represents the only or earliest known edition of a work published in the eighteenth century. Well-known works, with accurate listings elsewhere, are generally shown with curtailed short titles, while lesser-known works, or works which could have been plagiarized tend to have extended short titles. Where a work has never been listed before, an extended or, if possible, a complete recording of the original title-page has been given; but, in many such cases, only the briefest of titles has been found.

Any omission or excision from the original title-page is shown by three period points (...), except at the end of a title, when 'etc.' is used, and any added information to the original title-page is given in square brackets, except that any descriptive name for an author appearing on an original title-page is also given in square brackets; e.g. '[by a lady]' with a cross-reference from the heading 'LADY'. Capitalization of the original title-page has not been retained, except for the first letters of proper nouns; but the original punctuation and spellings have been adhered to at all times. Where any word is spelt incorrectly it is followed by '[*sic*]'; but eighteenth-century spellings which were good common usage have not been given this indication. Such eighteenth-century spellings include: almanack, cosmetick, physick, publick, inlarged, inquiry, intirely, compleat, chuse (or chusing), and cyder. The word 'curious' was, of course, used to mean 'specific', 'particular', or 'minutely careful', and was not interpreted in its modern sense as meaning 'odd' or 'inquisitive'.

Title-pages in the eighteenth century acted as advertisements, and were the equivalent of modern 'blurbs' on book jackets. Each gave not only a full résumé of the contents of a book, but also tried to flatter a potential buyer with key words. The two most frequently used words in the short titles of cookery books were 'complete' and 'accomplished', and the most commonly used descriptive name was 'A Lady'. The potential buyer's thriftyness, vanity, and snobbishness all seem to have been flattered. Having bought a 'complete' book, and thereby saving money (which could have been spent on two or more books, in order to obtain the same amount of information), the buyer, who is certain the complete book was written for people of her ability, because it says it is for those who are 'accomplished', is doubly reassured to know that the author, like herself, is 'A Lady'.

3. *Imprints*

In every instance in the catalogue, the imprint is a representation of the original, and not a reproduction of it. The place where the book was printed or published is given first; followed by the name of the printer (or printers) and then the name of the seller (or sellers), with the actual or approximate date of printing or publication in arabic numerals (even if shown in roman numerals in the original) as the last item. Where three or more sellers were given in the original, only the first three are listed. What has just been outlined is the most extensive recording of an imprint. In many cases, however, one or more items did not appear in the original, and where this occurred the maximum possible number of items have been recorded. All printers are indicated by the word 'by' on its own [printed by . . .], and all sellers can be detected by 'for' [printed for . . .] or the more obvious 'sold by' [printed . . ., and sold by . . .]. Where the place of printing or publishing was not given in the original, but the name of the printer or seller was shown, the place can often be found in Plomer/1 or Plomer/2, and where this has happened the place is shown in square brackets. Where a date was omitted on the original title-page, but has been confirmed from another source, it is given in square brackets. An approximate date follows the abbreviation '*c.*' and is also given in square brackets; e.g. [*c.*1745]. If a book was compiled in two or more volumes or parts, and if a book was not a first edition, this information is shown before the imprint.

4. *Information following imprints*

After the imprint the remaining details about the book (as far as they have been discovered) are always given in the following order: number of pages (p.);

frontispiece (frontis.); plate or plates (pl. or pls.); height to the nearest centi-metre (cm.); and the price in shillings and pence (sh. d.). Elements which did not appear in the book (frontis., pl. or pls., and often price) have received no symbol to show that they are absent. A symbol, a dash in square brackets, has been allocated to both pagination and size, and its significance depends upon the order, if it only appears once. If the number of pages is missing, then the symbol appears before the size that is listed. If the size is missing, then the symbol appears after the cited number of pages. If both details are missing, the symbol appears twice.

Pagination is given according to the printer's method of numeration. Un-numbered pages have been discounted. Pages with roman numbering appear first, according to the printer's method; e.g. vi–xxi. Then follow the pages with arabic numbering, on the same system; e.g. 5–501. Breaks in numbering have not been indicated, unless the book appeared in volumes (or parts) with continuous pagination. Where a book appeared in volumes (or parts) with separate pagination for each volume (or part), this has been shown. Where a whole book lacks pagination, but the pages have been counted, the figure is given in square brackets.

If the price was not printed on the original title-page, but has been confirmed by another source, it is entered with a numerical indicator to a 'Note', in which the full source is cited.

5. *Citations of bibliographies*

The bibliographies of both Bitting and Oxford are defective, but they are both still in print, and both are readily available in leading libraries for consultation. For the last two reasons they have been selected for inclusion under each work against the heading 'Cited', which is a short way of saying 'The work above is cited in . . .'. Where a dash appears against 'Cited' it indicates that neither Bitting nor Oxford included the work in their bibliographies. Where only one name appears, then it means only Bitting or only Oxford cited the work; and where both their names appear it shows that both cited the work.

6. *Locations of copies*

Giving the locations where copies of the work can be consulted is perhaps one of the most valuable aspects of the catalogue. Under each work appears the heading 'Copies', which is an abbreviation for 'Where copies of the above work can be located'. Against 'Copies' on two separate lines are the sub-heads '*BI*' and '*NA*', standing for 'British Isles' and 'North America'; and against each of these are the abbreviations representing the locations of libraries, up to a total of three in each case; giving a maximum of six locations for every work in the catalogue. The locations can be easily identified in 'The List of Abbreviations used for Libraries'. The maximum of six locations for every work was a target, which was only reached occasionally. If a work was a rarity, the present compiler was lucky to find one location to record; and in a minority of cases no locations could be found at all, and where that has occurred a dash appears against both '*BI*' and '*NA*'.

7. *Other editions*

Where any work had one or more subsequent editions, they are listed in strict chronological order after 'Copies'. Wherever possible the number or description of the edition has been given (e.g. 2nd ed., or A new ed.), and the identity of the edition has been followed (where appropriate) by any change in the title, and then by the imprint, which has been dealt with in the same manner as those which appear after title-page entries. Any unidentified edition has been called 'another edition' and placed with the others in strict chronological order. A dash in square brackets is used to represent a missing place of publication, and also to represent the name of a missing printer or seller. After the imprint the locations are shown, with those in the British Isles (up to a maximum of three) coming before those in North America (also up to a maximum of three), with a full colon separating the latter from the former. Where no locations could be found, a dash appears each side of the colon (—:—), and a numerical indicator indicates a source under 'Notes'. Where a location (or locations) could be found only in the British Isles, a dash appears after the colon; and where a location (or locations) could be found only in North America, a dash appears before the colon.

8. *Notes*

Notes (where they occur) come after other editions, or after 'Copies' if there are no other editions. The term is self-explanatory, and under it are cited sources and any matters of interest connected with the book or its author or authors. Notes are linked to the relevant detail or details by numerical indicators.

9. *Asterisk*

An asterisk * (throughout this short-title catalogue) indicates the library in which a book was inspected.

10. *Illustrations*

These are mostly of title-pages, and they have been positioned so that they face or are adjacent to the entries for the books to which they belong, rather than in chronological order. The selection has, however, been made with the purpose, among others, of showing how the content, design, and typography of title-pages evolved during the century. To follow this evolution, they should be looked at in the following order: page 120 (1710, but dating back to the seventeenth century); page 96 (1702); page 81 (1714); page 83 (1720); page 12 (1736, but dating back to the late 1720s); page 41 (1733); page 100 (1734); page xvi (1736, but the art of printing had not progressed as far in Scotland as in England!); page 110 (1746); page 58 (1747, our first example in large format); page 45 (1750); page 126 (1756); page 76 (1757); page 130 (1767); page 122 (1769); pages 53 and 80 (c.1780, and 1780); page 51 (1787, although originating a few years earlier); page 28 (1788); page 148 (1791); and page 130 (1798).

A SHORT-TITLE CATALOGUE
OF HOUSEHOLD AND
COOKERY BOOKS PUBLISHED IN
THE ENGLISH TONGUE
1701–1800

A

ABBOT, ROBERT (*fl.* 1790–1800?)

The housekeeper's valuable present: or, lady's closet companion. Being a new and complete art[1] of preparing confects, according to modern practice . . . working icecream . . . preparing cordials and made wines, etc. [London]: printed for the author;[2] and sold by C. Cooke, [*c.*1790].[3] xii, 13–100 p. 18 cm. 2 sh. sewed or 2 sh. 6 d. neatly bound.

Cited: Oxford, p. 126

Copies: *BI*: LBL; LWML; LeU(B)*[4]
       NA: KMK; MOSV; NYPL

1. *BMCat.* (1965) wrongly gives 'act' for 'art'.
2. The title-page states that the author was 'Robert Abbot, late apprentice to Messrs. Negri and Gunter, confectioners, in Berkeley Square'.
3. *B.&G.Cat.*, No. 37, p. 14, gives the date as 'ca.1798', but Pennell, p. 165, proves it was earlier by stating that her own copy has 'written on the inside of the cover "Anne Jones, Dec. 18, 1791"'; and the Whitney copy, now the property of NYPL, has the date marked in pencil on the title-page as 'circa 1791'.
4. The LeU(B) copy is lacking the last two pages.

ACCOMPLISH'D

The accomplish'd female instructor: or, a very useful companion for ladies, gentlewomen, and others. In two parts. Part I. Treating of generous breeding and behaviour; choice of company, friendship; the art of speaking well. etc. . . . Part II. Treating of making curious confectionaries, or sweetmeats, jellies, syrups, cordial-waters . . . to know good provisions, dye curious colours, whiten ivory . . . physical and chyrurgical [*sic*] receipts . . . and a great number of other useful and profitable things.[1] London: printed for J. Knapton, 1704. 184 p. 16 cm.

Cited: —

Copies: *BI*: LBL; LWML*
           NA: DCLC; ICJ; ICN

1. The preface is signed 'R. G.'; and *BMCat.* (1961) lists the work under 'G., R.'.

ACCOMPLISH'D

The accomplish'd housewife, and house-keeper's pocket-companion, or the compleat family cook. etc. [———]: printed by the author, 1736. 155 p. [———] 1 sh. 6 d.

Cited: Oxford, p. 68[1]

Copies: *BI*: —
           NA: —

1. The only known reference to this work is in Oxford.

ACCOMPLISH'D

The accomplish'd housewife; or, the gentlewoman's[1] companion.[2] etc. London: printed for J. Newbery, 1745.[3] 431 p. 17 cm. 3 sh.[4]

Cited: Bitting, p. 513; Oxford, p. 75

Copies: *BI*: LWML; LeU(B)*[5]
           NA: DCLC; ICU; MH

1. Oxford, p. 75, wrongly gives 'gentle*man's* companion'.
2. A note in this work recommends readers who want a larger system of cookery to consult Harrison, S., The house-keeper's pocket-book.
3. Pennell, p. 156, gives the date as '1748', which could indicate that there was a 2nd ed.
4. *Gents.Mag.*, vol. 15 (Aug. 1745), p. 448, confirms that the price was 3 sh., but *Scots Mag.*, vol. 7 (Aug. 1745), p. 400, quotes the price as '3 sh. 6 d.'. The LeU(B) copy contains the bookplate of Francis Otway, Esq[re]
5. Another LeU(B) copy is inscribed 'A. Cunningham'.

ACCOMPLISHED

The accomplished ladies rich closet of rarities; or, the ingenious gentlewoman and servant-maids delightful companion. etc.[1] 6th ed. London: printed for Nicholas Boddington, 1706. 7-188 p. frontis. 15 cm.

Cited: Oxford, pp. 43-4

Copies: *BI*: —
           NA: —

—7th ed. with additions. London: printed by E.M. for N. Boddington, 1715. LeU(B)*: CtY

1. The preface is signed 'John Shirley'. For earlier editions see Wing *STC*, vol. 3 (1951), p. 250.

ACCOMPLISHED

The accomplished lady's delight in cookery; or, the complete servant's-maid's [*sic*] guide. [by a lady].[1] Wolverhampton: printed for J. Smart, [*c.*1780]. 24 p. 18 cm.

Cited: Oxford, p. 112

Copies: *BI*: LBL*

    NA: —

—another ed. Accomplish'd lady's delight in cookery: or the complete servant-maids guide. Manchester: printed by G. Swindells, [*c*.1796]. In two parts. 24, 24 p. 18 cm.[2]

1. *BMCat.* (1962) gives the work under 'Lady'.
2. The only known reference to this edition is cited in *The Manchester Press before 1801*, Manchester Libraries Committee publication, Manchester, 1931, p. 22.

ACCOMPLISH'D

The accomplish'd lady's delight in preserving, physick, beautifying, cookery and gardening. etc. 9th ed. inlarged. London: printed and sold by Benjamin Harris, 1706.[1] 4, 176 p. frontis. 15 cm.

Cited: Bitting, p. 513; Oxford, pp. 37–8

Copies: *BI*: —

    NA: DCLC; KMK; MH*

—10th ed. inlarged. London: printed for D. Pratt, 1719. LBL: KMK

—11th ed. inlarged.[2] London: printed for John Willis and Joseph Boddington, [*c*.1720]. OBL: NPV

1. For earlier editions see Wing *STC*, vol. 3 (1951), p. 504, and *BMCat.* (1963) under P., T. Both attribute authorship to Hannah Woolley (or Wolley), whose life is given in *DNB*, vol. 31 (1909), pp. 902–3.
2. The preface is signed 'T.P.'.

ACCOUNT

An account of a meat and soup charity, established in the Metropolis, in the year 1797, with observations relative to the situation of the poor, and on the means of bettering the condition of the labouring people with regard to food. etc. [by a magistrate]. London: printed by H. Fry for C. Dilly, 1797. 24 p. 21 cm.

Cited: Oxford, p. 125[1]

Copies: *BI*: —

    NA: DCLC; MH-BA

1. The only known British reference to this work is given by Oxford. For a work on a similar theme, the growing conscience for the welfare of the poor, see later entry under BUCHAN, William, Observations concerning the diet of common people.

ADAM

Adam's luxury, and Eve's cookery; or, the kitchen-garden display'd, . . . in two parts to which is added, the physical virtues of every herb and root. etc.[1] London: printed for R. Dodsley, 1744.[2] xii, 216 p. 17 cm. 1 sh. 6 d.[3]

Cited: Bitting, p. 514; Oxford, p. 74

Copies: *BI*: GUL; LGL; LeU(B)*
         NA: KMK: MCR; NYPL

1. Although the majority of the receipts are vegetarian, some do use meat stock, e.g. Hodge-Podge on p. 184. The first part is devoted to the kitchen garden. The second part, cookery receipts.
2. An advertisement for this work appeared in *Scots Mag.*, vol. 18 (Oct. 1756), p. 527, which could indicate that a later edition was published.
3. *Gents.Mag.*, vol. 14 (May 1744), p. 288, confirms that the price was '1 sh. 6 d.' The LeU(B) copy is inscribed 'Mary Watson 1779 March 21'.

AGRICOLA SYLVAN

see FARMER (first entry).

ANTIQUARY

see PEGGE, Samuel.

APICIUS

Apicii Coelii[1] de opsoniis et condimentis, sive arte coquinaria, libri decem. Cum annotationibus Martini Lister, è medicis domesticis Serenissimae Majestatis Reginae Annae.[2] Et notis selectioribus, variisque lectionibus integris, Humelbergii, Caspari Barthii, & variorum. Londini: typis Gulielmi Bowyer, MDCCV [1705].[3] xiv, 231 p. 20 cm.

Cited: Bitting, p. 13; Oxford, p. 49.

Copies: *BI*: ERCP*; LBL; LeU(B)
         NA: DCLC; MH; NIC

1. Although the name of the author is invariably given as Apicius Coelius, only the name Apicius is certain. For information on the authorship and original date of compilation see B. Flower and E. Rosenbaum, *Apicius: The Roman Cookery Book* (London, 1974), pp. 9–18.
2. The publication of this edition by Dr Martin Lister, personal physician to Queen Anne, gave rise to a satirical poem; see KING, William, The art of cookery.
3. *B.&G.Cat.*, No. 37, p. 3, states that 'this edition was privately printed in an edition of 120 copies only, at the expense of 18 Gentlemen, among whom were Lord Somers, Robert Harley, Sir Christopher Wren, Isaac Newton and Sir Hans Sloane'. A 2nd ed. of this work, limited to 100 copies and edited by Theodore Jan Almeloveen, was published by Jan Waesberg in Amsterdam in 1709. For earlier editions see *BMCat.* (1965).

ARBUTHNOT, JOHN (1667-1735)

An essay concerning the nature of aliments, and the choice of them, according to the different constitutions of human bodies. etc.[1] London: printed for J. Tonson, 1731. [Part 1]. xxxii, 232 p. 20 cm. 4 sh. 6 d.

Practical rules of diet in the various constitutions and diseases of human bodies.[2] London: printed for J. Tonson, 1732. [Part 2]. 243-430 p. 20 cm. 2 sh. 6 d.[3]

Cited: —

Copies: *BI*: LBL; LWML*
    NA: DCLC; KU; MH

—another ed. Dublin: printed for G. Risk, G. Ewing and W. Smith, 1731. [Part 1 only]. LBL; LWML; OBL: —

—2nd ed. London: printed for J. Tonson, 1732. [Parts 1 and 2 in one volume]. LBL; LWML: CtY; DCLC; MH

—3rd ed. London: printed for J. Tonson, 1735-1736. LBL; LWML; OBL: CtY; DCLC; MiU

—another ed. London: printed for J. Tonson, 1741. LeU(B): —

—4th ed. London: printed for J. and R. Tonson, 1756. EUL; LWML: DCLC; DNLM; PPULC

1. For information on the author and his publications see G. A. Aitken, *The Life and Works of John Arbuthnot* (Oxford, 1892), p. 177.
2. The preface to Part 2 states: 'This treatise contains no recipes, but guides the reader to suitable food for differing illnesses.'
3. Confirmations of the prices for Parts 1 and 2 are given respectively in *RB* (May 1731), p. 103, and *Lond.Mag.* (Apr. 1732), No. 33 [no pagination].

ARMSTRONG, John (1709-1779)

The art of preserving health: a poem.[1] London: printed for A. Millar, 1744. 134 p. 25 cm. 5 sh. sewed[2]

Cited: Bitting, p. 16; Oxford, p. 74

Copies: *BI*: ENLS*; LBL; LWML
    NA: CaBVaUW; CtY; MH

—1st ed. Dublin: printed for J. Smith and W. Powell, 1744. LBL; LWML: —

—another ed. London: printed for A. Millar, 1744. LBL: —

—2nd ed. London: printed for A. Millar, 1745. ENLS; LWML: CtY; DCLC; MH

—another ed. London: printed; Philadelphia: reprinted and sold by B. Franklin, 1745. —: DCLC; CSmH; NYPL

—3rd ed. London: printed for A. Millar, 1748. ENLS; LWML: CtY; DNLM; TxU

—4th ed. London: printed for A. Millar, 1754. ENLS; LBL; LWML: CtY; CaBVaUW; ICJ

—another ed. London: printed for A. Millar, 1756. —: DCLC

—another ed. Dublin: printed for J. Rudd, 1756. LWML: —

—a new ed. London: printed for A. Millar, 1757. LBL; LWML: CtY; DNLM; MH

—4th ed. London: printed; Boston: reprinted and sold by Green and Russell, 1757. —: MH; MHi; NYPL

—a new ed. London: printed for A. Millar, 1765. ENLS; EUL: CtY

—another ed. Dublin: printed for [——], 1765. ENLS; LBL: NYPL

—a new ed. London: printed for T. Cadell, 1768. ENLS; LWML; LWS: DCLC; NNNAM; MWA

—a new ed. London: printed for T. Davies, 1774. ENLS; LBL: DNLM; NNNAM; PU

—another ed. Philadelphia: printed for T. Dobson, 1786. —: CSmH; DCLC; PHi

—another ed. Exeter: printed for [——], 1794. ENLS; LBL: PPULC

—another ed. London: printed for T. Cadell, jun. and W. Davies, 1795. ENLS; LBL: CtY; KMK; NYPL

—another ed. New York: printed for L. Wayland, 1795. —: DCLC

—another ed. London: printed for T. Cadell, jun. and W. Davies, 1796. ENLS; LBL: CtY; DCLC; MHi

—another ed. Manchester: printed for G. Nicholson, 1797.[3] LBL: —

1. For the life and publications of John Armstrong see Iolo Williams, *Seven XVIIIth-Century Bibliographies* (London, 1924).
2. *Scots Mag.*, vol. 6 (Apr. 1744), p. 200, confirms that the price was 5 sh.
3. Further editions were published in the 19th century.

ARMSTRONG, JOHN (1709-1779)

The muncher's and guzler's diary.[1] The wit's, the critic's, the farmer's and the petit-maitre's pocket companion . . . the gentleman's, the lady's, the old woman's, the child's manual . . . the universal almanack [by Noureddin Alraschin].[2] 2nd ed. London: printed for J. Cook, 1750. [——] [——]

Cited: Bitting, p. 16.

Copies: *BI*: —
      NA: DCLC

—1st ed. [——]: printed for [——], 1748.[3] —: —

—another ed. London: printed for R. Baldwin, 1749. LBL: —

1. *B.&G.Cat.*, No. 37, p. 25, states that this facetious work is very rare.
2. Iolo Williams, op. cit., p. 33, identifies 'Noureddin Alraschin' as pseudonym of John Armstrong. It is a poor version of the Arabic name Nur-ud-Din al-Rashid.
3. Although no copy of the 1st ed. has been located, it is certain that one was published in 1748; see John Armstrong, *Miscellanies* (London, 1770).

ARNAUD, JASPER (*fl.* 1740)

An alarm to all persons touching their health and lives . . .[1] To which are added, remarks . . . communicated to the author[2] by a learned physician. London: printed for T. Payne, 1740. 24 p. 19 cm.

Cited: Oxford, pp. 70–1

Copies: *BI*: LBL*; LWML
      NA: NYPL[3]

1. Typical of the many warnings in this work is that on p. 5 concerning the practice of selling rotten fish: 'Fish that is grown stale is usually soaked a little in water, and washed by some, and then laid on the shop-board for sale.'

2. The author identifies himself as 'Sometime past first cook to the late Duke of Orleans, and now for some time cook in London'.
3. See Pennell, p. 150, who originally owned a copy of this work and many other cookery books before donating her collection to the DCLC.

ART

The art of cheese-making; taught from actual experiments, by which more and better cheese may be made from the same quantity of milk. Concord: printed and sold by George Hough, 1793. 16 p. [——].

Cited: —

Copies: *BI*: —
        NA: NhHS[1]

—another ed. Boston: reprinted by Benjamin Edes, 1797. —: MH

—another ed. Windham: printed by John Byrne, 1798. —: MWA

1. See Lowenstein, p. 3.

ART of cookery
see GLASSE, Hannah.

ART of cookery
see KING, William.

ART of modern cookery
see MENON, [——].

ATKYNS, ARABELLA
see FAMILY magazine.

AUTHOR of the familiar catechism
see LAIRD and farmer.

B

B., T.
see LADIES companion.

BAILEY, NATHANIEL[1] (d. 1742)

Dictionarium domesticum, being a new and compleat houshold [*sic*] diction-ary. For the use both of city and country.[2] Shewing, the whole arts of brewing, baking, cookery and pickling . . . confectionary . . . the management of the kitchin [*sic*], pantry, larder, dairy, olitory,[3] and poultry . . . the herdsman, English vineyard . . . the apiary . . . the family physician. etc.

London: printed for C. Hitch, C. Davis and S. Austen, 1736. [614 p.] frontis. 20 cm. 6 sh.[4]

Cited: Bitting, p. 24; Oxford, p. 69

Copies: *BI*: AUL; LWML; LeU(B)*
     NA: DCLC; KMK; MH

1. The author was a school master in Stepney, and also compiled *The Universal Etymological English Dictionary*.
2. On the cover of the copy inspected is the short title: 'Bailey's Family Dictionary'.
3. An olitory is a kitchen garden.
4. *Ann.Cat.*, p. 3, confirms that the price was 6 sh.

BARKER, ANNE[1] (*fl.* 1760)

The complete servant maid: or young woman's best companion. Containing full, plain, and easy directions for qualifying them for service in general, but more especially for the places of lady's woman, housekeeper, chambermaid, nurserymaid, housemaid, laundrymaid, cookmaid, kitchen, or scullerymaid, dairymaid. etc.[2] London: printed for J. Cooke, [*c.*1762].[3] 48 p. 21 cm. 1 sh.

Cited: Oxford, pp. 94–5

Copies: *BI*: LBL*
     NA: —

1. Mrs Barker stated 'that for many years she discharged the office of Housekeeper in the most respectable families'.
2. Although no receipts are given in this work, there are, for example (on p. 46), directions for making butter and cheese, and the general household advice is absorbing.
3. The approximate date for this work has been arrived at from a comment on p. 44, where the cookmaid is advised to buy *The Complete English Cook* (see BROOKS, Catharine), which has a preface dated 'January 20th 1762'. This means that Anne Barker could have published her work in 1762, or soon thereafter.

BARRY, SIR EDWARD (1696–1776)

Observations historical, critical, and medical, on the wines of the ancients. etc. London: printed for T. Cadell, 1775. xii, 479 p. frontis. 27 cm. 15 sh.[1]

Cited: —

Copies: *BI*: ENLS*; LBL; LeU(B)
     NA: CaBVaUW; DCLC; NYPL

1. *Scots Mag.*, vol. 37 (Nov. 1775), p. 621, confirms that the price was '15 sh. boards'.

BASSE, J. H.

see FAUST, Bernard Christoph.

BATH

The Bath cookery book, and housekeepers' assistant: containing the most approved receipts, on roasting . . . made dishes . . . also the way to prepare hams, bacon . . . making wines. etc.[1] Bath: printed for the author by Henry Gye, [*c*.1780]. 204 p. 18 cm.

Cited: —

Copies: *BI*: LeU(B)*
   NA: —

1. The following comment is given in an advertisement in the work: 'It is presumed this work will be found particularly useful, more especially by inexperienced cooks, as it has ever been the practice to give two and often three receipts for the same article, which must necessarily confuse the person who searches for the one most approved.'

BATTAM, ANNE (*fl.* 1750)

A collection of scarce and valuable receipts, never before printed, and taken from the manuscripts of divers persons of the most refin'd taste and greatest judgement in the arts of cookery, preserving . . . concluding with many excellent prescriptions, of singular efficacy in most distempers, incident to the human body. London: printed for the author,[1] 1750. 198 p. 18 cm. 3 sh.

Cited: Oxford, p. 80

Copies: *BI*: LBL; LeU(B)*
   NA: —

—2nd ed. The lady's assistant in the œconomy of the table . . . originally published by the late Mrs. Anne Battam with near one hundred and fifty additional receipts, from several ladies, never before published. London: printed for R. and J. Dodsley, 1759. 300 p.[2] pls. 17 cm. 3 sh. LeU(B)*: KMK; NPV

1. Anne Battam described herself on the title-page as 'Mistress of Myon's Coffee-House in Great-Russel-Street Bloomsbury.'
2. The 2nd ed. is considerably enlarged, and it includes directions for marketing, and such recipes as Mrs Spender's Lemon Biscuits and Lady Berkeley's Cherry Wine.

BATTAM, ANNE (*fl.* 1750)

The new and complete cook.[1] With the addition of 150 scarce and valuable receipts. London: printed for R. Dodsley, 1797. [———] frontis. [———]

Cited: —

Copies: *BI*: —
   NA: —

1. The only known reference to this work is given in *B.&G.Cat.*, No. 37, p. 14, which states: 'Mrs. Battam's book [i.e. a collection of scarce and valuable receipts; see the previous entry for BATTAM, Anne] was first published in 1750, but this edition is so much altered that it may be considered a different work.' See also Aresty, p. 236.

BEAUTIES

Beauties treasury: or, the ladies vade mecum. Being a collection of the newest, most select and valuable receipts, for making all sorts of cosmetick-washes . . . To which are added receipts for making the best cordial-waters, as also the finest essences. etc. [by J.W. —— Philo-Chym. & Med.].[1] London: printed and sold by S. Malthus, 1705. ii, 117 p. frontis. 15 cm. 1 sh.

Cited: Oxford, p. 50[2]

Copies: *BI*: —
    NA: ICJ; ViSL

–another ed. London: printed and sold by S. Malthus, [*c.*1711] —: WU

1. The author 'J.W.' obviously wished to give himself or herself a credential by adding the subsidiary pseudonym 'Philo-Chym. & Med.', which presumably stands for 'Friend of Chemists and Physicians'.
2. In addition to Oxford, p. 50, there is a reference to this copy in *B.&G.Cat.*, No. 37, p. 34, which means there is (or was) a copy (or copies) of this work in the British Isles, but none has been located.

BENNET, CHRISTOPHER

see MOUFET, Thomas.

BEST

The best and easiest method of preserving uninterrupted health to extreme old age: established upon the justest laws of the animal œconomy and confirmed by the suffrages of the most celebrated practitioners among the ancients and moderns. From a manuscript found in the library of an eminent physician lately deceased. etc.[1] London: printed by order of his executors and sold by R. Baldwin, 1748. 204 p. 17 cm.

Cited: —

Copies: *BI*: LWML; LeU(B)*; OBL
    NA: DCLC; KMK; PPJ

1. Chapter II discusses: 'The various kinds of aliments, the several sauces or substances with which they are dress'd, the different methods of preparing them, and the unspeakable advantages arising from a moderate use of them.'

BEST

The best and most approved method of curing white-herrings, and all kinds of white fish. Containing particular directions how to slit, gut, salt. etc. [by a trader in fish]. London: printed for J. Davidson, 1750. 28 p. 21 cm.

Cited: —

Copies: *BI*: —
    NA: CtY;* IU; MH

BORELLA, [——] [Mr] (*fl.* 1770)

The court and country confectioner: or, the house-keeper's guide; to a more speedy, plain, and familiar method of understanding the whole art of confectionary ... and the making of fine flavoured English wines ... to which is added, a dissertation on the different species of fruits, and the art of distilling simple waters, cordials, perfumed oils and essences. [by an ingenious foreigner].[1] London: printed for G. Riley and A. Cooke, 1770. xxiii, 271, 46 p. 18 cm.

Cited: Bitting, pp. 49–50; Oxford, p. 102

Copies: *BI*: LeU(B)*; LBL
    NA: DCLC; KMK; NYPL

—2nd ed. London: printed for G. Riley, 1771.[2] —: —
—a new ed. London: printed for G. Riley, 1772. ENLS; LeU(B); LGL: MB; NPV

1. It is not until the publication of the new edition in 1772 that the 'Ingenious Foreigner' identifies himself as: 'Mr. Borella, now head confectioner to the Spanish Ambassador in England.'
2. No copy of the 2nd ed. has been located; see Murphy, p. 5.

BRADLEY, MARTHA (*fl.* 1760)

The British housewife:[1] or, the cook, housekeeper's, and gardiner's [*sic*] companion . . . containing a general account of fresh provisions of all kinds . . . the art of carving . . . the conduct of a family in respect to health . . . the whole embellished with a great number of curious copper plates, shewing the manner of trussing all kinds of game . . . also the order of setting out tables for dinners, suppers . . . by which even those who cannot read will be able to instruct themselves. etc. London: printed for S. Crowder and H. Woodgate, [*c*.1760].[2] Vol. 1. 752 p. frontis. pls. 21 cm.; Vol. 2. 469 p. 21 cm.

Cited: Bitting, pp. 54–5; Oxford, pp. 104–5

Copies: *BI*: ENLS[3]; LBL; LeU(B)*
    NA: MCR; NYPL; ViWC

1. *Scots Mag.*, vol. 18 (Jan. 1756), p. 54, contains the following advertisement: 'The British housewife, no. 1. To be continued weekly. 3d. Crowder.' It would seem that, from as early as 1756, Martha Bradley had the intention to publish her long work in instalments on the press of Stanley Crowder, but no copy of any instalment has been located, and no further advertisements appeared in *Scots Mag.*, and, although her printer was situated in London, no notices at all were inserted in *Gents.Mag.*
2. Henry Woodgate was in partnership with Stanley Crowder until a short time before the latter's death in 1766, which helps, with the information in note 1 above, to give an approximate date for publication; see Plomer/2, pp. 67–8, and 270.
3. The copy in the ENLS, which is incomplete, is inscribed 'E. Riddell 1773'.

BRADLEY, RICHARD
see CHOMEL, Noel.

BRADLEY, RICHARD (1688–1732)

The country housewife and lady's director, in the management of a house, and the delights and profits of a farm, . . . managing the brew-house . . . and making of wines . . . etc.[1] The sbcond [*sic*] edition.[2] London: printed for Woodman and Lyon, 1727. xi, 187 p. frontis. 20 cm. 2 sh. 6 d.

THE
Country Housewife
AND
LADY's DIRECTOR,
IN THE
Management of a HOUSE, and the Delights and Profits of a FARM.

CONTAINING

INSTRUCTIONS for managing the Brew-House, and Malt-Liquors in the Cellar; the making of Wines of all sorts.

DIRECTIONS for the DAIRY, in the Improvement of Butter and Cheese upon the worst of Soils; the feeding and making of Brawn; the ordering of Fish, Fowl, Herbs, Roots, and all other useful Branches belonging to a Country-Seat, in the most elegant manner for the Table.

Practical OBSERVATIONS concerning DISTILLING; with the best Method of making Ketchup, and many other curious and durable Sauces.

The whole distributed in their proper MONTHS, from the Beginning to the End of the Year.

With particular REMARKS relating to the Drying or Kilning of SAFFRON.

By R. BRADLEY,

Professor of Botany in the University of Cambridge; *and F. R. S.*

The Sixth Edition.
With ADDITIONS.

LONDON:

Printed for D. BROWNE, at the *Black-Swan* without *Temple-Bar*

MDCCXXXVI.

[Price 2 *s.* 6 *d.*]

Richard Bradley's two cookery books were published together as a single volume as early as 1732 when the second of the books first appeared. These two-in-one volumes retained two title-pages. This is the first title-page from a 1736 copy.

Cited: Bitting, pp. 55–6; Oxford, pp. 58–9

Copies: *BI*: LBL*
        NA: —

—another ed. Dublin: printed for J. Watts, 1727. LWML: DCLC

—3rd ed. London: printed for Woodman and Lyon, 1727. —: DCLC

—3rd ed. London: printed for Woodman and Lyon, 1728. OBL: NNNAM

—supplement. [Part 2 only, being a completely new addition to the original work.] The country housewife and lady's director, adorn'd with cuts. London: printed for D. Browne and T. Woodman, 1732. [Part 2] vii, 188 p. LBL: MH

—6th ed. with additions [being Parts 1 and 2 in one volume]. London: printed for D. Browne and T. Woodman, 1732. GUL; LBL; LWML: —

—6th ed. with additions [being Parts 1 and 2 in one volume]. London: printed for D. Browne, 1736. LBL; LeU(B): —

—6th ed. with additions. London: printed for D. Browne and L. Davis, 1753. LeU(B): —

—6th ed. London:[3] printed for W. Bristow and C. Ethrington, 1762. OBL: —

1. For a life of Richard Bradley, FRS, Professor of Botany, University of Cambridge, see *DNB*, vol. 2 (1908), p. 1080; also the Introduction, pp. 9–25, by Caroline Davidson to the reprint of the 6th ed. of this book by Prospect Books, 1980.
2. Although a 1st ed. must have been published, no copy of it has been located by the present compiler.
3. This was an abridged and re-arranged version.

BRADLEY, RICHARD (1688–1732)

A short historical account of coffee; containing the most remarkable observations of the greatest men in Europe. etc. London: printed and sold by Em. Mathews, [*c.*1715]. 30 p. frontis.[1] 14 cm.

Cited: Bitting, p. 55

Copies: *BI*: —
        NA: DCLC*

—another ed. The virtue and use of coffee etc. London: printed by Eman. Mathews and W. Mears, 1721. ENLS; LBL; LWML: CtY; DCLC; MB

1. There is a defect in the caption under the frontispiece: 'The Coffe [*sic*] Tree'.

BRADSHAW, PENELOPE (*fl.* 1750)

Bradshaw's family companion. Containing directions for marketing and housewifery; with . . . receipts in cookery . . . also curious extracts from a famous treatise on the teeth, their disorder and cure. etc. London: printed for the author, 1753. 9–96 p. 21 cm. 1 sh.

Cited: —

Copies: *BI*: LWML*[1]
        NA: —

1. The LWML copy contains an additional 98 pages of manuscript receipts.

BRADSHAW, PENELOPE (*fl.* 1750)

Bradshaw's valuable family jewel, and a store-house of such curious matters, as all ought to be acquainted with, being a collection of near three hundred of the most approved receipts in cookery, pastery [*sic*], confectionary [*sic*], preserving, pickling . . . brewing. etc. To which is added, a collection of near three hundred family receipts of medicines. etc. 5th ed. with very large additions. [London]: printed for P. Bradshaw, 1749. [Part 1] 48 p. [Part 2] 49–88 p. 16 cm. 1 sh.

Cited: Bitting, p. 56

Copies: *BI*: LeU(B)*
          NA: —

—6th ed. [London]: printed for P. Bradshaw, 1749. GPL(M): KMK

—9th ed. with additions. [London]: printed for P. Bradshaw, [*c.*1750]. —: DCLC

—10th ed. [London]: printed for P. Bradshaw, 1748.[1] —: KMK

—12th ed. [London]: printed for the author, 1752.[2] LeU(B): —

—a new ed. [London]: printed for the author, [*c.*1755]. LeU(B): —

1. This edition gives a joint authorship: Mrs Penelope Bradshaw and 'the late ingenious Mr. Lambart, [*sic*] confectioner', who was probably Edw. Lambert; see LAMBERT, Edward, The art of confectionary. It is odd that this edition, the 10th, which was *certainly* printed in 1748, has a higher edition number than the 6th ed., which was *certainly* printed in 1749, and the 9th ed., which was *probably* printed in 1750. If the figures for the years were not wrongly printed (and such a mistake seems unlikely), then Mrs Bradshaw could have been misusing edition numbers to imply by 1748 that she had written a work that was much in demand.
2. Although the contents of this edition are, with certain exceptions, identical to all the other known editions of this work, the title-page has been altered considerably. The main title, for instance, is Bradshaw's valuable family companion, with 'companion' in place of 'jewel'. It is also interesting to note that in this edition Mrs Bradshaw describes herself as 'a Housekeeper to *several* Noble Families *many* Years', but in another of her works says she was 'Housekeeper *Forty* Years to *a* Noble Family; see next entry: BRADSHAW, Penelope, The family jewel.

BRADSHAW, PENELOPE (*fl.* 1750)

The family jewel, and compleat housewife's companion: or, the whole art of cookery made plain and easy. In a method entirely new, and suited to every capacity; calculated for the preservation of health, and on the principles of frugality, including things useful, substantial and splendid. Containing compleat directions in marketing, and other branches of housewifry [*sic*], and above 400 receipts . . . Being the result of forty years experience, and an attentive observation on all the books of cookery that have ever yet been published. With an index directing to every receipt . . . With remarks by a London pastry-cook, of long and extensive practice. Also an addition of about 200 receipts, and a bill of fare for every month in the year; with the manner of placing the dishes. 6th ed.[1] London: printed for R. Whitworth, 1754. 144 p. 17 cm.

Cited: —

Copies: *BI*: LeU(B)*[2]
       NA: NNNAM

1. No other editions have been located, and it is possible that this edition, although numbered '6th', was the only one published. From note 1, under the previous entry, it has been shown that Mrs Bradshaw could have misused edition numbers.
2. The LeU(B) copy is inscribed 'Thoˢ Grover's Booke 1755'.

BRAIDLEY, A. (*fl.* 1786)

The complete English cook, etc. [——]: printed for the author, 1786.[1] [——] [——]

Cited: —

Copies: *BI*: —
      NA: —

1. The only known reference to this work is *Sotheby Cat.* (4 Nov. 1971), p. 81, which shows that a copy of it was bound with the 22nd ed. of the Rev. John Wesley's *Primitive Physic*, and that this copy was sold on the aforesaid date to S. Pottesman.

BREWER, SAMUEL CHILD[1] (d. 1743?)

Everyman his own brewer. A small treatise explaining the art and mystery of brewing porter, ale, twopenny and table-beer. etc. 3rd ed. London: printed for Dring & Co., [*c.*1792].[2] [——] [——]

1. This entry is included because *Maggs Bros. Cat.*, No. 645, p. 101, wrongly assumed that the author's occupation (a brewer) was his surname, and thereby made the error of ascribing the work to 'BREWER (Samuel Child)'. For the correct ascription; see under later entry: CHILD, Samuel, Everyman his own brewer (under 3rd ed.).
2. The same source wrongly dates the edition *c.*1790 when it was probably published *c.*1792.

BRIGGS, RICHARD[1] (*fl.* 1788–1798)

The English art of cookery, according to the present practice; being a complete guide to all housekeepers, on a plan entirely new . . . containing . . . directions for markets . . . the art of carving . . . made wines . . ., brewing . . . with bills of fare for every month of the year. etc. London: printed for G. G. J. and J. Robinson, 1788. xx, 656 p. pls. 22 cm. 7 sh²

Cited: Bitting, p. 60; Oxford, pp. 115–16

Copies: *BI*: ANLW; DoCL; OBL*
      NA: DCLC; MCR

—2nd ed. London: printed for G. G. and J. Robinson, 1791. LWML: —

—a new ed. Dublin: printed for P. Byrne, 1791. —: NBu

—another ed. The new art of cookery. etc. Philadelphia: printed for W. Spotswood, R. Campbell and B. Johnson, 1791.[3] —: —

—another ed. Philadelphia: printed for W. Spotswood, R. Campbell and B. Johnson, 1792. LBL: DCLC; MWA; NYPL

—a new ed. Cork: printed for J. Connor, [*c.*1792]. DNLI: —

—3rd ed. London: printed for G. G. and J. Robinson, 1794. LWML: DCLC: MiD

—a new ed. Dublin: printed for P. Byrne, 1798. LGL: DCLC; KMK

—another ed. Philadelphia: printed for H. and P. Rice, 1798. MWA; NjP; ViU

—another ed. Boston: printed for W. Spotswood, 1798. —: MWA

1. The author described himself as 'many years Cook at the White-Hart Tavern, Holborn: Temple Coffee-House, and other Taverns in London'.
2. *Scots Mag.*, vol. 51 (May 1789), p. 243, confirms that the price was '7 sh. bound'.
3. The only known reference to this edition is Bitting, p. 60. This and all subsequent *American* editions have the same alteration in the title: The new art of cookery; with 'new' in place of 'English'.

BRITISH

The British jewel, or complete housewife's best companion . . . directions for making English wines . . . Everyman his own physician . . . a method of restoring to life people drowned . . . to which is added the complete farrier. etc. London: printed and sold by J. Miller, 1769.[1] 104 p. pls. 17 cm. 1 sh.

Cited: Bitting, p. 524; Oxford, pp. 112–13

Copies: *BI*: —
     NA: DCLC*

—another ed. [——]: printed for [——], 1776.[2]

—a new ed. London: printed and sold by J. Miller, 1780. LBL: —

—a new ed. London: printed and sold by J. Miller, 1782.[3] —: NYPL

—a new ed. London: printed and sold by J. Miller, 1785. LeU(B): —

—a new ed. London: printed for Osborne and Griffin; and Gainsborough: printed for H. Mozley, 1788. LeU(B)[4]: —

—a new ed. London: printed and sold by T. Sabine, [c.1790]. —: KMK

1. Oxford, p. 113, wrongly states that the 1st ed. was published in 1780. Although no copies of this edition have been located in the British Isles, they have been offered for sale in Germany and England; see Drexel, (1888), p. 28, and *B.&G.Cat.*, No. 37, p. 11.
2. The only known reference to this edition is given in *Christie's Cat.* (1 Aug. 1972), p. 51. This copy was sold to 'Edwards'.
3. See Stark, p. 17
4. This edition is entitled The new British jewel.

BRITISH

The British legacy: or, fountain of knowledge, containing among upwards of two hundred other curious particulars, of the utmost service to families in general. etc. London: printed for Thomas Chandler, 1754. x, 11–176 p. pls. 19 cm. 2 sh.

Cited: Bitting, pp. 379–80

Copies: *BI*: OBL*
     NA: CtY; PPULC

—another ed. The fountain of knowledge, or British legacy. etc. London: printed by T. Bailey, [c.1760]. LBL: CtY; MH

—another ed. . . . upwards of five hundred . . . London: printed by W. Bailey, [c.1785].[1] —: DCLC

1. Up to p. 83 of this work there is domestic advice, including cookery receipts. Thereafter it is devoted to a treatise: 'Everyone their own physician'; see Bitting, p. 380.

BROADBENT, Humphrey (*fl.* 1722)

Domestick coffee man, shewing the true way of preparing and making chocolate, coffee and tea. etc. London: printed for E. Curll and T. Bickerton, 1722. 26 p. 20 cm.

Cited: —

Copies: *BI*: LBL*
     NA: MH-BA

BROOKS, Catharine (*fl.* 1760)

The complete English cook; or prudent housewife. Being an entire new collection of the most genteel, yet least expensive receipts in every branch of cookery and good housewifery . . . to which is added the physical director. etc.[1] 2nd ed. with additions.[2] London: printed for the authoress, and sold by J. Cooke, [c.1762].[3] 5–132 p. frontis.[4] 16 cm. 1 sh.

Cited: Bitting, pp. 61–2; Oxford, p. 93

Copies: *BI*: LBL; LeU(B)*; MU(JR)
    NA: DCLC; MH

—another ed. The experienced English housekeeper, for the use and ease of ladies. London: printed for the authoress, [c.1766]. LeU(B): —

—4th ed. with additions. London: printed for the authoress, [c.1770]. LBL: DNLM

—another ed. Manchester: printed by Alice Swindells, [c.1796].[5]

—another ed. Manchester: printed for T. Thomas and J. Sadler, [c.1800]. LWML: —

1. The present compiler has compared the 2nd ed. of Catharine Brooks's work with the 2nd ed. of Ann Peckham's work (see PECKHAM, Ann, The complete English cook), and the title-pages were found to be identical. The contents of each work, however, are entirely different. Indeed, although the two women used identical title-pages more than once, there is no evidence that they plagiarized each other's texts. See also RAFFALD, Elizabeth, The experienced English house-keeper, footnote 2.
2. No copy of the 1st ed. has been located, but Mrs Brooks clearly implied that she had published one by using the words 'with additions' after '2nd ed.'.
3. The approximate year of publication has been arrived at from the preface, which is dated 'January 20th 1762'.
4. The frontispiece is missing from the LeU(B) copy.

5. *The Manchester Press before 1801*, op. cit., p. 222, and Arthur John Hawkes, *Lancashire Printed Books* (Wigan, 1925), p. 105, give the only known references to this edition.

BRUES, JOHN (*fl.* 1754)

The servant's sure guide to favour and fortune, etc.[1] London: printed for [——] Robinson, [*c.*1754]. In two parts. [——] [——] 3 sh.

Cited: —

Copies: *BI*: —
   NA: —

1. The only known reference to this work is in *Scots Mag.*, vol. 16 (Apr. 1754), pp. 207–8. A 'reviewer' writing under 'miscellaneous' states: 'In this work, though the author protests that he neither understands nor desires to understand grammar . . . his book is an epitome of all knowledge; and contains almost every species of literary composition, from a receipt in cookery to a theological dissertation.'

BUCHAN, WILLIAM (1729–1805)

Domestic medicine; or, the family physician . . . chiefly calculated to recommend a proper attention to regimen and simple medicines.[1] Edinburgh: printed by Balfour, Auld and Smellie, 1769. xv, 624 p. 21 cm. 6 sh.[2]

Cited: —

Copies: *BI*: ENLS*; GUL; LWML
   NA: DNLM; ICU; NNNAM

—1st American ed. Philadelphia: printed for R. Aitken, [*c.*1771]. —: DCLC; DNLM; PPULC

—2nd ed. with additions. Edinburgh: printed for W. Strahan and T. Cadell, 1772. ENLS: MH; PPULC

—2nd ed. with additions. London: printed for W. Strahan and T. Cadell, 1772. —: DNLM; MH; ViSL

—another American ed. Philadelphia: printed by John Dunlap for R. Aitken, 1772. —: CtY; MHi; NYPL

—3rd ed. with additions. London: printed for W. Strahan and T. Cadell, 1774. ENLS; LWML: ICJ; MiU; PPC

—2nd American ed. Philadelphia: printed by Joseph Crukshank for R. Aitken, 1774. —: CtY; DCLC; PHi

—5th ed. corrected. London: printed for W. Strahan and T. Cadell, 1776. —: CtY; DNLM; PPULC

—6th ed. corrected. Dublin: printed by W. Sleator, 1777. —: DNLM

—3rd American ed. Norwich [Connecticut]: printed by John Trumbull, 1778. —: CtY; DCLC; NNNAM

—6th ed. corrected. London: printed for W. Strahan and T. Cadell, 1779. LWML: PPULC; WU-M

—7th ed. corrected. London: printed for W. Strahan and T. Cadell, 1781. LWML: DNLM

—another ed. London: printed for W. Strahan and T. Cadell, 1783. —: NNNAM

—another American ed. Philadelphia: printed for Joseph Crukshank, 1784. LWML: DCLC; NNNAM; PHi

—8th ed. corrected and enlarged. London: printed for W. Strahan and T. Cadell, 1784. EUL: DNLM; NNNAM

—9th ed. Dublin: printed by H. Chamberlaine, 1784. —: NNNAM; PPULC

—9th ed. with additions. London: printed for A. Strahan and T. Cadell, 1786. ERCP: CtY; DNLM

—10th ed. London: printed for A. Strahan and T. Cadell, 1788. ENLS; LWML: —

—11th American ed. corrected. Hartford [Connecticut]: printed by Nathaniel Patten, 1789. —: CtY; DNLM; MB

—11th ed. corrected. London: printed for A. Strahan and T. Cadell, 1790. ERCP: CtY; MiU

—12th ed. London: printed for A. Strahan and T. Cadell, 1791. LWML: CtY-M; DCLC; TxU

—13th ed. London: printed for A. Strahan and T. Cadell, 1792. LBL: DCLC; PPC; TxU

—13th American ed. Philadelphia: printed for J. Crukshank, 1793. —: MWA; NNNAM; NYPL

—14th American ed. Boston: printed by Joseph Bumstead, 1793. —: CtY; DCLC; MWA

—14th ed. London: printed for A. Strahan and T. Cadell, 1794. LBL: DCLC; NNNAM; PPULC

—another American ed. revised and adapted to the diseases and climate of the United States by S. P. Griffiths.[3] Philadelphia: printed by T. Dobson, 1795. —: MWA

—18th American ed. New London [Connecticut]: printed by Thomas C. Green, 1795. —: DCLC; MWA; PPULC

—15th ed. to which is added observations concerning the diet of the common people.[4] London: printed for A. Strahan, T. Cadell, jun. and W. Davies, 1797. LBL: DNLM

—another American ed. Philadelphia: printed by Richard Folwell for T. Allen, 1797. ENLS: DCLC; ICJ; NNNAM

—17th ed. London: printed for A. Strahan, T. Cadell, jun. and W. Davies, 1800.[5] —: DNLM

1. On p. 68 Buchan states: 'The arts of cookery render many things unwholesome, which are not so in their own nature. By jumbling together a number of different ingredients, in order to make a poignant sauce, or rich soup, the composition proves almost a rich poison . . . It were well for mankind if cookery, as an art, were intirely prohibited. Plain roasting or boiling is all that nature points out, and all that the stomach requires.'

2. *Scots Mag.*, vol. 31 (June 1769), p. 315, confirms that the price was 6 sh.
3. Further editions were published in the 19th century.
4. For a similar theme, see earlier entry under ACCOUNT.
5. Publication of British editions continued in the 19th century. No copy of the 4th ed. has been located.

BUCHAN, WILLIAM (1729-1805)

Observations concerning the diet of common people, recommending a method of living less expensive, and more conducive to health, than the present. etc.[1]
London: printed for A. Strahan, T. Cadell, jun. and W. Davies, 1797.[2] 44 p. 22 cm. 1 sh. 6 d.[3]

Cited: —

Copies: *BI*: EUL*
      NA: CtY; DNLM

1. For a life of William Buchan see *DNB*, vol. 3 (1908), pp. 180-1.
2. This work was published for the same people in the same year as an additional part of the 15th ed. of the author's earlier work; see previous entry: BUCHAN, William, Domestic medicine. It here stands as a separate book in its own right.
3. An advertisement in *Scots Mag.*, vol. 59 (Oct. 1797), p. 767, confirms that the price was 1 sh. 6 d.

BUC'HOZ, PIERRE JOSEPH (1731-1807)

The toilet of Flora; or, a collection of the most simple and approved methods of preparing baths, essences, pomatums . . . and sweet-scented waters. etc.[1]
London: printed for W. Nicoll, 1772.[2] [———] [———] 3 sh.

Cited: —

Copies: *BI*: —
      NA: —

—a new ed. improved. London: printed for J. Murray and W. Nicoll, 1775. BPL: —

—a new ection [*sic*]. London: printed for J. Murray and W. Nicoll, 1779. LBL; LeU(B): —

—a new ed. improved. London: printed for J. Murray and W. Nicoll, 1784. LBL: NYPL[3]

1. A translation, with alterations, of *La Toilette de Flore* by Pierre Joseph Buc'hoz (Valade, Paris, 1771). The name of the English translator is not known. The surname 'Buc'hoz' must be a French version of the German surname Buchholz or Buchholtz.
2. The entry is based on the only known reference to this edition, which is a notice in *Scots Mag.*, vol. 34 (Aug. 1772), p. 437.
3. The NYPL copy is part of the Whitney Cookery Collection.

BUTLER

The butler's assistant. etc. London: printed for R. Dodsley, 1749.[1] [———] [———] 1 sh. 6d.

Cited: —

Copies: *BI*: —
    NA: —

1. The only known reference to this work is an advertisement in *Gents.Mag.*, vol. 19 (Apr. 1749), p. 192.

BUTLER, Caroline[1] (*fl.* 1760)

The new London and country cook, or, the whole art of cookery displayed in the newest and most fashionable taste. etc. London: printed for J. Cooke, [*c.*1760]. 108 p. frontis. [——] [——] 1 sh.

Cited: Oxford, p. 103

Copies: *BI*: —
    NA: NNNAM; WU

1. The author stated she was 'of Charlotte-Street [London]' and that she had practised cookery in all its various branches, and in the best families upwards of thirty years!

C

CAMPBELL, Duncan (*fl.* 1735)

A poem upon tea. Wherein its antiquity, its several virtues and influences are set forth; and the wisdom of the sober sex commended in chusing so mild a liquor for their entertainments. Likewise, the reason why the ladies protest against all imposing liquors, and the vulgar terms used by the followers of Bacchus. Also, the objections against TEA answered; the complaint of the fair sex redress'd, and the best way of proceeding in love-affairs; together with the sincere courtship of Dick and Amy, etc. London: printed and sold by Mrs. Dodd, 1735. 9–32 p. 21 cm. 6 d.

Cited: —

Copies: *BI*: ENLS*; LBL
    NA: IU

CAREY, Henry (1687?-1743)

A learned dissertation on dumpling; its dignity, antiquity . . . with a word upon pudding. etc. [Anon.][1] London: printed for J. Roberts, 1726. 2, 25 p. 19 cm. 6 d.

Cited: Bitting, p. 76.

Copies: *BI*: LeU(B); OBL*
    NA: —

—2nd ed. London: printed for J. Roberts, 1726. —: CtY; KMK; MiU

—3rd ed. London: printed for J. Roberts, 1726. —: MH

—4th ed. London: printed for J. Roberts, 1726. OBL: —

—5th ed. London: printed for J. Roberts, 1726. LBL: MH

—6th ed. London: printed for J. Roberts, 1726. —: DCLC

—7th ed. London: printed for Thos. Worrall, 1727. LBL: CtY

1. See *NUCat.*: 'The authorship is attributed to Henry Carey on strong internal and external evidence.' He was a well-known English poet and playwright who wrote, among other things, *Sally in our Alley*; see *DNB*, vol. 3, (1908), pp. 980–1.

CARRUTH, P. (*fl.* 1800)

Domestic economy; or, general recipe book: containing a number of useful recipes, compiled from valuable private manuscripts and expensive works of eminent men.[1] Edinburgh: printed by Robert Menzies, [*c.*1800]. 12 p. 15 cm.

Cited: —

Copies: *BI*: ENLS*
      NA: —

1. This is a chapbook, containing household hints and recipes, including 'how to make spruce beer and instantaneous ginger beer'. At the end there is a notice for 'Carruth's vegetable corn plaster . . . prepared only by P. Carruth, Chiropedist [*sic*]'.

CARTER, [——] [Mrs]

The British jewel or art of cookery made perfectly easy.[1] [London]: printed for J. Bailey, [*c.*1795]. [——] [——]

Cited: —

Copies: *BI*: —
      NA: —

1. No copy of this work has been located. The only known reference to it is given in *Sotheby Cat.*, (1 Aug. 1968), p. 15. It is possible that this Mrs Carter is the same person as Susannah Carter; see later entry: CARTER, Susannah, The frugal housewife.

CARTER, CHARLES (*fl.* 1730–1750)

The compleat city and country cook: or, accomplish'd housewife . . . illustrated with forty-nine copper plates . . . to which is added by way of appendix, near two hundred of the most approv'd receipts in physick and surgery for the cure of the most common diseases incident to families: the collection of a noble lady deceased. etc. London: printed for A. Bettesworth, C. Hitch and C. Davis, 1732. viii, 280 p. pls. 20 cm. 5 sh.[1]

Cited: Bitting, p. 78; Oxford, p. 62

Copies: *BI*: BaCE; LWML; LeU(B)*
      NA: CLSU; DCLC; NYPL

—2nd ed. with large additions. London: printed for A. Bettesworth, C. Hitch and C. Davis, 1736. LBL; LWML; OBL: DCLC; NIC

—3rd ed. London: printed for [——] 1749.[2]

1. *RB* (Mar. 1732), p. 69, confirms that the price was 5 sh.
2. The only known reference to this edition is *B.&G.Cat.*, No. 37, p. 8.

CARTER, CHARLES (*fl.* 1730–1750)

The complete practical cook: or, a new system of the whole art and mystery of cookery . . . adorned with sixty curious copper plates. etc.[1] London: printed for W. Meadows, C. Rivington and R. Hett, 1730. 224, 58 p. pls. 26 cm. 16 sh.[2]

Cited: Bitting, p. 77; Oxford, pp. 61–2

Copies: *BI*: ENLS*[3]; LBL; LeU(B)
   NA: KMK; MSaE; NYPL[4]

1. The author, whose father was also a cook, described himself as 'Lately Cook to his Grace the Duke of Argyll, the Earl of Pontefract, the Lord Cornwallis, etc.'.
2. *Mon.Cat./2* (vol. 2), p. 2 (Jan. 1730), confirms that the price was 16 sh.
3. The ENLS copy contains the bookplate of Sir George Steuart of Grantully, Bart.
4. The NYPL copy is part of the Whitney Cookery Collection, which was donated by the will of Mrs Helen Hay Whitney.

CARTER, CHARLES (*fl.* 1730–1750)

The London and country cook: or, accomplished housewife, containing practical directions and the best receipts in all the branches of cookery and housekeeping; . . . such as roasting . . . confectionary . . . English wines; interspersed with many sovereign and approved medicines, used by private families . . . revised and much improved by a gentlewoman. etc. 3rd ed. London: printed for Charles Hitch, Stephen Austen and John Hinton, 1749.[1] vii, 363 p. frontis. pls.[2] 20 cm.

Cited: Oxford, p. 77

Copies: *BI*: LeU(B)*[3]
   NA: KMK; MWelC; NYPL

1. The date is misprinted in *NUCat.* as '1799'.
2. The 49 plates are the same as those used by the author in a previous work; see CARTER, Charles, The compleat city and country cook.
3. The LeU(B) copy is inscribed: 'Elizabeth Griffith Her Booke 1750'.

CARTER, SUSANNAH (*fl.* 1765–1790?)

The frugal housewife, or, complete woman cook. Wherein the art of dressing all sorts of viands, with cleanliness, decency and elegance, is explained in five hundred approved receipts . . . also two copper plates, displaying the method of trussing game and poultry. etc. London: printed for F. Newbery,[1] [*c.*1765]. 168 p. pls. 17 cm. 1 sh.

Cited: Bitting, pp. 78–9; Oxford, pp. 122–3

Copies: *BI*: —

     NA: KMK; MHi*; MWA

—another ed. Dublin: printed by James Hoey,[2] [*c*.1765]. DNLI: —

—another ed. London: printed for F. Newbery; and Boston: reprinted and sold by Edes and Gill,[3] [*c*.1772]. —: DCLC; MWA

—another ed. London: printed for E. Newbery, [*c*.1790]. LBL: —

—another American ed. New York: printed for Berry and Rogers, [*c*.1792]. —: DCLC; MWA

—another ed. revised and corrected. London: printed for E. Newbery, 1795. LBL; LWML; LeU(B): NPV

—another American ed. revised and corrected. Philadelphia: printed by James Carey, 1796. —: MSaE; NYPL

—another ed. London: printed for E. Newbery, [*c*.1800]. —: MH

1. For a history of the Newbery family see S. Roscoe, *John Newbery and Successors: 1740–1814* (London, 1973).

2. As the printer was described as John Hoey, *senior*, in (and probably before) 1765 [see Plomer/2, p. 389], it is possible that this edition was published at an earlier date. James Hoey was a printer from 1730 to 1774.

3. The two plates are by the celebrated Paul Revere, hero at the outbreak of the American Revolution, who was a Boston silversmith. See Lowenstein, p. 2.

CARTWRIGHT, CHARLOTTE (*fl.* 1790)

The lady's best companion; or, a complete treasure for the fair sex. Containing the whole arts of cookery, pastry, confectionary, potting, pickling, preserving, candying, collaring, brewing, etc. . . . To which is added, the approved family physician; consisting of physical receipts for most disorders that grown people, and young children are subject to. etc. London: printed for W. Clements and James Sadler, 1789. 48 p. 19 cm. 6 d.

Cited: —

Copies: *BI*: LeU(B)*

     NA: —

—another ed. London: printed for A. Hambleton, 1790. —: MiD

—another ed. London: printed for W. Clements and J. Sadler, 1791. —: KMK

—an American ed. Elizabeth Town [now Hagerstown, Maryland]: printed by Thomas Grieves, 1798.[1]

1. The only known reference to this edition is given in Evans, vol. 12 (1798–9), who records the place-names as 'Elizabeth (Hager's) Town'. See CHAMBERS, Amelia.

CELLAR

The cellar book, or the butler's assistant in keeping a regular account of his liquors. London: printed for R. Dodsley, 1754.[1] [——] [——] 1 sh. 6 d.

Cited: —

Copies: *BI*: —

     NA: —

—3rd ed. London: printed for R. Dodsley, 1763.[2] —: —

1. The only known reference to this work is an advertisement in *Gents.Mag.*, vol. 24 (Nov. 1754), p. 535. It is almost certainly the 2nd ed. of a work published in 1749 for Dodsley for 1 sh. 6 d.; see under BUTLER.
2. The only known reference to this work is Simon, p. 36.

CHAMBERS, AMELIA (*fl.* 1800)

The ladies best companion; or, a golden treasure for the fair sex. Containing the whole arts of cookery . . . with plain instructions for making English wines . . . the art of preserving beauty . . . every lady her own and family's physician . . . also the family instructor. etc. London: printed for J. Cooke, [*c*.1800]. vii, 196 p. frontis.[1] 17 cm. 3 sh.

Cited: Oxford, pp. 127–8

Copies: *BI*: LBL; LeU(B)*[2]
      NA: —

1. See earlier entry: BUTLER, Caroline, The new London and country cook, which has an identical frontispiece. As both works were printed for J. Cooke, it is possible that he decided to use again an apt illustration for another similar but completely separate work. The contents of the two books are entirely different.
2. The LeU(B) copy is inscribed: 'E. Villars'.

CHAPMAN, THOMAS (*fl.* 1760)

The cyder-maker's instructor, or sweet-maker's assistant, and victualler's and housekeeper's director. etc. In three parts. Cirencester: printed for the author by S. Rudder, [*c*.1757]. xii, 15–49 p. 16 cm. 2 sh.

Cited: —

Copies: *BI*: LBL[1]; OBL*
      NA: —

—another ed. Boston: printed by Green and Russell, 1762. —: DCLC; MHi; MWA

—another ed. Philadelphia: printed for Andrew Steuart, 1762. —: PPL

—a new ed. London: printed for Richardson and Urquhart, 1780. OBL: —

1. The British Library copy has been lost or mislaid.

CHILD, SAMUEL (*fl.* 1768?–1800)

Everyman his own brewer. A small treatise explaining the art and mystery of brewing porter, ale, twopenny and table-beer.[1] etc. London: printed for the author, [*c*.1790]. 19 p. 21 cm.

Cited: —

Copies: *BI*: LBL*
      NA: MH

—2nd ed. carefully revised. London: printed for the author, [*c*.1792]. LBL: MH

—3rd ed. London: printed for J. Ridgeway, [*c*.1792]. —: NYPL

—3rd ed. carefully revised. London: printed for Dring & Co., [*c*.1792].[2]

—4th ed. revised. London: printed for J. Ridgeway, [*c*.1794].[3] ENLS: MH

—2nd American ed. Philadelphia: printed for T. Condie, 1796.[4] —: DCLC; MWA

—5th ed. corrected and enlarged. London: printed for J. Ridgeway, 1798. —: MH

—6th ed. corrected and enlarged. London: printed for J. Ridgeway, 1798. LBL: MH-BA

—7th ed. corrected and enlarged. London: printed for J. Ridgeway, 1799. —: MH

—9th ed. corrected and enlarged. London, printed for J. Ridgeway, 1800. —: CU

1. See WATKINS, George, The compleat English brewer, for a similar work.
2. The only known reference to this 3rd ed. is given in *Maggs Bros. Cat.*, No. 645, p. 101, where the authorship is wrongly ascribed to Samuel Child's occupation of brewer, instead of to his surname; see under earlier entry: BREWER, Samuel Child, Everyman his own brewer.
3. On p. 19 of the 4th ed. the author states: 'Women are the chief home-brewers throughout England; and I have endeavoured to render every part intelligible and easy to the meanest capacity.'
4. See Lowenstein, p. 5.

CHILD, SAMUEL (*fl.* 1768?-1800?)

Everyman his own brewer; or a compendium of the English brewery. Containing the best instructions for the choice of hops, malt and water; and for the right management of the brewing utensils. Likewise, the most approved methods of brewing London porter and ale. Of brewing amber, Burton, western and oat ales . . . and of manufacturing pure malt wines. etc. [by a gentleman]. [London]: printed for the author, and sold by J. Almon, 1768. xxviii, 29-256 p. 18 cm.[1]

Cited: —

Copies: *BI*: CUL
              NA: MH-BA; NYPL

1. The entry is based on the copy in CUL-Rare Books Dept.

CHOICE

A choice collection of cookery receipts. Newcastle: printed in this present year for [——], [*c*.1775]. 24 p. [——]

Cited: Oxford, p. 107

Copies: *BI*: LBL
              NA: —

CHOMEL, NOEL (1632–1712)

Dictionnaire oeconomique; or, the family dictionary. Containing . . . the best and cheapest way of providing and improving all manner of meats and drinks . . . of preserving all kinds of fruits . . . the whole illustrated throughout with very great variety of figures. etc. [revised and recommended by Mr R. Bradley].[1] In two volumes. London: printed for D. Midwinter, 1725.[2] n.p. pls. 35 cm.

Cited: Bitting, pp. 87–8; Oxford, pp. 57–8

Copies: *BI*: CUL; EUL*; LBL
      NA: DCLC; KMK; MH

—another ed. Dublin: printed by J. Watts, 1727. —: OClW

—another ed. Dublin: printed by L. Flinn, 1758. —: MH

1. Professor Richard Bradley revised the English translation of the 2nd French ed. of the Rev. Noel Chomel's work (1st ed., Lyon, 1709; 2nd ed., Paris, 1718); see Vicaire, p. 173.
2. *Mon.Cat./2* (vol. 1), p. 1 (May 1723) gives a note on proposals for funding the printing by subscription.

CLELAND, ELIZABETH (*fl.* 1755–1770)

A new and easy method of cookery [by Elizabeth Cleland] . . . chiefly intended for the benefit of the young ladies who attend her school. etc.[1] Edinburgh: printed for the author by Gordon and Wright, 1755. 204 p. 20 cm. 3 sh. 6 d.[2]

Cited: Bitting, p. 91; Oxford, pp. 88–9

Copies: *BI*: RAL*[3]
      NA: NYPL

—2nd ed. with appendix. Edinburgh: printed by C. Wright & Co., 1759. ENLS[4]; LBL: MiD; NYPL

—2nd ed. with appendix. Edinburgh: printed by W. Gordon and Wright, 1759. ENLS; LeU(B); OBL: —

—2nd ed. London: printed for [——], 1759.[5] —: —

—3rd ed. with appendix. Edinburgh: printed for and sold by R. Fleming and W. Gray, 1770. CUL; ENLS; GUL: DCLC

1. For Elizabeth Cleland, who was a teacher of cookery in Edinburgh, see Alexander Law, 'Teachers in Edinburgh in the Eighteenth Century', *Book of the Old Edinburgh Club*, vol. 32 (1966), p. 120.
2. *Scots Mag.*, vol. 17 (Apr. 1755), p. 216, confirms that the price was 3 sh. 6 d.
3. The 1st ed. of 1755 is not listed by either Bitting or Oxford. The present compiler located a copy in Sir Walter Scott's Library, Abbotsford House, near Melrose, Roxburghshire, and then found it listed in J. G. Cochrane [compiler], *Catalogue of the Library at Abbotsford* (Edinburgh, 1838), p. 298. There is also a copy of the 1st ed. in NYPL. It is a scarce item.
4. The ENLS copy is a microfilm of the LBL copy.
5. The only known reference to this London printed 2nd ed. is given by Lewer, p. 222.

CLERMONT, B[ERNARD?]

see MENON, [——].

THE
LADY's COMPLETE GUIDE;
OR
COOKERY IN ALL ITS BRANCHES.

CONTAINING

The moſt approved Receipts, confirmed by Obſervation and Practice, in every reputable Engliſh Book of Cookery now extant,
beſides a great Variety of others which have never before been
offered to the Public. Alſo ſeveral tranſlated from the Productions of COOKS of Eminence who have publiſhed in FRANCE,
particularly M. COMMO's HISTOIRE DE CUISINE, M. DI-
SANG's MAITRE D'HOTEL, M. DUPONT and M. VALOIS,
M. TROAS, and M. DELATOUR, with their reſpective Names
to each Receipt; which, with the ORIGINAL ARTICLES,
will form the moſt complete Syſtem of Cookery ever yet exhibited, under the following Heads, viz.

ROASTING,	SOUPS,	TARTS,
BOILING,	SAUCES,	PIES,
MADE-DISHES,	GRAVIES,	PASTIES,
FRYING,	HASHES,	CHEESECAKES,
BROILING,	STEWS,	JELLIES,
POTTING,	PUDDINGS,	PICKLING,
FRICASSEES,	CUSTARDS,	PRESERVING,
RAGOUTS,	CAKES,	CONFECTIONARY, &c,

TO WHICH IS ADDED,

In order to render it as complete and perfect as poſſible,

THE COMPLETE BREWER;

CONTAINING

Familiar Inſtructions for brewing all Sorts of Beer and Ale; including the proper Management of the Vault or Cellar.

ALSO

THE FAMILY PHYSICIAN;

Conſiſting of a conſiderable Collection of approved Preſcriptions by
MEAD, SYDENHAM, TISSOT, FOTHERGIL, ELLIOT, BUCHAN,
and others, including a certain Remedy for that formidable Diſ-
order, the DROPSY, recommended by Perſons reſpectable in the
higheſt Degree.

BY MRS. MARY COLE,

COOK TO THE RIGHT HON. THE EARL OF DROGHEDA.

LONDON:
PRINTED FOR G. KEARSLEY, NO. 46, FLEET-STREET.
MDCCLXXXVIII.

Mrs Mary Cole deserves praise for being among the first cookery writers to cite in a systematic
way the sources of her recipes. Even in instances where she has combined versions from other
writers into something which she could have called her own, she cites the other writers. In her
preface she claims full credit for this innovation, and castigates those writers who simply
plagiarized their predecessors without acknowledgement. An earnest, moral approach. It is all
the more strange that of the six French authors cited on her title-page, and three others (Dupont,
Verno, and Troas) mentioned in her preface, only one (Clermont) has been identified. Was she
making fun of authors who paraded foreign names on their title-pages? Or did she have eight
French cookery books of which no other trace has survived? The latter hypothesis seems
incredible; while the former would involve modifying the impression we otherwise have of a
wholly serious and straightforward person.

CLIFTON, ELIZABETH (*fl.* 1750)

The cookmaid's assistant, or art of cookery, made plain and easy . . . With a bill of fare for each month in the year. etc.[1] London: printed for the Proprietors, [*c.*1750]. xii, 216 p. 17 cm.

Cited: Bitting, p. 92[2]

Copies: *BI*: —
NA: DCLC*

1. This work was 'by the late Mrs. Eliza. Clifton, of Richmond in Surrey'.
2. According to Bitting this work is very scarce.

COACHMAN

see TREATISE on . . . the steward's table.

COCCHI, ANTONIO CELESTINO (1695–1758)

The Pythagorean diet, of vegetables only, conducive to the preservation of health, and the cure of diseases. A discourse delivered in Florence, in the month of August 1743 . . . translated from the Italian.[1] London: printed for R. Dodsley, 1745. 91 p. 20 cm. 1 sh. 6 d.[2]

Cited: Oxford, p. 76

Copies: *BI*: ENLS*; LBL; LWML
NA: DCLC; TxU

1. This vegetarian pamphlet contains no receipts.
2. *Scots Mag.*, vol. 7 (Feb. 1745), p. 100, confirms that the price was 1 sh. 6 d.

COLE, MARY[1] (*fl.* 1788–1791)

The lady's complete guide; or cookery in all its branches . . . to which is added the complete brewer . . . also the family physician. etc.[2] London: printed for G. Kearsley, 1788. xxvii, 564 p. 22 cm. 6 sh.[3]

Cited: Bitting, p. 94; Oxford, pp. 117–18

Copies: *BI*: LBL; LeU(B)*
NA: CoU; DCLC; KMK

—a new ed. improved. London: printed for G. Kearsley. 1789. —: MCR, NNNAM

—3rd ed. very much improved. London: printed for G. Kearsley, 1791. LWML; LeU(B): NYPL

1. Mrs Cole described herself as 'Cook to the Right Hon. The Earl of Drogheda'.
2. See Hazlemore, M., Domestic economy, for a very similar work.
3. *Scots Mag.*, vol. 51 (June 1789), p. 284, confirms the prices as 6 sh. boards, 7 sh. bound.

COLLECTION

see KETTILBY, Mary.

COLLECTION

A collection of one hundred and thirty-seven approved receipts, in pastry and cookery . . . to which are added directions for making the best cosmetics, washing gauzes, muslins, etc. and painting of rooms, staircases. Aberdeen: printed for Alexander Thomson, 1774. iii, 52 p. 13 cm.

Cited: Oxford, p. 107

Copies: *BI*: LBL[1]; LeU(B)*
   NA: —

1. The British Library copy has been lost or mislaid.

COLLECTION

A collection of ordinances and regulations for the government of the Royal Household made in divers reigns. From King Edward III to King William and Queen Mary. Also receipts in ancient cookery. London: printed for The Society of Antiquaries by John Nichols, 1790. xxii, 476 p. 21 cm.[1]

Cited: Bitting, p. 532; Oxford, p. 119

Copies: *BI*: LeU(B)*; MCL; MPL
   NA: KMK; MiD; NYPL

1. The Society had previously published, in 1787, the account of the Comptroller of the Ward-robe, of the 28th year of King Edward I. Being in Latin, this work is not here listed; but it includes a 64-page introduction in English by John Topham, Esq., and an 11-page glossary by R. G., which contain interesting material on food as well as other household matters.

COLLECTION

A collection of the most approved receipts for pastry viz. bread pastes baken meat seed-cake plumb-cake sugar biscuits preserves marmalades jellies confections. Aberdeen: printed for Francis Douglas, 1750.[1] 56 p. 16 cm.

Cited: —

Copies: *BI*: AUL; ENLS*[2]
   NA: —

—2nd ed. Aberdeen: printed for F. Douglas, 1766. —: NNNAM

1. The authorship of this work has been attributed to Francis Douglas.
2. The ENLS copy is incomplete, and the AUL copy is wanting a title-page.

COLLINGWOOD, Francis, and WOOLLAMS, John (*fl.* 1790)

The universal cook, and city and country housekeeper . . . bills of fare . . . and proper subjects for the improvement of the art of carving, elegantly engraved on fourteen copper-plates.[1] London: printed by R. Noble for J. Scatcherd and J. Whitaker, 1792.[2] 451 p. frontis. pls. 22 cm.

Cited: Bitting, pp. 94–5; Oxford, pp. 120–1

Copies: *BI*: ENLS*; GUL; LBL
   NA: KMK; MCR; NIC

—2nd ed. London: printed for J. Scatcherd, 1797.[3] —: MB
—3rd ed. London: printed by C. Whittingham for J. Scatcherd, [?1792].[4] —: —

1. *Lyle Cat.*, No. 3 [1976], states that this is a 'well printed book by the chefs of the Crown and Anchor Tavern in the Strand, a notable London dining-house with a banqueting room which could take 2,500 people, and was consequently the scene of many famous gatherings, such as Charles James Fox's 2,000 strong birthday party . . . it was also the meeting place of the Royal Society Club'.

2. See Vicaire, p. 189, for the French edition of this work.

3. For an abridged version of this edition see under later entry: WILLIAMS, T., The accomplished housekeeper.

4. The only known reference to this 3rd ed. is *Maggs Bros. Cat.*, No. 645, p. 101, where the date of publication is given as '1792', which must be an error.

COMPLEAT

The compleat cook: prescribing the most ready ways for dressing flesh and fish, ordering sauces, pickles, jellies, etc. and making pastry after the newest manner. London: printed for J. Phillips, H. Rhodes and J. Taylor, 1710. 138 p. 16 cm.

Cited: Bitting, p. 533

Copies: *BI*: LeU(B)*[1]
      NA: CU-B; NcD

—another ed. London: printed for J. Phillips, H. Rhodes and J. Taylor, [*c*.1710]. LWML: —

1. The LeU(B) copy of this work is bound with the 11th ed. of The queen's closet opened; see later entry: QUEEN.

COMPLEAT

The compleat English family companion. Consisting of a collection of near a thousand curious and uncommon receipts in cookery, pastry . . . wine making . . . pickling . . . brewing . . . with plain and easy instructions for chusing all sorts of eatables . . . to which is added, the compleat servant maid, likewise the art of clear starching, etc. London: printed for [——], 1769. viii, 9–200 p. pls. 19 cm.

Cited: —

Copies: *BI*: LeU(B)*[1]
      NA: —

1. The LeU(B) copy is inscribed: 'John Taylor, Wigan'.

COMPLEAT

The compleat family companion: or, the whole art of cookery made plain and easy; in a method intirely new and suited to every capacity . . . Also curious extracts from a famous treatise on the teeth, their disorder and cure. Directions for marketing . . . with an excellent method for preserving of metals from rust, such as guns, grates, candlesticks, etc. [by a gentlewoman]. London: printed for the author, 1753.[1] viii, 9–128 p. 18 cm.

Cited: —

Copies: *BI*: —
      NA: ICJ; NYPL

—another ed. London: printed for [——], [*c*.1787].[2]

1. This work could have been written by Penelope Bradshaw. The phrase in the title-page about teeth is identical to the one employed in another 1753 work; see under earlier entry: BRADSHAW, Penelope, Bradshaw's family companion.
2. The only known reference to this edition is given by Hazlitt, p. 177. If the assumption in note 1 above is correct the probable date of publication is nearer 1757 than '1787'.

COMPLEAT

The compleat family cook. Consisting of a collection of near a thousand curious and uncommon receipts in soops [*sic*] made-dishes . . . also bills of fare for every month in the year . . . a book necessary for mistresses of families, higher and lower women servants . . . and calculated for the preservation of health . . . revised and corrected by an eminent cook . . . To which is added the London and country brewer . . . with a copious treatise on malt liquors . . . the art of clear starching, ironing, . . . the servant maid's best companion. etc. Hull: printed by J. Rawson and Son, 1766. 216 p. pls. 17 cm.

Cited: Bitting, p. 534[1]

Copies: *BI*: —
       NA: DCLC

1. This work is certainly a pirated or spurious version of Elizabeth Moxon's book (see under later entry: MOXON, Elizabeth, English housewifry).

COMPLEAT

The compleat servant maid: or, the young maidens tutor. directing them how they may fit, and qualifie themselves for any of these employments. viz. . . . cook-maid . . . housemaid . . . a supplement containing the choicest receipts and rarest secrets in physick and chirurgery. etc.[1] 7th ed. with additions. London: printed for Eben. Tracy, [*c*.1702]. [——] [——]

Cited: —

Copies: *BI*: —
       NA: —

—8th ed. with additions. London: printed for E. Tracy, 1711.[2] —: —

—9th ed. with large additions. London: printed for D. Midwinter, 1729. —: ICN

1. The only known reference to this edition is *Bib.Ann.*, vol. 2 (1701–3), p. 16.
2. The only known reference to this edition is *Sotheby Cat.* (5 Nov. 1971), p. 78.

COMPLETE

The complete caterer, or directions to choose the best provisions of flesh, fish and fowl.[1] [London]: printed for and sold by John Nutt, [1701]. [——] [——] 6 d.

Cited: —

Copies: *BI*: —
       NA: —

1. The only known reference to this work is *Bib.Ann.*, vol. 2 (1701–3), p. 39.

COMPLETE

The complete distiller; combining theory and practice; and explaining the mysteries and most recent improvement of distilling and brewing, in a most simple, easy and familiar manner. [by a gentleman of extensive practice and long experience]. Edinburgh: printed for P. Hill, 1793. viii, 151 p. 22 cm.

Cited: —

Copies: *BI*: LBL*; LGL
     NA: CtY

COMPLETE

The complete family brewer, or the best method of brewing or making any quantity of good strong ale and small beer, in the greatest perfection, for the use of private families . . . to which is added, the method of making a cheap and wholesome beer . . . which is so easy to make, that a child of ten years of age may learn to do it in five minutes. London: printed for J. Walker, 1789. iv, 5–24 p. 19 cm.

Cited: —

Copies: *BI*: LBL*[1]
     NA: —

1. Listed in *BMCat*. under 'FAMILY BREWER'.

COMPLETE

The complete family-piece: and, country gentleman, and farmer's best guide. etc. In three parts.[1] London: printed for and sold by J. Roberts, 1736. xii, 456 p. 17 cm. 3 sh. 6 d.[2]

Cited: Bitting, p. 534; Oxford, pp. 66–8

Copies: *BI*: LWML; LeU(B)*
     NA: CtY; ICJ; NNNAM

—another ed. London: printed by T. Longman, J. Clarke and S. Birt, 1736. LWML: NNNAM

—2nd ed. improved. London: printed for A. Bettesworth and C. Hitch, 1737. LWML; LeU(B): CtY; KMK

—3rd ed. improved. London: printed for C. Rivington and S. Birt, 1741. LBL; LeU(B); MPL: CtY; MH; MnU

—5th ed. improved. Dublin: reprinted and sold by G. Faulkner, 1749. —: CtY

1. Part 1 is devoted to cookery receipts and medical hints. Part 2 to hunting, coursing, setting and shooting . . . and Part 3 practical rules . . . for the improving of land.
2. *Gents.Mag.*, vol. 6 (Mar. 1736), p. 172, confirms that the price was 3 sh. 6 d.

COMPLETE CONFECTIONER

see NUTT, Frederic.

COMPLETE FAMILY COOK
  see MENON, [——].

COMPLETE HOUSEWIFE (or COMPLEAT HOUSEWIFE)
  see SMITH, Eliza.

CONCISE

Concise observations on the nature of our common food, so far as it tends to promote or injure health; with remarks on water, bread, meat, cheese, butter, milk, wine, punch, beer, coffee, tea, sugar. etc. [by a gentleman of the faculty].[1] London: printed by W. Justins for W. Stanes at Chelmsford, 1787. 56 p. 21 cm. 1 sh.[2]

Cited: —

Copies: *BI*: LBL*; LWML
        NA: DNAL

—2nd ed. London: printed for [——]; New York: reprinted by J. and T. Swords for Berry and Rogers, 1790. —: DCLC; MHi; MWA

1. The authorship has been ascribed to at least two people. In the LWML copy he is identified as John Tweed (who wrote *Popular Observations on Regimen and Diet*, *c*.1820); and the *NUCat*. states it was Thomas Hayes.
2. *Scots Mag.*, vol. 50 (Jan. 1788), p. 33, confirms that the price was 1 sh.

COOK

The cook's pocket companion.[1] [——]: printed for [C. ?] Henderson, 1756. [——] [——] 1 sh.

Cited: —

Copies: *BI*: —
        NA: —

1. The only known reference to this work is in *Lond.Mag.* (May–June 1756), p. 359. See under later entry: HONEYWOOD, Lydia, The cook's pocket-companion.

COOK, ANN

The new system of cookery.[1] Newcastle: printed for [——], 1753. [——] [——] 5 sh.

Cited: —

Copies: *BI*: —
        NA: —

1. The only known reference to this work is given in the *Newcastle Journal* (17 Feb. 1753), and this advertisement is referred to in F. J. G. Robinson, 'Trends in Education in Northern England during the Eighteenth Century: a biographical study', 3 vols., University of Newcastle Ph.D. thesis, 1972 [in vol. 3, appendix 6].

COOK, ANN (*fl.* 1754–1760)

Professed cookery: containing boiling, roasting, pastry, preserving, pickling, potting, made-wines. gellies [*sic*] and part of confectionaries . . . together with a plan of house-keeping. etc.[1] Newcastle: printed for J. White, 1754.[2] [——] [——] [?6 sh.][3]

Cited: Bitting, p. 98; Oxford, pp. 91–2

Copies: *BI*: —
      NA: -

—2nd ed. Newcastle: printed for the author, 1755. EUL; NPL: DCLC; KMK

—3rd ed. Newcastle: printed for the author, 1760. NPL: —

—3rd ed. London: printed for and sold by the author, at Holborn, [*c.*1760]. GUL; LWML: KMK; ViWC

1. Ann Cook, a teacher of cookery, had a very troubled life, and she used her book partly to attack Hannah Glasse (see under later entry), but mainly (in the last 100 pages under the misnamed 'A Plan of Housekeeping') as an autobiography; see Regula Burnet, *Ann Cook and Friend* (London, 1936).
2. For this entry see Madeleine Hope Dodds, 'The Rival Cooks: Hannah Glasse and Ann Cook', *Archaeologia Aeliana*, Series 4, vol. 15, pp. 43–68; and Dr F. J. G. Robinson's University of Newcastle Ph.D. thesis, op. cit., vol. 3, for 'A List of Educational Works Published in the North of England in the Eighteenth Century'. He also discusses schools of cookery in northern England.
3. As the 2nd ed. (see Madeleine Hope Dodds, op. cit., p. 52) and the 3rd London ed. (see Oxford, p. 92) cost 6 sh., it is probable that the 1st ed. was also sold at 6 sh.

COOKERY

Cookery reformed: or the lady's assistant . . . to which is added the family physician . . . published at the request of a physician of great experience, who for the benefit of the purchaser, has carefully corrected this work; and shewn why several things heretofore used in cookery, and inserted in other books, have been prejudicial to mankind.[1] London: printed for P. Davey and B. Law, 1755. 254 p. [——] 4 sh. 6 d.[2]

Cited: Oxford, pp. 86–7

Copies: *BI*: —
      NA: —

1. The entry for this rare book is based on Murphy, p. 11.
2. *Lond.Mag.* (May 1755), No. 17 [no pagination], confirms that the price was 4 sh. 6 d.

COOPER, AMBROSE (*fl.* 1757–1800?)

The complete distiller. To which are added descriptions of the several drugs, plants, flowers, fruits, etc. used by distillers, and instructions for chusing the best of each kind. London: printed for P. Vaillant and R. Griffiths, 1757. 266 p. pl. 20 cm.

Cited: —

Copies: *BI*: LBL*; LWML
　　　　NA: CtY; MH; PPULC

—another ed. [same contents, but entirely new title-page:] The complete distiller: containing I. The method of performing the various processes of distillation. II. The manner of distilling all kinds of simple waters from plants . . . III. The method of making all the compound waters and rich cordials so largely imported from France and Italy. London: printed for P. Vaillant and R. Griffiths, 1757.[1]

—2nd ed. with additions. London: printed for P. Vaillant and R. Griffiths, 1760. LWML: DCLC; PPULC; WU

—another ed. London: printed for Hamilton, 1797. LGL: —

—another ed. London: printed for Vernor, Hood, and J. Cuthell, 1800.[2] LBL: NYPL; PPULC

1. For this edition see Crahan, p. 30.
2. There were further editions in the 19th century.

CORNARO, Louis

see Lessius, Leonardus.

COUNTRY

The country gentleman, farmer and housewifes compendious instructor.[1] Dublin: printed for [——], 1761. [——] [——]

Cited: —

Copies: *BI*: —
　　　　NA: —

1. The only known reference to this work is given in *Sotheby Cat.* (30 July 1969), p. 8.

COUNTRY

The country magazine. Calculated for the gentleman; the farmer and his wife: containing everything necessary for the advantage and pleasure of a country life. etc. London: printed for T. Waller, 1763. [——] frontis. pls. 21 cm.

Cited: —

Copies: *BI*: —
　　　　NA: CtY; MH

COUNTRY

The country magazine, or, the gentleman and lady's pocket companion. London: printed for the authors, 1736–1737.[1] [——][2] 21 cm.

Cited: —

Copies: *BI*: —
　　　　NA: NNNAM; NYPL

1. This was a periodical, although a short-lived one, and not a 'magazine' in a single volume, as many other 18th-century works were (including the previous entry). The first section of each issue of this magazine was devoted to recipes for cookery; see Stark, p. 14.
2. The pagination undoubtedly varied with each issue.

COURT AND COUNTRY COOK
see MASSIALOT, François.

CROFT, JOHN (1732–1820)
A treatise on the wines of Portugal; and what can be gathered on the subject and nature of the wines . . . also, a dissertation on the nature and use of wines in general, imported into Great-Britain, as pertaining to luxury and diet. etc.[1] In two parts. York: printed by Crask and Lund, 1787. 27 p. 21 cm.

Cited: —

Copies: *BI*: LBL; OBL*
      NA: CtY

—2nd ed. corrected and enlarged. York: printed by A. Ward for J. Todd, 1788. ENLS; LBL: MH-BA

1. John Croft was a member of the English Factory at Oporto in northern Portugal, and wine-merchant in York.

CURIOUS
A curious collection of receipts in cookery, pickling, family physic . . . with the best and cheapest methods of brewing all sorts of malt liquors, and preparing sundry kinds of excellent made wines, not inferior to the best French. etc. London: printed for R. Montagu, 1742. 103 p. 15 cm.

Cited: —

Copies: *BI*: GPL(M)*[1]
      NA: KMK

1. The Mitchell Library copy is inscribed: 'Mrs. James Gordon'.

CURZON, H.
see UNIVERSAL library.

D

DALRYMPLE, GEORGE (*fl.* 1781)
The practice of modern cookery; adapted to families of distinction, as well as to those of the middling ranks of life. etc.[1] Edinburgh: printed for the author, and sold by C. Elliot and T. Longman at London, 1781. vi, 475 p. 21 cm.

Cited: Bitting, p. 114; Oxford, p. 113

Copies: *BI*: ENLS*; GPL(M); LBL
    NA: DCLC; KMK

1. George Dalrymple describes himself as 'late cook to Sir John Whitefoord, Bart.', and he dedicated his work to Lady Whitefoord. It is interesting to note that he named receipts in both English and French, and that he was one of the first cookery writers to give a glossary of terms.

DICTIONARIUM RUSTICUM

see WORLIDGE, John.

DIRECTIONS

Directions to lords and ladies, masters and mistresses, for the improvement of their conduct to servants and tenants, tradesmen and humble friends and cousins. Designed as a return for their impertinent directions to servants. [Anon.].[1] London: printed for M. Cooper, 1766. 16, 28 p. [——]

Cited: —

Copies: *BI*: —
    NA: NYPL

1. This is an attack on the upper classes for the alleged neglect of their servants' welfare, and is in much the same vein as a work printed *c.*1758; see under later entry: TREATISE on . . . the steward's table.

DODD, JAMES SOLAS (1721–1805)

An essay towards a natural history of the herring . . . with receipts for divers methods of dressing and preparation. etc. 2nd ed. London: printed for T. Vincent, 1752. xxii, 23–178 p. pl.[1] 21 cm.

Cited: —

Copies: *BI*: ENLS*; LBL; LeU(B)
    NA: CtY; DCLC; ICJ

1. This is a particularly fine folding plate, showing the composition of the herring.

DOMESTIC

Domestic management, or the art of conducting a family; with instructions to servants in general. Addressed to young housekeepers. etc. London: printed for H. D. Symonds, [*c.*1800]. 108 p. 17 cm.

Cited: Oxford, p. 128

Copies: *BI*: LBL; OBL*
    NA: —

DOSSIE, ROBERT (d. 1777)

An essay on spirituous liquors, with regard to their effects on health; in which the comparative wholesomeness of rum and brandy are particularly considered. London: printed for J. Ridley, [*c.*1770]. 50 p. 20 cm. 1 sh.

Cited: —

Copies: *BI*: OBL*
      NA: CtY-M

DOUGLAS, Francis

see COLLECTION of the most approved receipts.

DOUGLASS, C. (*fl.* 1746)

The summer's amusements: or, the young ladies companion. Containing above 150 receipts. Newcastle: printed by William Cuthbert, 1746.[1] viii, 70 p. [——]

Cited: —

Copies: *BI*: NPL
      NA: —

1. This entry is based on Richard Welford, *Early Newcastle Typography: 1639–1800* (Newcastle upon Tyne, 1907), p. 69. See also under later entry: SUMMER.

DUNBAR, James (*fl.* 1737)

The industrious country-man and virtuous house-wife's companion.[1] Edinburgh: printed for the author, who is to be found at the Laigh Coffee-House, 1737. iv, 47 p. 18 cm.

Cited: —

Copies: *BI*: ENLS*; MPL
      NA: —

1. It is dedicated to 'The Ladies of the Assembly'.

DUNCAN, Daniel (1649–1735)

Wholesome advice against abuse of hot liquors, particularly of coffee, chocolate, tea, brandy and strong-waters. etc. London: printed for H. Rhodes and A. Bell, 1706. 280 p. 19 cm.

Cited: —

Copies: *BI*: ENLS*; LBL; LeU(B)
      NA: ICJ; MH; NYPL

E

EALES, Mary (*fl.* 1718–1730?)

The compleat confectioner: or, the art of candying and preserving in its utmost perfection. Being a collection of all the receipts of the late ingenious Mrs. Eales . . . Familiarly adapted for the use of the ladies, and very necessary for all who are willing to excel in the most excellent qualifications of a good house-wife.

Publish'd with the consent of her executors. London: printed for J. Brindley and R. Mountagu [*sic*], 1733. 100 p. 18 cm. 2 sh. 6 d.

Cited: —

Copies: *BI*: LBL; LeU(B)*
      NA: ICJ; KMK; MCR

—3rd ed. to which is added, a second part. Containing a curious collection of receipts in cookery, pickling, family physick . . . methods of brewing all sorts of malt liquors, and preparing sundry kinds of excellent made wines. etc. London: printed for R. Montagu, 1742.[1] 100, 103 p. 18 cm. OBL*: NYPL

—5th ed. London: printed for C. Hitch and A. Millar, 1753. LBL; LeU(B): ViWC

—a new ed. . . . collected by several hands. London: printed for W. Cavell, [*c*.1788]. LeU(B): —

1. This 'second part' was almost certainly not the work of Mary Eales, although it was 'added' to her book. The additional 'part' is identical in content to a work published separately in the same year for the same person, R. Montagu; see under entry: CURIOUS.

EALES, MARY

Mrs. Mary Eales's receipts. Confectioner to her late Majesty Queen Anne. London: printed by H. Meere, 1718.[1] 100 p. 18 cm. 2 sh. 6 d.

Cited: Bitting, p. 139; Oxford, p. 55

Copies: *BI*: EUL*; LWML; OBL
      NA: DCLC; NIC; NYPL

—another ed. London: printed for J. Brindley, and F. Montagu, 1733. LeU(B): NYPL

—2nd ed. corrected with additions. London: printed for J. Robson, 1767. LBL; LeU(B): —

1. Although this work by Mary Eales bears great similarity to her later published work, The compleat confectioner (see previous entry), there are sufficient differences to allow them to be regarded as separate books. It is interesting to note a sale in or about 1934; see *B.&G.Cat.*, No. 37, p. 7, which lists 'Mrs. Mary Eales's Receipts . . . [London, *c*.1720]. An English MS. on 54 leaves, easily legible. This is a transcript of the first edition (1718).'

EASY

An easy way to prolong life, by a little attention to what we eat and drink. Containing a chemical analysis; or, an enquiry into the nature and properties of all kinds of food. etc. [by a medical gentleman]. London: printed for J. Bell, 1773. [Part 1]. [——] [——] 2 sh.[1] [and] London: printed for J. Bell, 1774. [Part 2]. [——] [——] 1 sh. 6 d.[2]

Cited: —

Copies: *BI*: —
    NA: —

—another ed. Dublin: printed for J. Potts, 1773. —: DNLM; WU

The COMPLEAT

CONFECTIONER:

OR, THE

ART of *Candying* and *Preserving*
in its utmoft Perfection.

BEING

A Collection of all the RECEIPTS
of the late ingenious Mrs. *EALES*,
Confectioner to their late Majefties
King *William* and Queen *Anne*.

Familiarly adapted for the

USE of the LADIES,

And very neceffary for all who are willing
to excel in the moft excellent Qualifications of a good Houfe-Wife.

Publifh'd with the Confent of her Executors.

L O N D O N:

Printed for J. BRINDLEY, Bookfeller, at the *King's
Arms* in *New Bond-Street*, and Bookbinder to Her
Majefty and His Royal Highnefs the Prince of *Wales*;
and R. MOUNTAGU at the *General Poft-Office*, the
Corner of *Great Queen-Street*, near *Drury-Lane*.
MDCCXXXIII. [Price Bound *2s. 6d.*]

Mrs Eales's main work is very explicitly directed to 'the ladies'. Her executors managed to pack
much impressive prose, and her impeccably royal credentials, into a title-page which is pleasantly
uncrowded.

—3rd ed. London: printed for J. Bell, [*c*.1774]. —: DNLM

—4th ed. London: printed for the author and J. Bell, [*c*.1775]. LWML: NNNAM

—5th ed. improved. London: printed for the author, [*c*.1790]. LWML: MH

—4th ed. improved. Dover [Delaware]: printed by Samuel Bragg, jun. for Wm. T. Clap at Boston, 1794. —: CSmH; MHi

1. The only known reference for Part 1 of this edition is given in *Scots Mag.*, vol. 35 (June 1773), p. 311.
2. The only known reference for Part 2 of this edition is given in *Scots Mag.*, vol. 36 (Feb. 1774), p. 92.

ECONOMIST

The economist. Shewing, in a variety of estimates, from fourscore pounds a year to upwards of 800 l. how comfortably and genteely a family may live, with frugality, for a little money. Together with the cheapest method of keeping horses and carriages. [by a gentleman of experience]. London: printed for the author and sold by J. Bell, 1774. 21 p. 18 cm. 1 sh.

Cited: —

Copies: *BI*: —

     NA: MH-BA

—3rd ed. London: printed for the author, 1774. —: NYPL

—4th ed. London: printed for the author, and sold by J. Bell, 1774. GSU(A): —

—8th ed. London: printed for the author, and sold by J. Bell, 1774. ENLS: —

—10th ed. London: printed for the author, and sold by J. Bell, 1774. —: CtY

—14th ed. London: printed for the author, and sold by J. Bell, 1776. —: ICU; MH-BA

—15th ed. London: printed for the author, and sold by J. Bell, 1781. LBL; OBL: CtY

ECONOMY

The economy of an institution, established in Spitalfields, London, for the purpose of supplying the poor with a good meat soup. [Anon.]. [——]: printed for [——], 1799. [——] [——]

Cited: Oxford, p. 125[1]

Copies: *BI*: —

     NA: —

1. Oxford gives the only known reference to this work.

EDMONDS, W. (*fl.* 1767)

A new and easy way of making wines from herbs, fruits, and flowers, the growth of England; viz. goosberries [*sic*], currants, rasberries [*sic*] etc., with their physical virtues. Also, to make artificial wines, as malaga, claret, rhenish, etc., recovering faded wines, and such as have lost their colour, with the true way of making ordinary and rich cordial waters; likewise to make cyder equal to canary; to make the best mead, perry, mum,[1] etc., with divers other sorts of English liquors never before treated of. London: printed for J. Williams, 1767. 84 p. 17 cm.

Cited: —

Copies: *BI*: LBL*
     NA: IaAS

1. 'Mum' is a kind of beer originally brewed in Brunswick.

ELLIS, JOHN (d. 1776)

An historical account of coffee. . . . To which are added, sundry papers relative to its culture and use, as an article of diet and commerce. London: printed for Edward and Charles Dilly, 1774. iv, 71 p. frontis. 27 cm. 3 sh.[1]

Cited: Bitting, p. 142

Copies: *BI*: ENLS*; LBL; LeU(B)
     NA: CtY; DCLC; MiU

1. *Scots Mag.*, vol. 36 (Mar. 1774), p. 148, confirms that the price was 3 sh.

ELLIS, WILLIAM[1] (d. 1758)

The country housewife's family companion: or profitable directions for . . . the management and good oeconomy of the domestick concerns of a country life . . . shewing how great savings may be made in housekeeping, . . . methods of cookery . . . method of making butter and cheese . . . brewing good beer. etc. London: printed for James Hodges; and for B. Collins, bookseller at Salisbury, 1750. x, 379 p. frontis. 20 cm.

Cited: Bitting, p. 143; Oxford, pp. 79-80

Copies: *BI*: ANLW; LWML; LeU(B)*
     NA: KMK; NPV; NYPL

1. For information on the author see Vicars Bell, *To Meet Mr. Ellis* (London, 1956).

ELLIS, WILLIAM (d. 1758)

The London and country brewer, to which is added the cellar man. etc. [Anon.]. In three parts. London: printed for W. Meadows, 1734-1738. [———] [———] 2 sh.[1]

Cited: —

Copies: *BI*: LBL[2]
     NA: —

—another ed. Dublin: printed by M. Rhames and R. Gunne, 1735-1738. —: DCLC; MH-BA

William Ellis's frontispiece, which accompanied the title-page opposite, was not unusual in showing a rustic farmyard scene rather than a kitchen or a portrait of the author. A somewhat similar scene was used as frontispiece for *The Farmer's Wife*, of which the title-page is reproduced on page 53.

THE
COUNTRY HOUSEWIFE's
Family Companion:

OR

PROFITABLE DIRECTIONS for whatever relates
to the Management and good Œconomy

OF THE

Domeſtick Concerns of a Country Life,

According to the

PRESENT PRACTICE of the Country Gentleman's, the
Yeoman's, the Farmer's, &c. Wives, in the Counties
of *Hertford, Bucks,* and other Parts of *England:*

SHEWING

How great SAVINGS may be made in Houſekeeping:

And wherein, among many others,

The following HEADS are particularly treated of and explained:

I. The Preſervation and Improve-
ment of Wheat, Barley, Rye, Oats,
and other Meals; with Directions
for making ſeveral Sorts of Bread,
Cakes, Puddings, Pies, &c.
II. Frugal Management of Meats,
Fruits, Roots, and all Sorts of
Herbs; beſt Methods of Cookery;
and a cheap Way to make Soups,
Sauces, Gruels, &c.
III. Directions for the Farm Yard;
with the beſt Method of increaſing
and fatning all Sorts of Poultry, as
Turkies, Geeſe, Ducks, Fowls,&c.

IV. The beſt Way to breed and
fatten Hogs; ſundry curious and
cheap Methods of preparing Hogs
Meat; Directions for curing
Bacon, Brawn, pickled Pork,
Hams,&c. with the Management
of Sows and Pigs.
V. The beſt Method of making
Butter and Cheeſe, with ſeveral
curious Particulars containing the
whole Management of the Dairy.
VI. The ſeveral Ways of making
good Malt; with Directions for
brewing good Beer, Ale, &c.

With Variety of CURIOUS MATTERS,

Wherein are contained frugal Methods for victualling Harveſt-men,
Ways to deſtroy all Sorts of Vermine, the beſt Manner of ſuckling
and fattening Calves, Preſcriptions for curing all Sorts of Diſtempers
in Cattle, with Variety of curious Receits for Pickling, Preſerving,
Diſtilling, &c.

The Whole founded on near thirty Years Experience by
W. ELLIS, *Farmer, at* Little Gaddeſden, *near* Hempſted, Hertfords.

LONDON:
Printed for JAMES HODGES, at the *Looking-glaſs,* facing *St. Magnus*
Church, *London-Bridge;* and B. COLLINS, Bookſeller, at *Saliſbury.* 1750.

The title-page of William Ellis's book brings out one of the features which makes it of special
interest, namely the fact that is firmly based on experience in a given region—Essex and the
country round about. It is one of the eighteenth-century books which conveys a feeling of direct
communication and of confidence that the author invariably knew what he was talking about.

—3rd ed. corrected. London: printed for J. and J. Fox, 1736–1738. —: NYPL

—4th ed. London: printed for Thomas Astley, 1742. —: DNAL; MH-BA

—5th ed. London: printed for Thomas Astley, 1744. —: CtY; KU

—6th ed. to which is added a supplement. London: printed for Thomas Astley and Richard Baldwin, 1750. LBL: KyU; MH

—7th ed. London: printed for Thomas Astley, 1759. CUL; LBL: DNAL; ICJ

1. *Gents.Mag.*, vol. 6 (Aug. 1736), p. 492, confirms that the price was 2 sh.
2. The British Library copy has been lost or mislaid.

EMINENT POULTERER
see HEALTH's preservative.

ENGLISH
The English pocket gardener: or, country gentleman's vade mecum . . . to which is added, the art of preserving fruits, and directions for making English wines. etc. London: printed for Hamilton & Co., 1794. 48 p. 14 cm. 6 d.

Cited: —

Copies: *BI*: LBL*
     NA: —

ENUMERATION
An enumeration of the principal vegetables, and vegetable productions, that may be substituted, either in part or wholly, in place of wheat and other bread-corn, in times of scarcity.[1] etc. Birmingham: printed for Thomas Pearson, 1796. vi, 26 p. 20 cm.

Cited: —

Copies: *BI*: LBL*
     NA: —

1. For further details see Henrey, vol. 3, pp. 40 and 136. She ascribes the authorship to John Winthorp.

ESSAY
An essay on tea, sugar, white bread and butter, country alehouses . . . and other modern luxuries. Salisbury: printed for [——], 1777. [——] [——]

Cited: —

Copies: *BI*: LBL[1]
     NA: —

1. The entry is based on the *BMCat.*, but the British Library copy to which it refers has been lost.

ESSAY
An essay on the nature, use and abuse of tea, in a letter to a lady; with an account of its mechanical operation.[1] London: printed by J. Bettenham for James Lacy, 1722.[2] 3–63 p. 20 cm. 1 sh.

Cited: —

Copies: *BI*: ENLS*; LBL
    NA: —

1. On p. 14 the author states: 'Among many other Novelties in our Diet, there is one which seems particularly to be the cause of the Hypochondriack disorders; and it is generally known by the Name of Thea or Tea. It is a Drug. . . .'
2. *BMCat.* (1961), ascribes the authorship to Robert Helsham.

ESSAY ON CULINARY POISONS

see ROBERTSON, Joseph.

EVELYN, JOHN (1620–1706)

Acetaria. A discourse of sallets.[1] 2nd ed.[2] London: printed for B. Tooke, 1706. 191 p. pl. 17 cm.

Cited: Bitting, p. 149; Oxford, p. 46

Copies: *BI*: ENLS; LBL*; LeU(B)
    NA: DCLC; ICJ; KMK

1. For a life of the author; see: *DNB*, vol. 6 (1908), pp. 943–6.
2. The 1st ed. was published in 1699. The recipes are given in an appendix. The first part of this work is a botanical and historical description of plants and herbs.

EVERYWOMAN

see PERKINS, John.

EXPLANATION

An explanation and translation of a modern bill of fare. [——]: printed for [——], [1751].[1] [——] [——] 6 d.

Cited: —

Copies: *BI*: —
    NA: —

1. The only known reference to this work is given in *Scots Mag.*, vol. 13 (June 1751), p. 359.

F

FAIRFAX, ARABELLA[1] (*fl.* 1753)

The family's best friend: or the whole art of cookery made plain and easy; . . . by his Majesty's authority. . . . Being the result of above thirty years practice and experience; together with an attractive observation of all the books hitherto published in cookery. To which is added, . . . Dr. Mead's cure for the bite of a mad dog; and instructions for preparing such diets as are proper for sick persons. etc.[2] 5th ed. London: printed for the author only, 1753. 258 p. 16 cm. 2 sh sewed

Cited: Oxford, p. 85

Copies: *BI*: —
         NA: KMK*; NNNAM; NYPL

—another ed. London: printed for C. Henderson,[3] [*c.*1755]. —: —

1. The author had her work set in a peculiar typeface 'in order to prevent unfair Traders from reprinting, or in any wise defrauding the Author or the Publick, by publishing . . . this Book'.
2. This work is probably either a slightly earlier edition of a book by Penelope Bradshaw using a pseudonym, or, more likely, a pirated version of it; see BRADSHAW, Penelope, The family jewel. There are certain similarities in the title-pages that seem to be more than coincidental.
3. The only known British reference to this work is given in *B.&G.Cat.*, No. 27, p. 10.

FALCONER, WILLIAM (1744–1824)

Observations on some of the articles of diet and regimen usually recommended to valetudinarians.[1] London: printed for Edward and Charles Dilly, 1778. 63 p. 17 cm. 1 sh.[2]

Cited: —

Copies: *BI*: LBL*
         NA: ICJ; MH

1. For a life of William Falconer see *DNB*, vol. 6 (1908), pp. 1029–31.
2. *Scots Mag.*, vol. 40 (Apr. 1778), p. 202, confirms that the price was 1 sh.

FAMILY

The family chronicle. etc.[1] [——]: printed for Cooper, 1757. [——] [——] 2 sh.

Cited: —

Copies: *BI*: —
         NA: —

1. The only known reference to this work is given in *Scots Mag.*, vol. 19 (Dec. 1757), p. 672.

FAMILY

The family companion for health: or plain, easy and certain rules . . . which . . . will . . . keep families free from diseases, and procure them long life.[1] London: printed for F. Fayram and J. Leake, 1729. 426 p. 20 cm.

Cited: —

Copies: *BI*: LBL*[2]; LWML
         NA: —

1. The following passage appears in the introduction: 'By this small volume, the charitable housekeepers, for whose use it is written, will be enabled to give relief to their menials, without the assistance of an apothecary or physician: it is charity on all hands.'
2. *BMCat.* (1961), has the following note under 'Family': '*The practical physician for travellers*

was published by the author of *The family companion for health*; to which this treatise is intended for a supplement.' The former is outwith the terms of this short-list, but the latter, which was published separately, is not.

FAMILY

Family œconomist or compleat cook and caterer . . . to which is prefixed the servant's best companion. etc.[1] Dublin: printed for [——], 1766. [——] [——]

Cited: —

Copies: *BI*: LBL [ref. only]
     NA: —

1. This entry is based on the *BMCat.*, but the British Library copy to which it refers was destroyed in the Second World War.

FAMILY

The family magazine: in two parts. Part I. Containing useful directions in all the branches of house-keeping and cookery . . . together with the art of making English wines. . . . Part II. Containing a compendious body of physick . . . with a supplement containing a great variety of experienced receipts, from two excellent family collections.[1] etc. [Anon.]. London: printed for J. Osborn, 1741. xiv, 123, 324 p. 19 cm. 5 sh.[2]

Cited: Bitting, p. 550; Oxford, pp. 71-2

Copies: *BI*: LGL; LBL*; LePL
     NA: DCLC; MH; NNNAM

—2nd ed. revised and inlarged. London: printed for J. Osborn, 1743. LBL: —

—3rd ed. revised and corrected. London: printed for J. Osborn, 1747. LWML: CtY; KMK

—4th ed. [——]: printed for [——], 1754.[3]

1. The following statement appears in the preface: 'Being still teized [*sic*] for some name, I will, tho' not my right one, subscribe that of Arabella Atkyns.' The author also states that Part II was taken from a commonplace book of her late brother, a physician, but it contains so many revolting remedies that her claim must be regarded with suspicion. Part I is good.
2. *Gents.Mag.*, vol. 10 (Oct. 1740), p. 128, confirms that the price was 5 sh., but *Scots Mag.*, vol. 2 (Oct. 1740), p. 488, quotes the price as 5 sh. 6 d.
3. See Oxford, p. 72, for reference to this edition; and next entry: FAMILY, The family magazine.

FAMILY

The family magazine, or accomplish'd housewife and house-keeper's pocket-companion; containing several hundred curious and most useful recipes in cookery, pickling, preserving. etc. 4th ed.[1] [London]: printed for the author, 1754. [——] [——]

Cited: —

Copies: *BI*: —
     NA: MH

1. This work is probably the 4th ed. of the previous entry (see FAMILY, The family magazine) without Part II, but with a changed title-page. Unfortunately, the present compiler has not been able to verify this probability with Harvard University Library. See ACCOMPLISH'D (1736).

FARLEY, [——] [Mr] (*fl.* 1800?)

The guide to preferment; or, complete art of cookery: containing directions for marketing; . . . the forms of placing the dishes on table, and a plate shewing the proper method of trussing.[1] London: published by Dean and Munday, [*c.*1800]. xi, 13–116 p. pl. 15 cm. 1 sh.

Cited: Bitting, p. 152[2]

Copies: *BI:* —
    NA: KMK

1. The present compiler has not found one cataloguer of 18th-century cookery books who has assumed that the 'Mr. Farley' who produced this work was the same person as John Farley; see next entry.
2. Bitting states that this work is entirely different from another with the same main title; see under later entry: POWELL, B., The guide to preferment. This work is not part of her collection in the DCLC.

FARLEY, JOHN (*fl.* 1783–1800?)

The London art of cookery,[1] and housekeeper's complete assistant. . . . to which is added, an appendix, containing considerations on culinary poisons; . . . embellished with a head of the author[2] . . . and a bill of fare for every month in the year, elegantly engraved on thirteen copper-plates. London: printed for John Fielding; J. Scatcherd and J. Whitaker, 1783. xvi, 459 p. frontis. pls. 21 cm. 6 sh. bound.

Cited: Bitting, pp. 152–3; Oxford, p. 114

Copies: *BI:* ENLS*[3]; LBL
    NA: DCLC; MB; NYPL

—another ed. Dublin: printed for S. Price and W. Sleator, 1783. —: NIC; PV

—2nd ed. London: printed for J. Scatcherd and J. Whitaker, 1784. DoCL: —

—3rd ed. London: printed for J. Scatcherd and J. Whitaker, 1785. LePL: NYPL

—4th ed. with additions. London: printed for J. Scatcherd and J. Whitaker, 1787. LeU(B); OBL: MiD

—6th ed. with additions. London: printed for J. Scatcherd and J. Whitaker, 1789. ShCL: NIC

—7th ed. with additions. London: printed for J. Scatcherd and J. Whitaker, 1792. CUL; LGL; LeU(B): KMK

—8th ed. with additions. London: printed for J. Scatcherd and J. Whitaker, 1796. ANLW; LWML; LeU(B): —

—9th ed. with additions. London: printed by John Barker for James Scatcherd, 1800.[4] GSU(S); LWML; LeU(B): —

THE

London Art of Cookery,

AND

HOUSEKEEPER's COMPLETE ASSISTANT.

On a NEW PLAN.

Made Plain and Eafy to the Underftanding of every HOUSEKEEPER,
COOK, and SERVANT in the Kingdom.

CONTAINING,

Proper Directions for the Choice of all Kinds of Provifions.
Roafting and Boiling all Sorts of Butchers Meat, Poultry, Game, and Fifh.
Sauces for every Occafion.
Soups, Broths, Stews, and Hafhes.
Made Difhes, Ragoos, and Fricaffees.
All Sorts of Pies and Puddings.
Proper Inftructions for dreffing Fruits and Vegetables.

Pickling, Potting, and Preferving.
The Preparation of Hams, Tongues, and Bacon.
The whole Art of Confectionary.
The Preparation of Sugars.
Tarts, Puffs, and Pafties.
Cakes, Cuftards, Jams, and Jellies.
Drying, Candying, and Preferving Fruits, &c.
Made Wines, Cordial Waters, and Malt Liquors.

To which is added,

AN APPENDIX,

Containing

Confiderations on Culinary Poifons; Directions for making Broths, &c.
for the Sick; a Lift of Things in Seafon in the different
Months of the Year; Marketing Tables, &c. &c.

Embellifhed with

A HEAD of the AUTHOR, and a BILL of FARE for every Month
in the Year, elegantly engraved on Thirteen Copper-plates.

By JOHN FARLEY,

PRINCIPAL COOK AT THE LONDON TAVERN.

THE FOURTH EDITION,

With the Addition of upwards of One Hundred and Fifty new and
elegant RECEIPTS in the various Branches of COOKERY.

LONDON:
Printed for J. SCATCHERD and J. WHITAKER, N° 12,
B. LAW, N° 13, Ave-Maria-Lane; and G. and T. WILKIE,
St. Paul's Church-Yard. 1787.
[Price Six Shillings Bound.]

As the frontispiece of the present volume shows, John Farley's title-page had a portrait of himself facing it. It would be hard to fault the layout of the title-page, and the printing of it is less irregular than that of many earlier title-pages, but the general effect is unexciting.

1. An anonymous work with a similar main title was printed in 1797, and was almost certainly a pirated and spurious version of this book; see under later entry: LONDON, The London complete art of cookery.
2. John Farley was the principal cook at The London Tavern.
3. The ENLS copy is a microfilm of the LBL copy, which is bound with pages of MS receipts.
4. There were further editions in the 19th century.

FARMER

The farmer's magazine, and useful family companion . . . consisting of . . . a miscellaneous collection of family receipts, recommended from experience. [Agricola Sylvan]. 5 volumes. London: printed for Charles Dilly, April 1776–December 1780. [——][1] pls. 23 cm.

Cited: —

Copies: *BI*: ERHAS[2]; LBL*
      NA: DNAL

1. The pagination varied with each volume.
2. ERHAS holds vols. 1 to 4 only.

FARMER

The farmer's wife; or the complete country housewife . . . to which is added the art of breeding and managing song birds. etc. London: printed for Alex. Hogg, [*c*.1780]. 125 p. frontis. 17 cm. 1 sh. 6 d.

Cited: Oxford, pp. 111–12

Copies: *BI*: LBL; LeU(B)*[1]
      NA: NYPL

1. The LeU(B) copy is inscribed: 'for Mr. Dow Wm Dow his Book Needham Hall'; and opposite: 'Sarah Dow'.

FAUST, BERNARD CHRISTOPH (1755–1842)

Catechism of health: for the use of schools, and for domestic instruction. etc. [translated by J. H. Basse]. Dublin: printed by P. Byrne, 1794. 112 p. frontis. pls. 17 cm. 2 sh.

Cited: —

Copies: *BI*: —
      NA: DCLC; IU; PPC

—another ed. Boston: printed and sold by William Spotswood; and for H. & P. Rice at Philadelphia, 1795. —: DCLC; MH

—another ed. London: printed for Dilly, 1796.[1]

—another ed. Edinburgh: printed for William Creech, 1797.[2] ENLS: —

—another ed. New York: printed by R. Wilson for Samuel Campbell, 1798. —: DCLC; MH

1. The only known reference to this edition is given in *Scots Mag.*, vol. 58 (Nov. 1796), p. 769.
2. 'Now first published for the use of the inhabitants of Scotland, by the recommendation of Dr. Gregory.' The ENLS copy is inscribed: 'Mr. Wemyss from Lord Wemyss'.

THE
FARMER's WIFE;
OR THE COMPLETE
COUNTRY HOUSEWIFE.

CONTAINING

Full and ample DIRECTIONS for the Breeding and Management of TURKIES, FOWLS, GEESE, DUCKS, PIGEONS, &c.

INSTRUCTIONS for fattening HOGS, pickling of PORK, and curing of BACON.

How to make SAUSAGES, HOGS-PUDDINGS, &c.

Full INSTRUCTIONS for making WINES from various Kinds of English Fruits, and from Smyrna Raisins.

The METHOD of making CYDER, PERRY, MEAD, MUM, CHERRY-BRANDY, &c.

DIRECTIONS respecting the DAI-RY, containing the best Way of making BUTTER, and likewise Gloucestershire, Cheshire, Stilton, Sage, and Cream CHEESE.

How to pickle common English FRUITS and VEGETABLES, with other useful Receipts for the Country HOUSE-KEEPER.

Full INSTRUCTIONS how to brew BEER and ALE, of all the various Kinds made in this Kingdom.

Ample DIRECTIONS respecting the Management of BEES, with an Account of the Use of HO-NEY.

To which is added

The Art of Breeding and Managing SONG BIRDS:

Likewise a Variety of RECEIPTS in COOKERY,

And other Particulars, well worthy the Attention of Women of all Ranks residing in the COUNTRY.

Instructions, full and plain, we give,
To teach the Farmer's Wife,
With Satisfaction, how to live
The happy Country Life.

LONDON,

Printed for ALEX. HOGG, in Pater-noster Row.

(Price One Shilling and Six-pence.)

This title-page is *c.*1780. Comparison with the somewhat similar but earlier title-page of William Ellis (page 45) shows that the author of this work lays more emphasis on making beverages, and thought it appropriate to introduce not only bees but also song birds into the list of matters covered.

FEMALE

The female glossary: being a particular description of the principal commodities of this island. Wherein the various names, qualities and properties of each one are handsomely handled. Collected for the benefit of the inquisitive, and the help of weak memories. [by an old trader].[1] [——]: printed for W. Shaw, [c.1733] [——] [——] 6 d.

Cited: —

Copies: *BI*: —
     NA: —

1. The only known reference to this work is given in *Gents.Mag.*, vol. 3 (Jan. 1733), p. 50(a).

FISHER, [——] [Mrs]

see FISHER, Lydia.

FISHER, LYDIA (*fl.* 1750?–1800?)

The prudent housewife: or, complete English cook for town and country . . . and, in order to render it still more valuable than any other publication that hath appeared, a treasure of valuable medicines,[1] for the care of every disorder, crowns the whole of this work. etc. [Written by Mrs Fisher of Richmond]. London: printed by T. Sabine, [c.1750]. 142 p. frontis. 18 cm. 1 sh.

Cited: Bitting, p. 159; Oxford, p. 82

Copies: *BI*: LBL*
    NA: DCLC; ICJ; MH

—4th ed. with additions. London: printed by T. Sabine, [c.1755]. LeU(B): DCLC; NNNAM

—12th ed. London: printed by T. Sabine, [c.1758]. —: MCR

—15th ed. London: printed by T. Sabine and Son, [c.1760]. —: NIC

—20th ed. London: printed by Sabine and Son, [c.1760].[2] —: —

—24th ed. London: printed by Sabine and Son, [c.1788]. LeU(B)[3]: MiD

—25th ed. London: printed by T. Sabine and Son, [c.1800]. —: DNLM

1. In the opinion of Oxford, p. 82, 'the medical portion' is 'excellent and far above any preceding book'.
2. The only known reference for this edition is given in *B.&G.Cat.*, No. 27, p. 7.
3. The 24th ed. of Mrs Fisher's The prudent housewife, or compleat English cook; etc., has the spelling 'compleat' instead of 'complete' and other changes in the title-page, together with a frontispiece of the author, who described herself as 'Late Cook & House-keeper to the Duke of Newcastle, Marquis of Rockingham, &c.—upward of 50 years'.

FORME OF CURY

see PEGGE, Samuel, and WARNER, Richard.

FOUNTAIN OF KNOWLEDGE

see BRITISH legacy.

FRAZER, [——] [Mrs] (*fl.* 1791–1827?)

The practice of cookery, pastry, pickling, preserving, containing . . . a full list of supper dishes . . . directions for choosing provisions: with two plates, showing the method of placing dishes upon a table. etc.[1] Edinburgh: printed for Peter Hill and T. Cadell, 1791. xiii, 254 p. pls. 18 cm. 3 sh.[2]

Cited: Bitting, p. 167; Oxford, p. 120

Copies: *BI*: ENLS*; LBL; LeU(B)
    NA: NYPL

—another ed. Dublin: printed for R. Cross, G. Burnet and P. Wogan, 1791. DNLI; LeU(B): CaBVaUW; MCR

—2nd ed. corrected with additions. Edinburgh: printed for Peter Hill; and Vernor and Hood, 1795. ENLS; OBL: NYPL

—3rd ed. improved and enlarged. Edinburgh: printed by J. Ruthven and Sons, for Peter Hill, 1800.[3] ENLS: DNAL

1. The author describes herself as 'sole teacher of these arts in Edinburgh, several years colleague and afterwards successor to Mrs. M'Iver [*sic*] deceased'. Her work is clearly based on a book published by her colleague in 1773; see under later entry: MACIVER, Susanna, Cookery and pastry. See also Alexander Law, 'Teachers in Edinburgh in the eighteenth century', op. cit., pp. 127 and 140.
2. *Scots Mag.*, vol. 53 (Feb. 1791), p. 83, confirms that the price was 3 sh.
3. Further editions were published in the 19th century, including an 8th ed. in 1827.

FRENCH FAMILY COOK

see MENON, [——].

FRIEND, MY

see POISON detected.

FRUGAL

The frugal house-keeper, or, the compleat cook . . . going to market . . . pickling . . . brewing . . . To which is added the art of clear starching . . . useful receipts from ['] The toilet of Flora ['][1] . . . with receipts for cosmetics of every kind. etc. London: printed in the year 1778 for [——]. 3–206 p. 18 cm.

Cited: Bitting, p. 554

Copies: *BI*: LeU(B)*
    NA: DCLC

1. For this work see under earlier entry: BUC'HOZ, Pierre Joseph, The toilet of Flora.

G

G., R.

see ACCOMPLISH'D female instructor.

GARNETT, THOMAS (1766–1802)

A lecture on the preservation of health.[1] Liverpool: printed by J. McCreery and sold by Cadell and Davies at London, 1797. v, 6–72 p. 21 cm.

Cited: Bitting, p. 177

Copies: *BI*: EUL*; GPL(M); LBL
    NA: DCLC; MH

—2nd ed. London: printed by R. Noble, 1800. LBL: CtY; NNNAM

1. For a life of Dr Thomas Garnett see *DNB.* vol. 7 (1908), pp. 886–7. His best-known work is the excellent *Observations on a Tour through the Highlands and Part of the Western Isles of Scotland* (London, 1800). The work listed here is a lecture against the dangers of drinking and over-eating; and, wrote the author, it 'has been honoured with the attention of numerous audiences, in some of the most populous towns in England, where it has generally been read for the benefit of charitable institutions'.

GELLEROY, WILLIAM (*fl.* 1762)

The London cook, or the whole art of cookery made easy and familiar . . . to which is prefixed, a large copper-plate, representing His Majesty's table, with its proper removes, as it was served at Guild-Hall, on the 9.th of November last, being the Lord Mayor's Day. etc.[1] London: printed for S. Crowder & Co.; and J. Coote and J. Fletcher, 1762. iv, 486 p. pl. 20 cm.

Cited: Bitting, p. 179; Oxford, p. 92

Copies: *BI*: DoCL; LBL; LeU(B)*
    NA: KMK; NPV; NYPL

—another ed. Dublin: printed by T. and J. Whitehouse, 1762. DNLI: —

1. The author describes himself as 'William Gelleroy, late cook to her Grace the Dutchess [*sic*] of Argyle [*sic*], and now to the Right Hon. Sir Samuel Fludger, Bart., Lord Mayor of the City of London'.

GENTLEMAN

The gentleman's companion: or, tradesman's delight . . . to which is added the method of curing and preserving all sorts of wines . . . also some excellent receipts in cookery, physick, and surgery. etc.[1] London: printed for J. Stone, 1735. 259 p. 16 cm. 2 sh. 6 d.[2]

Cited: Bitting, p. 556; Oxford, pp. 65–6

Copies: *BI*: —
    NA: KMK; MH-BA

1. This entry is based on Rudolph, pp. 25–6. Apart from Oxford, pp. 65–6 (which gives slightly different wording for the title-page; e.g. '... English wines ...' for '... all sorts of wines ...'), the only known reference to a copy that is (or was) in the British Isles is given in *BABCat.*, No. BA/20, p. 93.
2. *Gents.Mag.*, vol. 6 (Aug. 1736), p. 491, confirms that the price was 2 sh. 6 d.

GENTLEMAN
see CHILD, Samuel.

GENTLEMAN OF EXPERIENCE
see ECONOMIST.

GENTLEMAN OF EXTENSIVE PRACTICE
see COMPLETE distiller.

GENTLEMAN OF THE FACULTY

see CONCISE observations.

GENTLEWOMAN
see CARTER, Charles, The London and country cook.

GENTLEWOMAN
see COMPLEAT family companion.

GENTLEWOMAN
see LADIES companion.

GENTLEWOMAN
see YOUNG ladies companion.

GLASSE, A. (*fl.* 1797)
The accomplished family cook. etc.[1] London: printed for J. Bell, 1797. [——] [——]
Cited: Oxford, pp. 124–5
Copies: *BI*: —
   NA: —

1. The only known reference to this work is Oxford, who says that the title-page is identical to one used for another book; see under later entry: MENON, [——], The French family cook. Oxford also implies that the contents are identical, and that the famous name Glasse was pirated in an attempt to stimulate sales.

T H E
A R T
OF
C O O K E R Y,

Made PLAIN and EASY;

Which far exceeds any THING of the Kind ever yet Publifhed.

CONTAINING,

I. Of Roafting, Boiling, &c.
II. Of Made-Difhes.
III. Read this Chapter, and you will find how Expenfive a *French* Cook's Sauce is.
IV. To make a Number of pretty little Difhes fit for a Supper, or Side-Difh, and little Corner-Difhes for a great Table; and the reft you have in the Chapter for *Lent*.
V. To drefs Fifh.
VI. Of Soops and Broths.
VII. Of Puddings.
VIII. Of Pies.
IX. For a Faft-Dinner, a Number of good Difhes, which you may make ufe for a Table at any other Time.
X. Directions for the Sick.
XI. For Captains of Ships.
XII. Of Hog's Puddings, Saufages, &c.

XIII. To Pot and Make Hams, &c.
XIV. Of Pickling.
XV. Of Making Cakes, &c.
XVI. Of Cheefecakes, Creams, Jellies, Whip Syllabubs, &c.
XVII. Of Made Wines, Brewing, *French* Bread, Muffins, &c.
XVIII. Jarring Cherries, and Preferves, &c.
XIX. To Make Anchovies, Vermicella, Ketchup, Vinegar, and to keep Artichokes, French-Beans, &c.
XX. Of Diftilling.
XXI. How to Market, and the Seafons of the Year for Butcher's Meat, Poultry, Fifh, Herbs, Roots, &c. and Fruit.
XXII. A certain Cure for the Bite of a Mad Dog. By Dr. *Mead*.

BY A LADY.

L O N D O N:
Printed for the AUTHOR; and fold at Mrs. *Afhburn*'s, a China-Shop, the Corner of *Fleet-Ditch*. MDCCXLVII.

[*Price* 3 s. *ftitch'd, and* 5 s. *bound.*]

The first edition of Mrs Glasse's principal book was in a large format and had this handsome title-page. In later editions the main list of contents was preserved without any change of substance except for the addition of 'XXIII A Receipt to keep clear from Buggs'.

GLASSE, Elizabeth
see Price, Elizabeth.

GLASSE, Hannah (1708–1770)

The art of cookery, made plain and easy; which far exceeds any thing of the kind ever yet published. etc. [by a lady].[1] London: printed for the author,[2] and sold at Mrs. Ashburn's, a china-shop, the corner of Fleet-Ditch, 1747. ii, 166 p. 29 cm. 3 sh. stitched and 5 sh. bound.

Cited: Bitting, pp. 186–9; Oxford, pp. 76–7

Copies: *BI*: ENLS*[3]; LBL; LeU(B)
    NA: KMK; MH; NYPL

—2nd ed. with additions.[4] London: printed for the author, 1747. DoCL; LeU(B): DCLC; KMK

—3rd ed. London: printed for the author, 1748. BPL; CUL; LeU(B): ICJ; KMK; MCR

—3rd ed. Dublin: printed for E. and J. Exshaw, 1748. —: DCLC; MH

—another ed.[5] London: printed for the author, [*c*.1750]. GUL: MCR

—4th ed. with additions. London: printed for the author, 1751. LBL; LWML; LeU(B): MCR; MH; NYPL

—another ed. [with changed title: the *new* art of cookery]. Dublin: printed for John Exshaw, 1753. DNLI: KMK

—5th ed. with additions. London: printed; and sold at Mrs. Ashburn's, 1755. LBL; LGL; LeU(B): CtY; KMK; PHi

—supplement. An appendix to Mrs. Glasse's cookery: containing many new and useful receipts, in all branches of the art . . . to which is added a copious index to this and all the octavo editions. London: printed for the author, and sold by A. Millar and T. Trye, 1758. 3–48 p. 20 cm. 1 sh. EUL; LeU(B): —

—6th ed. with additions. London: printed for the author, and sold by A. Millar and T. Trye, 1758. GPL(M); LBL; LeU(B): KMK; MOSV; NB

—7th ed. London: printed for A. Millar; and J. and R. Tonson, 1760. LBL; LeU(B): KMK; NPV; ViWC

—another ed. [The *new* art of cookery]. Dublin: printed by John Exshaw, 1762. —: KMK

—8th ed. with additions. London: printed for A. Millar; and J. and R. Tonson, 1763. LBL; LWML; LeU(B): CtY; MB; MiD

—9th ed.[6] London: printed for A. Millar; and J. & R. Tonson, 1765. LeU(B): CaOTUTF; KMK; MiD

—a new ed. London: printed for A. Millar; and J. & R. Tonson, 1765. LeU(B): —

—a new ed. London: printed for A. Millar; and J. & R. Tonson, 1767. LBL; LeU(B): KMK; NYPL; OCl

—a new ed. with additions. London: printed for W. Strahan; and J. & F. Rivington, 1770. LWML; LeU(B): DCLC; KMK; MiD

—a new ed.[7] London: printed for W. Strahan; and J. & F. Rivington, 1771. —: —

—another ed. Edinburgh: printed for Alexander Donaldson, 1774. ENLS[8]; LBL; LWS: KMK; MiD

—a new ed. with additions. London: printed for W. Strahan, 1774. LBL; LWML: CU; DCLC; NNNAM

—a new ed. London: printed for a company of booksellers, and sold by L. Wangford, [c.1775]. LBL; LWML; LeU(B): DCLC

—a new ed. with additions. London: printed for W. Strahan, etc., 1778. LBL; LWML: DCLC; KMK; MiD

—another ed. Edinburgh: printed for Alexander Donaldson, 1781. ENLS; LBL: KMK; MiD

—a new ed. London: printed for a company of booksellers, [c.1781]. LeU(B): MH-BA

—a new ed. London: printed for W. Strahan, etc., 1784. LBL; LeU(B); RUL: ICJ; KMK; NYPL

—another ed. Edinburgh: printed for Alexander Donaldson, 1786. LWS: —

—a new ed. London: printed for J. Rivington and Sons, 1788. LBL; LWML; LeU(B): KMK; NBu; NPV

—17th ed. Edinburgh: printed for James Donaldson, 1788. GSU(S); LWML: —

—a new ed. London: printed for A. Millar; W. Law, and R. Cater, 1789. OBL: IaAS; OrU

—20th ed. Edinburgh: printed for James Donaldson, 1791. LBL; LWML: —

—a new ed. with additions. Dublin: printed for W. Gilbert, 1791. —: DNAL; NSyU

—a new ed. London: printed for A. Millar, 1796. LWML: —

—a new ed. London: printed for T. Longman, 1796. ENLS; LWML; LeU(B): KMK; MCR; NIC

—a new ed. Dublin: printed for W. Gilbert, 1796. LBL: —

—a new ed.[9] London: printed for [———], 1799.

—a new ed. Dublin: printed for W. Gilbert, 1799. CUL; LeU(B): —

—a new ed.[10] London: printed for a company of booksellers and sold by L. Wangford, [c.1800]. —: KMK

1. Hannah Glasse did not identify herself until the publication of the 4th ed. in 1751, when she described herself as 'Habit Maker to Her Royal Highness the Princess of Wales, in Tavistock Street, Covent Garden'.

2. This author deserves more than a cursory note. She is certainly the best-known cookery writer of the 18th century, and wrote in the title of her 1st ed.; that it far exceeded 'any thing of the kind ever yet published'. Her works were best-sellers for nearly 100 years, the last edition being printed in 1843, and they remained popular until Mrs Beeton took over her mantle. It can be stated, with some certainty, that Hannah Glasse (1708–70) née Allgood, was the London-born daughter of a clergyman of a respectable family from Hexham in Northumberland, and, at an early age, married Peter Glasse, a solicitor, by whom she had

several children. Her brother is said to have been Sir Lancelot Allgood, who might have been indirectly involved in the troubles of Ann Cook, one of the rival cookery writers who envied or resented Hannah's success; see Madeleine Hope Dodds, op. cit.; and earlier entry under COOK, Ann; and the interesting book by Mary Aylett and Olive Ordish, *First Catch your Hare: A History of the Recipe-makers* (London, 1965), pp. 112-25. It is a myth that Mrs Glasse was responsible for the joke: 'First catch your hare'. The recipe on p. 6 of her 1st edition begins: 'Take your Hare when it is cas'd'; and 'cased' meant 'skinned'. It is also a myth that her works were written by the notorious John Hill. Dilly, the bookseller, while host to Dr Samuel Johnson on 15 April 1778, asserted: 'Mrs. Glasse's *Cookery*, which is the best, was written by Dr. Hill. Half the *trade* know this'; which Dr Johnson, perhaps for the wrong reasons, refuted; see *Boswell's Life of Johnson*.

3. The National Library of Scotland holds a typescript of Dr Robb-Smith's bibliography: Hannah Glasse. Notes on Editions and Variants (catalogued 22 January 1962; pressmark 6.98) [hereafter referred to as Robb-Smith Bib.]. For owners of the very rare 1st eds. see Crahan, p. 42.

4. A so-called '2nd ed.' [London: printed for J. Fairburn, 1812 (see Robb-Smith Bib., p. 2)] was published, and some libraries (e.g.: NYPL) have it wrongly listed as 'ca. 1747'. In a letter to the present compiler, Dr. Robb-Smith says: 'This is an undated "second edition" of a shortened version of the pre-1784 text, of which there are about ten editions . . . dating between *1802* and *1846*.'

5. This rare edition is listed as entry No. 54 in the typescript handlist entitled 'Women and Books from the sixteenth century to the Suffragettes: An Exhibition held in the Hunterian Library, University of Glasgow, November 1971', (p. 11), and a copy at MCR, which is part of the Samuel and Narcissa Chamberlain Cookery Book Collection, and is housed in the Sarah Wyman Whitman Room of the Arthur and Elizabeth Schlesinger Library on the History of Women.

6. Robb-Smith Bib., p. 1, states: 'Some copies have a misprint on title—RECEIPS FOR RECEIPTS.' The LeU(B) copy of the 9th edition is inscribed: 'Maria Kirkman 1780'.

7. No copy located. *Pub.Adv.*, 18 Jan. 1771, p. 1—'This day is published a new edition . . . of The Art of Cookery Made Plain and Easy.'

8. The ENLS copy of the Edinburgh edition of 1774 is inscribed: 'Mrs Sinclair 25 Sept. 1775'.

9. Bitting describes a copy, said to be identical with the 1778 eds., which is said to have been in her collection, but there is no such copy in the collection of her books, which are now in the Library of Congress.

10. There were further editions of this work in the 19th century; until 1843 for certain, perhaps until 1852; see Robb-Smith Bib., p. 2. The first American edition was probably published in Alexandria in 1805. For a brief analysis of Hannah Glasse's work see T. G. H. Drake, OBE, MB, FRCP(C), 'Eighteenth Century Cookery: *The Art of Cookery Made Plain and Easy, by a Lady* (Hannah Glasse)', *Journal of the American Dietetic Association*, vol. 28 (1952), pp. 422-4. Dr Drake makes the important point that Mrs Glasse, unlike many of her contemporary cookery writers, did not include large sections on home medication in her editions—although she was not the first to concentrate on cookery.

GLASSE, HANNAH (1708-1770)

The compleat confectioner: or, the whole art of confectionary made plain and easy. etc. London: printed; and sold at Mrs. Ashburner's [*sic*] china shop[1] [and] by I. Pottinger; and J. Williams, [*c.*1760]. iv, 304, xvi p. 21 cm.

Cited: Bitting, p. 190; Oxford, pp. 90-1

Copies: *BI*: LBL*; OBL
     NA: CtY; MH; NYPL

—another ed. with the new art of brewing. Dublin: printed for J. Exshaw, 1762.[2] DNLI; LBL; LWS: NB; NYPL

—another ed. London: printed for J. Cooke, [*c*.1765]. DoCL; ESBL: MWelC; MiD

—another ed. London: printed for J. Cooke, 1772. LWML: DCLC; KMK

—another ed. London: printed for J. Cooke, 1787. CUL: —

—another ed. with additions and corrections by Maria Wilson. London: printed by J. W. Myers, for West and Hughes, 1800.[3] —: ICJ; KMK

—another ed. with considerable additions and corrections by Maria Wilson. London: printed by J. D. Dewick . . . and sold by R. Dutton for West and Hughes, 1800.[4] LWML: NcU

1. See previous entry: GLASSE, Hannah, The art of cookery, where the name in the main entry and for the 5th ed. is given as 'Ashburn' and not 'Ashburner'.
2. Robb-Smith Bib., p. 3, states that the year 1762 was misprinted 'MDCCXLII' [1742].
3. For a copy that is (or was) in the British Isles see *BABCat.*, No. BA/20, p. 31.
4. See later entry: HOLLAND, Mary, The complete British cook, which contains the following advertisement: 'On Saturday, November 30, 1799, was published Number 1 price sixpence, to be continued Weekly, and completed in 10 Numbers, of The Complete Confectioner; or, Housekeeper's Guide, . . . by Mrs. H. Glasse, author of the Art of Cookery, with considerable additions and corrections, by Maria Wilson. London: printed by J. D. Dewick, for Lackington, Allen and Co., and West and Hughes.'

GLASSE, HANNAH (1708–1770)

The servant's directory, or house-keeper's companion: wherein the duties of the chamber-maid, nursery-maid, house-maid, landery-maid [*sic*], scullion, or under-cook . . . to which is annexed . . . directions for keeping accounts.[1] etc. London: printed for the author, and sold by W. Johnston . . . [and] at Mrs. Ashburnham's [*sic*] china-shop,[2] 1760. viii, 4–80, 432 p. 21 cm.

Cited: Bitting, p. 190; Oxford, pp. 89–90

Copies: *BI*: ENLS*; LBL; LeU(B)
            NA: DCLC; KMK; NPV

—another ed. New York: printed for [———], 1760.[3] —: —

—another ed. Dublin: printed by James Potts, [*c*.1761].[4] —: —

—4th ed. improved. Dublin: printed by James Potts, 1762. —: MNU[5]

1. The majority of the part devoted to accounts is ruled for 366 days.
2. See the two previous entries for GLASSE, Hannah, where, in the first, the name is given as 'Ashburn' and, in the second, is listed as 'Ashburner'. Here it changes to 'Ashburnham' (or, according to Rudolph, p. 47, to 'Asburnham').
3. It would seem that Hugh Gaine did not continue to hold copies of this work for sale at his bookstore in Hanover Square, New York City; but 'by 1792 his catalog of importations, which he published in book form, offered three titles: "Glasse's New Art of Cookery made plain and easy, which far exceeds any thing of the kind ever yet published. Mrs. Frazer's Practice of Cookery, Pastry, Pickling, Preserving, with Figures of Dinners. Mrs. Maciver's Cookery and Pastry." These titles are entered under Miscellany in his roughly classified catalog'; see Hugh Gaine, *Catalogue of Books, Lately Imported* (New York, 1792), p. 15. Hugh Gaine's *Journals* were edited by Paul Leicester Ford and published in New York in 1902.
4. There are copies of this edition in Dublin Public Library and the Bibliothèque Nationale, Paris.
5. *NUCat.* confirms that a copy of this edition is held by the University of Minnesota at Minneapolis, and Robb-Smith Bib., p. 3, states: 'There was a copy in the John Hodgkin collection [in Minneapolis] said to be dated 1762.'

GODFREY, BOYLE (d. 1756?)

Miscellanea vere utilia: or miscellaneous experiments and observations on various subjects. etc. In three parts.[1] London: printed for J. Robinson, [c.1735]. 138 p. 18 cm.

Cited: —

Copies: *BI*: ENLS*; LBL
    NA: CLU-C; WU

—2nd ed. with additions. London: printed for [——], 1737 LBL: DNLM; MH; OClW

—another ed. Dublin: printed for the author, 1746. —: ICU; PPL

—another ed. Dublin: printed for James Hunter, 1760. —: DNLM

—another ed. with additions. Dublin: printed for James Hunter, 1761. —: DCLC

1. Part 1 covers 'observations upon aliments, in order to give health and longer life'.

GRAHAM, WILLIAM (*fl.* 1750-1783)

The art of making wines of fruits, flowers and herbs, all the native growth of England.[1] Particularly of grapes, gooseberries, currants, raspberries . . . with a succinct account of their medicinal virtues, and the most approved receipt for making raisin wine. etc. London: printed for J. Williams, [c.1750]. vi, 42 p. 20 cm. [1 sh.]

Cited: —

Copies: *BI*: —
    NA: CtY*

—2nd ed. to which is now added, the complete method of pickling and preserving. Revised, corrected and greatly enlarged. London: printed for W. Nicoll, [c.1760]. [1 sh.][2] —: DNAL

—5th ed. revised, corrected and greatly enlarged. London: printed for W. Nicoll, [c.1765]. —: CtY; ICJ

—6th ed. revised and corrected. London: printed for W. Nicoll, [c.1765]. LWML; LeU(B): —

—a new ed. enlarged. London: printed for W. Nicoll, 1770. LBL[3]: —

—8th ed. London: printed for W. Nicoll, [c.1780]. LGL: —

—a new ed. London: printed for R. Baldwin, 1783. LBL: MB

1. It is interesting to note that although 'England' was used in the 1st ed., all subsequent editions used 'Great-Britain'.
2. *Lond.Mag.* (Jan. 1760), p. 56, confirms that the price was 1 sh.
3. The British Library copy has been lost or mislaid.

GREY (or DE GREY), ELIZABETH, COUNTESS OF KENT (1581-1651)

A choice manuall, of rare and select secrets in physick and chirurgery: collected, and practised by the Right Honourable the Countesse of Kent, late deceased.

As also most exquisite ways of preserving, conserving, candying. etc. [Anon.].[1]
London: printed for H. Mortlock, 1708. [——] [——]

Cited: Bitting, p. 201; Oxford, pp. 22–3

Copies: *BI*: —
    NA: ICJ

1. The 1st ed. was printed in London by R[oger] Norton in 1653, two years after the Countess's
death, and the publisher was given as 'W. J., Gent.', who might have been the author.
According to Oxford, p. 22, the author was 'W. Jar.', but he does not give the source for his
assertion. 'Jar.' could be an abbreviation of a name such as Jarvis, Jardine, or Jarman, or
Oxford could have misread the indistinct printing and misquoted the word. The work is
listed, with its several 17th-century editions, under the name of the Countess in the *BMCat*. It
is largely devoted to home cures of the most disgusting sort. See also Elizabeth David, 'A True
Gentlewoman's Delight', *Petits Propos Culinaires*, vol. 1 (1979), pp. 43–53.

GREY (or DE GREY), Elizabeth, Countess of Kent (1581–1651)

A true gentlewoman's delight, Wherein is contained all manner of cookery:
together with preserving, conserving, drying, and candying. Very necessary for
all ladies and gentlewomen. [Anon.].[1] London: printed for H. Mortlock, 1707.
68 p. frontis. 15 cm.

Cited: Bitting, p. 201; Oxford, pp. 22–3

Copies: *BI*: —
    NA: ICJ

1. According to Bitting this and the previous work are nearly always found together, bound as
one volume, although they are certainly separate works. The 1st ed. of this work, in common
with the previous work, was printed in London by R. Norton in 1653, and published by 'W. J.,
Gent.' (and written, according to Oxford, by 'W. Jar.'). For earlier editions see Wing *STC*,
vol. 2 (1948), p. 293.

GRIFFITHS, Samuel Powell

see Buchan, William, Domestic medicine.

GRINDAL, Martin (*fl* 1724–1741?)

Warm beer, a treatise; proving . . . that beer so qualify'd, is far more wholesome
than that which is drank cold. etc. London: printed for J. Wilford, 1724.[1] 48 p.
[——]

Cited: —

Copies: *BI*: LBL
    NA: DCLC*

—another ed. London: printed for T. Read, 1741. LBL; LWML: CLU-C

1. The British Library copy of the 1724 edition has been lost or mislaid.

GUIDE

A guide to gentlemen and farmer's [*sic*] for brewing malt-liquors, also directions for the right managing utencles [*sic*]. London: printed for [——], 1703.[1]
[——] [——]

Cited: —

Copies: *BI*: LBL
    NA: —

—2nd ed. with additions.[2] London: printed and sold by S. Popping, 1718. [6 d.]
    ENLS: ICJ

—4th ed. London: printed for J. Mills, 1724. —: CtY

—5th ed.[3] Dublin: printed for [——], 1727. —: —

1. This is a revised edition of a work published three years earlier: Directions for brewing malt
   liquors. etc. [by a countrey gentleman]. London: printed for J. Nutt, 1700. 28 p. 16 cm. LBL:
   CLU-C; DFo; NYPL
2. The 'additions' are receipts for physical ales.
3. The only known reference to this 5th ed. is given in *Maggs Bros. Cat.*, No. 645, p. 80.

H

H., J.
    see SALMON, William.

HALL, T. (*fl.* 1709–1730?)

The queen's royal cookery: or, expert and ready way for the dressing of all sorts
of flesh . . . also making several sorts of English wines . . . together with several
cosmetick or beautifying waters. etc.[1] London: printed for C. Bates; and
A. Bettesworth, 1709. 178 p. frontis. 16 cm.

Cited: Bitting, p. 210; Oxford, pp. 51–2

Copies: *BI*: LeU(B)*[2]
    NA: MH; NYPL

—2nd ed. London: printed for C. Bates; and A. Bettesworth, 1713. LBL;
    LWML; LeU(B): DCLC; KMK

—3rd ed. London: printed for S. Bates; and A. Bettesworth, 1719. LGL;
    LeU(B): MH; NPV

—4th ed. London: printed for S. Bates; and A. Bettesworth, 1729. OBL: —

—5th ed. London: printed for A. Bettesworth; and C. Hitch, [*c.*1730]. LBL:
    DCLC

—another ed. London: printed for A. Bettesworth; and C. Hitch, [*c.*1734]. —:
    NNNAM

1. The author described himself as 'Free-Cook of London'.
2. The LeU(B) copy is wanting its frontispiece, which has a portrait of Queen Anne (marked
   'AR') above a kitchen, and below the kitchen a division, with a pastry room on the left and
   a room for 'chymistry' on the right, in which a woman is distilling.

HARRISON, Sarah (*fl.* 1733-1777)

The house-keeper's pocket book, and compleat family cook . . . concluding with many prescriptions of the most eminent physicians. etc.[1] London: printed for T. Worrall, 1733. xii, 217 p. 17 cm. 2 sh. 6 d.[2]

Cited: Bitting, p. 217; Oxford, pp. 63-4

Copies: *BI*: —
     NA: KMK; MiD

—2nd ed. London: printed for T. Worrall, 1738. LeU(B): —

—2nd ed. corrected and improved. London: printed for R. Ware, 1739. LBL: MCR; NYPL

—3rd ed. corrected and improved. Dublin: printed for Edward Exshaw, [*c*.1739].[3] —: NRU; NYPL

—3rd ed. corrected and improved. London: printed for R. Ware, 1743. CUL: CtY; NNNAM

—4th ed. corrected and improved. London: printed for R. Ware, 1748. LeU(B): DCLC; KMK

—5th ed. corrected and improved. London: printed for R. Ware, 1751. LeU(B): ICJ

—6th ed., revised and corrected. To which is now added several modern receipts . . . Also, every one their own physician; . . . Carefully compiled by Mary Morris.[4] London: printed for R. Ware, 1755. ANLW; LWML; LeU(B): DCLC; KMK; NPV

—7th ed. revised and corrected. London: printed for C. and R. Ware, 1760.[5] GUL; LBL; LeU(B): —

—8th ed. revised and corrected. London: printed for C. and R. Ware, 1764. LBL; LeU(B): NIC; OCl

—9th ed. revised and corrected. London: printed for J. Rivington, 1777. LBL: KMK

1. The main entry is based on Rudolph, p. 24, as no copy of the 1st ed. has been located in the British Isles. Mrs Harrison was a Devonshire woman.
2. *Gents.Mag.*, vol. 2 (Dec. 1732), No. 15 [no pagination], confirms that the price was 2 sh. 6 d.
3. One source seems to have a positive date; see Stark, p. 14, where part of the entry reads: '. . . The third edition . . . Dublin: Printed by S. Powell, for Edward Exshaw . . . MDCCXXXVIII. [1738]'. In the present compiler's opinion, an 'X' could be missing from the Stark entry, and the date of publication was *c*.1748 rather than 1738 or *c*.1739. It is more likely that a 3rd ed. printed in Dublin was published after and not before the 3rd ed. printed in London in 1743.
4. For this edition see Rudolph, pp. 43-4.
5. *Sotheby Cat.* (17 Dec. 1971), p. 61, wrongly lists the 7th ed. as 'ca. 1750'.

HAY, D[aniel?]
    see Lémery, Louis.

HAYES, Thomas
    see Concise observations.

HAYWOOD, Eliza Fowler (1693?-1756)

A new present for a servant-maid:[1] containing rules for her moral conduct both with respect to herself and her superiors: the whole art of cookery . . . in ten books.[2] etc. [by Mrs Haywood].[3] London: printed for G. Pearch; and H. Gardner, 1771. xiii, 272 p. frontis. 19 cm. 2 sh.[4]

Cited: Bitting, p. 220

Copies: *BI*: LeU(B)[5]
        NA: DCLC; KMK; NYPL

—another ed. London: printed for G. Pearch; and H. Gardner, [c.1775]. —: ICJ

1. The main title in Murphy, p. 19 contains the misprint 'serving-maid' in place of 'servant-maid'.
2. The term 'books' in this (as in many other) 18th-century works means 'part' or 'section', and includes directions for marketing, the art of preserving, making English wines, the whole art of distilling, and instructions for carving.
3. For biographies of Mrs Eliza Fowler Haywood see *DNB*, vol. 9 (1908), pp. 313-15; and M. Priestley, *The Female Spectator* (London, 1929).
4. *Scots Mag.*, vol. 34 (Apr. 1772), p. 205, confirms that the price was 2 sh.
5. Inscribed 'Elizabeth Baker Her Book, London October 9th 1780'.

HAYWOOD, Eliza Fowler (1693?-1756)

A present for a servant-maid:[1] or, the sure means of gaining love and esteem . . . to which are added, directions for going to market; . . . with some rules for washing. etc. [Anon.]. London: printed and published by T. Gardner, 1743. 76 p. 19 cm. 1 sh. (or 25 for a guinea to those who give them away)

Cited: Oxford, p. 73

Copies: *BI*: ENLS*; LBL
        NA: MH; NYPL

—another ed. Dublin: printed by and for George Faulkner, 1743, LeU(B): —

—another ed. Dublin: printed by and for George Faulkner, 1744. LBL: CSmH; ICN

—another ed. London: printed and published by T. Gardner, 1745. —: CtY; NcU

—another ed. Boston: reprinted by Rogers and Fowle, [c.1747].[2] —: —

—another ed. London: printed and published by T. Gardner, 1749. LeU(B): CtY; NPV

1. This work contains few receipts and, notwithstanding the similar main-title of Mrs Haywood's other work which was published nearly thirty years later (see previous entry), the two books are entirely different. The later work contains a considerable number of receipts. The following sub-headings give an idea of the content of this earlier book: Sluttishness; Telling Family Affairs; Fortune-Tellers; Giving Saucy Answers; Apeing the Fashion; Delaying to give Change; Washing Victuals; Being too free with Men-Servants; Mispending Time; etc.
2. For this edition see Lincoln, p. 7, where it is stated: 'This book is advertised in the *Boston Evening Post* for August 24, 1747 . . . no copy placed.'

HAZLEMORE, MAXIMILIAN (*fl.* 1794)

Domestic economy; or, a complete system of English housekeeping . . . also the complete brewer . . . likewise the family physician. etc.[1] London: printed for J. Creswick and Co., 1794. xxxii, 392 p. 21 cm.

Cited: Oxford, p. 122

Copies: *BI*: LBL; LeU(B)*
      NA: MB; NYPL

  1. This work is either a revised and pseudonymous edition or, much more likely, a pirated version of a book which was first published six years before; see under earlier entry: COLE, Mary, The lady's complete guide.

HEALTH

Health's preservative: being a dissertation on diet, air, and down-beds. And of the cause and cure of buggs [*sic*] . . . directions how to buy, feed and fatten fowl. etc.[1] [eminent poulterer deceas'd]. London: printed for F. Cogan, 1750. 104 p. 20 cm. 1 sh.

Cited: —

Copies: *BI*: LBL*
      NA: DCLC

  1. The section on poultry gives valuable evidence on the great number and variety of land and water birds which were eaten in the 18th century.

HEASEL, ANTHONY (*fl.* 1773)

The servant's book of knowledge, containing . . . tables for marketing . . . to which are added plain and easy instructions for servants of both sexes.[1] London: printed for J. Cooke, 1773. 87 p. [——] 1 sh. 6 d.[2]

Cited: —

Copies: *BI*: —
      NA: CtY; NYPL

  1. Many references from this book are contained in two works by Dr J. Jean Hecht, *The Domestic Servant Class in Eighteenth-Century England* (London, 1956), and 'Continental and Colonial Servants in Eighteenth-century England', *Smith College Studies in History*, vol. 40. Dr Hecht has also drawn on the more personal but equally valuable and interesting work by John Macdonald, *Memoirs of an Eighteenth-century Footman*, (ed.) John Beresford (London, 1927).
  2. *Scots Mag.*, vol. 35 (Jan. 1773), p. 39, confirms that the price was 1 sh 6 d.

HELSHAM, ROBERT

see ESSAY on the nature . . . of tea.

HENDERSON, WILLIAM AUGUSTUS (*fl.* 1790?–1800?)

The housekeeper's instructor; or, universal family cook, containing . . . confectionary, pickling . . . British wines . . . brewing malt liquor . . . complete art of carving . . . bills of fare . . . directions for marketing, etc.[1] London: printed for W. and J. Stratford, [*c.*1790]. 448 p. frontis. pls. 22 cm.

Cited: Oxford, pp. 133-4[2]

Copies: *BI*: DoCL; LWML*
    NA: TxU

—another ed. London: printed for W. and J. Stratford, [*c.*1793]. ENLS; LWML: —

—5th ed. London: printed by W. and J. Stratford, [*c.*1793]. LeU(B): LU

—6th ed. London: printed by W. and J. Stratford, [*c.*1795]. LeU(B): KMK; MCR; NYPL

—8th ed. London: printed by W. and J. Stratford, [*c.*1800]. —: MB

—10th ed. London: printed by W. and J. Stratford, [*c.*1800]. LWML: MH; OrU

1. Simon, p. 81, claims 'this was probably the most popular cookery book in England during the last decade of the eighteenth century. There were ten editions published before 1800.' Notwithstanding the 'probably' this is a bold assertion, and the present compiler has found no evidence to justify it. On the contrary, the claim could be made for several other works, especially those of Hannah Glasse and certain of her contemporaries.
2. Oxford cites no editions which were published in the 18th century. His only entry is for the 12th ed. which was 'corrected, revised, and considerably improved . . . by Jacob Christopher Schnebbelie, late apprentice to Messrs. Tupp and Perry, Oxford-Street; afterwards principal cook at Melun's Hotel, Bath; and now of the Albany, London'; which was printed and sold in London by J. Stratford, 1804. Henderson is described as 'many years eminent in the culinary profession'.

HILL, JOHN (1716?-1775)

The old man's guide to health and longer life, with rules for diet, exercise and physick. etc.[1] 2nd ed. London: printed for M. Cooper, [*c.*1750]. 54 p. 21 cm.

Cited: —

Copies: *BI*: —
    NA: DNLM; NIC; WU

—5th ed. London: printed for R. Baldwin and J. Ridley, 1764. ENLS; EUL; LBL: ViSL

—6th ed. corrected and enlarged. London: printed for E. and C. Dilly, 1771. LBL: DCLC

—another ed. London: printed; Philadelphia: reprinted by John Dunlap, 1775. —: DCLC

1. For a life of the notorious Dr John Hill see *DNB*, vol. 9 (1908), pp. 848-52. He is, perhaps, best known as the racketeer who ran a show called 'The Bed of Venus' with which the celebrated Lady Emma Hamilton, in her youth, was associated. His published work promised to the elderly either through herbs or special disciplines a new lease of life, and, though considered a quack, some of his diets are interesting. There is no evidence to suggest that he ever wrote a cookery or household book, even though Edward Dilly, who sold the 6th ed. of this work (see above), told Dr Samuel Johnson in 1778 that Hill was the real author of the major work of Hannah Glasse; see under earlier entry: GLASSE, Hannah, The art of cookery (note 2).

HILL, John (1716?-1775)

The useful family herbal; or, an account of all those English plants, which are remarkable for their virtues . . . with an introduction. etc. London: printed for W. Johnston and W. Owen, 1754. iv, 404 p. pls. 21 cm.

Cited: Bitting, p. 229[1]

Copies: *BI*: OBL*
          NA: MnU; PU

—2nd ed. London: printed for W. Johnston and W. Owen, 1755. LBL: CtY; MH

—another ed. London: printed for W. Johnston, 1759. —: PU

—3rd ed. London: printed for W. Owen, 1770. —: NIC

—a new ed. corrected. London: printed for A. Millar, 1789. —: KMK; PPL

1. For a more recent citation see *Sotheby Cat.* (21 June 1971), p. 34.

HINTS

Hints for the relief of the poor.[1] [——]: printed for [——], [*c*.1795]. [——] [——]

Cited: Oxford, p. 125

Copies: *BI*: —
          NA: —

1. The only known reference to this pamphlet is a footnote in Oxford, p. 125, who says it contains 'recipes for soups and other cheap foods'.

HOFFMAN, Frederick (1660-1742)

A treatise on the nature of aliments, or foods in general, shewing their good and bad qualities . . . to which is added an essay on digestion. etc.[1] [London]: printed by L. Davis and C. Reymers, 1761. [——] [——]

Cited: Bitting, p. 231

Copies: *BI*: —
          NA: —

1. This entry is based on Bitting, p. 231, and is not part of her collection in the DCLC rare books department.

HOLLAND, Mary (*fl.* 1800)

The complete British cook: being a collection of the most valuable and useful receipts, for rendering the whole art of cookery plain and familiar to every capacity. etc.[1] London: printed by J. D. Dewick for West and Hughes, 1800. 104 p. frontis. 17 cm.

Cited: Oxford, p. 127

Copies: *BI*: LBL*[2]
          NA: —

1. This book contains an advertisement for one of the two 1800 editions of the work of the late Mrs Glasse, which had been revised by Maria Wilson; see under earlier entry: GLASSE, Hannah, The compleat confectioner.
2. The British Library copy is bound with several other cookery works under 'Tracts on Cookery: 1699-1808', (press-mark 1037.e.41).

HONEYWOOD, LYDIA (*fl.* 1755?)

The cook's pocket-companion, and complete family-guide . . . to which is added, the universal physician. etc.[1] London: printed for C. Henderson, [*c.*1756]. [——] [——] 1 sh.[2]

Cited: —

Copies: *BI*: —

      NA: —

—another ed. London: printed for Thomas Caslon, 1760.[3] 143 p. pls. 16 cm. 1 sh. LeU(B): —

1. This entry is based on *B&GCat.*, No. 37, p. 10.
2. *Scots Mag.*, vol. 18 (Sept. 1756), p. 472, confirms 1 sh.
3. This edition contains excellent illustrations on trussing of poultry and game. See p. xi.

HONOURS OF THE TABLE

see TRUSLER, John.

HOUDLSTON, THOMAS[1] (*fl.* 1753)

A new method of cookery, or, expert and ready way for the dressing of all sorts of flesh, fowl, fish. etc. [Dumfries]: printed for the author, [*c.*1760]. 6-186 p. 15 cm.

Cited: —

Copies: *BI*: ENLS*

      NA: —

—another ed. Edinburgh: printed for E. Wilson at Dumfries, [*c.*1760]. LBL[2]: —

1. Although printed for the author, it must be presumed that he saw no proofs of the title-page giving his surname as 'Houdlston', which must be a printer's error. The author's surname was, without any doubt, HUDDLESTON; see William McDowall, *History of Dumfries* (Edinburgh, 1867), p. 598 (footnote), which states: 'Education in other useful occupations was also promoted by the [Dumfries Town] Council. On the 24th of December, 1753, Thomas Huddleston, cook and confectioner, was admitted a freeman and burgess [of Dumfries] on condition that he should teach three poor girls "the arts of cookery and confectionery or paistry [*sic*]".' George Fraser Black, *The Surnames of Scotland: Their Origin, Meaning and History* (New York, 1962), p. 358, gives only Hiddleston, Hiddlestone, and Huddleston, as variants of a surname which had its 'local origin from Huddleston in the parish of Westerkirk, Dumfriesshire.
2. The British Library states that this copy has been destroyed.

HOUSE-KEEPER

The house-keeper's guide, in the prudent management of their affairs, being several observations relating to the orderly and discreet government of private

families, grounded upon reason, experience, and the Word of God. etc.[1]
London: printed for A. Bosvile, 1706. 264 p. frontis. [——]

Cited: Oxford, pp. 50–1[2]

Copies: *BI*: —
  NA: DFo; MH; PU

1. The preface is signed 'C. R.'.
2. Oxford states: 'The book is purely devotional, and is entered here as a warning to collectors who may see the title in a catalogue'; and then goes on to quote from 'A Servants Prayer', which is self-demeaning in the extreme.

HOUSE-KEEPER

The house-keeper's pocket book, and compleat family cook.[1] Containing several hundred curious receipts . . . to which is added, every man his own doctor, shewing the nature and faculties of the different sorts of foods. etc.[2]
[London]: printed by Thomas Martin, 1776. 168 p. frontis. [——]

Cited: Oxford, p. 115

Copies: *BI*: LBL*; LWML
  NA: —

—another ed. London: printed by Thomas Martin, 1783. LBL; LeU(B): —

—another ed. London: printed by Henry Fenwick, [*c*.1785]. —: CtY

—another ed. [London]: printed for the booksellers in town and country, [*c*.1790].[3] —: NYPL

1. The contents of this work are entirely different from a book with an identical main title, which was first published over thirty years before and went into its 9th ed. in 1777; see under earlier entry: HARRISON, Sarah, The house-keeper's pocket book, and compleat family cook. None the less, there was an attempt to associate the two books by lettering the frontispiece: 'Engraved for Mrs. Harrisons Cookery Book'.
2. According to the *Catalogue of Printed Books in the Wellcome Historical Medical Library: 1641–1850*, vol. 3 (London, 1976), p. 305, this work could be an adaption from Mrs Glasse's major book; see under earlier entry: GLASSE, Hannah, The art of cookery. If so, it had nothing to do with the 'official' editions of Hannah's work.
3. For this edition see Stark, p. 18.

HOWARD, HENRY (*fl.* 1703–1729)

The British cook's companion: being a collection of four hundred of the newest and best receipts. 5th ed.[1] London: printed for R. Knaplock, 1729. 224 p. pls. 16 cm. 2 sh. 6 d.[2]

Cited: —

Copies: *BI*: —
  NA: NYPL

1. This entry is based on Stark, p. 13, who implies that this work is an edition of the following entry: see HOWARD, Henry, England's newest way in . . . cookery. The author described himself as 'Henry Howard, Free-Cook of London, and late Cook of his Grace the Duke of Ormond, and since to the Earl of Salisbury, and Earl of Winchelsea.'
2. *Mon.Cat./2* (vol. 2), pp. 95–6 (Aug. 1729), confirms that the price was 2 sh. 6 d.

HOWARD, HENRY (*fl.* 1703-1729)

England's newest way in all sorts of cookery, pastry, and all pickles that are fit to be used. etc.[1] London: printed for and sold by Chr[istopher] Coningsby, 1703. [——] pls. [——]

Cited: Bitting, p. 235; Oxford, p. 51

Copies: *BI*: —

      NA: DCLC; NYPL

—2nd ed. with additions and amendments.[2] London: printed for Chr. Coningsby, 1708. CUL: NYPL

—3rd ed. with additions. London: printed for Chr. Coningsby, 1710. ENLS; LBL; LeU(B): —

—4th ed. with additions. London: printed for Chr. Coningsby, 1717.[3] LeU(B): KMK; NYPL

—5th ed. London: printed for J. Knapton, 1726. LBL: MB; MCR; NIC

1. This entry is based on Bitting, p. 235.
2. The 'additions' include 'receipts of beautifying waters, and other curiosities'.
3. See Stark, p. 13.

HOWARD, HENRY

    see MIDDLETON, John.

HUDDLESTON, THOMAS

    see HOUDLSTON, Thomas.

I

INGENIOUS FOREIGNER

    see BORELLA, [——] [Mr].

J

J., W.

    see GREY (or DE GREY), Elizabeth, Countess of Kent.

JACKSON, H. (*fl.* 1758)

An essay on bread; wherein the bakers and millers are vindicated . . . to which is added, an appendix; explaining the vile practices committed in adulterating wines, cider, porter, punch. etc. London: printed for J. Wilkie, 1758. 55 p. 20 cm. 1 sh.

Cited: —

Copies: *BI*: LBL*
     NA: —

JACKSON, SARAH (*fl.* 1754–1770)

Complete family cook; or young woman's best companion.[1] etc. London: printed for [——], 1754. [——] [——]

Cited: —

Copies: *BI*: —
     NA: —

1. The only known reference to this work is given in Vicaire, p. 459. It is almost certainly another edition or a slightly altered version (with a changed main title and rearranged or truncated sub-titles) of the next entry; see JACKSON, Sarah, The director.

JACKSON, SARAH (*fl.* 1754–1770)

The director: or, young woman's best companion, . . . in cookery . . . physick, and surgery . . . directions for carving . . . made wines . . . collected for the use of her own family . . . being one of the plainest and cheapest of the kind. The whole makes a complete family cook and physician. London: printed for J. Fuller;[1] and for S. Neale at Chatham, 1754. 112 p. 17 cm.

Cited: Oxford, p. 86

Copies: *BI*: ENLS*; LBL; LeU(B)
     NA: NNNAM

—another ed. London: printed for S. Crowder and H. Woodgate, 1754.[2] —: —

—2nd ed. corrected and greatly improv'd. London: printed for S. Crowder and H. Woodgate, 1755. LeU(B): NIC; NYPL

—a new ed. corrected and greatly improved. London: printed for S. Crowder and R. Baldwin, 1770.[3] —: —

1. 'This work may be had complete, or the numbers delivered weekly at their own houses upon giving notice to the proprietor J. Fuller.'
2. The only known reference to this edition is given in *B.&G.Cat.*, No. 37, p. 10.
3. The only known reference to this edition is given in *BABCat.*, No. BA/20, p. 32.

JAMES, ROBERT
see MOUFET, Thomas.

JAMES, ROBERT
see PAULI, Simon.

JAR., W.
see GREY (or DE GREY), Elizabeth, Countess of Kent.

JENKS, JAMES (*fl.* 1768)

The complete cook: teaching the art of cookery in all its branches; . . . and dishes for Lent and fast-days, . . . with an appendix teaching the art of making wine . . . and receipts for preserving and restoring health. etc. London: printed for E. and C. Dilly, 1768. xx, 364 p. 17 cm.

Cited: Bitting, p. 245; Oxford, pp. 97–8

Copies: *BI*: ENLS*; LBL
 NA: DCLC; KMK; NYPL

—another ed. Dublin: printed by J. Potts for J. Williams, 1769. —: NNNAM

NAMES of WOMEN.

A.	D.	I.	Phyllis
Abigail	Damaris	Jane	Priscilla
Alice	Deborah	Joan	Prudence
Agnes	Diana	Isabel	
Amelia	Dinah	Judith	R.
Ann	Dorothy		Rachel
Arabella		L.	Rebecca
	E.	Laura	Rosamond
B.	Eleanor	Louisa	Rose
Barbara	Elizabeth	Lucy	
Beatrice	Esther	Lucretia	S.
Betty			Sarah
Bridget	F.	M.	Sophia
	Flora	Magdalen	Susanna
C.	Frances	Margaret	
Caroline		Margery	T.
Catherine	G.	Mary	Theresa
Cecily	Gertrude	Martha	
Charlot	Grace	Maud	U.
Christian			Ursula
Constance	H.	P.	
	Hellen	Penelope	
	Henrietta		

The above reproduction shows the girls' names which Madam Johnson thought worthy of inclusion in her compendium of useful and universal knowledge (see entry below, Note 1)

JOHNSON, MARY (*fl.* 1754–1772)

Madam Johnson's present: or, the best instructions for young women, in useful and universal knowledge. etc.[1] London: printed for M. Cooper and C. Sympson, 1754. xiv, 222 p. frontis.[2] 17 cm. 1 sh. 3 d. sewed, or 1 sh. 6 d. bound.

Cited: Bitting, p. 247; Oxford, p. 83

Copies: *BI*: LeU(B)*
 NA: CaOTP; NPV; NYPL

—another ed. London: printed for M. Cooper, 1755. LWML; LeU(B): —
—2nd ed. London: printed for J. Fuller, 1759. ENLS; LeU(B): KMK

Madam JOHNSON's Present:

Or, the best

INSTRUCTIONS

FOR

YOUNG WOMEN,

IN

Useful and Universal KNOWLEDGE,

WITH A

Summary of the late MARRIAGE ACT,
and Instructions how to marry pursuant thereto.
Digested under the following HEADS.

I. An Estimate of the Expences of a Family in the middling Station of Life.	IV. The young Woman's Guide to Knowledge.
II. The Art and Terms of Carving, Fish, Fowl, and Flesh.	V. A new English Spelling Dictionary.
III. A Bill of Fare for every Month in the Year for Dinner and Supper, and also for extraordinary Occasions.	VI. The Compleat Market-woman.
	VII. The Cook's Guide for dressing all Sorts of Flesh Fowl and Fish.
	VIII Pickling, Pastry, and Confectionary.

With several useful TABLES, being the compleatest
Book of the Kind ever published.

The Compiler, Madam JOHNSON, in order to make
this Book come as cheap as possible to the Purchasers,
has, out of her Benevolence, fixed the Price at
1 s. 6 d. bound, tho' it contains double the Quantity that is usually sold for that Sum.

LONDON:

Printed for M. COOPER, Pater-noster-row; and
C. SYMPSON, at the Bible, Chancery-lane. 1754.
Price sewed. 1 s. 3 d. bound 1 s. 6 d.

Madame Johnson included much miscellaneous information for the 'Young Women' to whom
she addressed herself, and explicitly declared her book to be a bargain in comparison with others.
(It was in fact relatively cheap.)

—2nd ed. London: printed for H. Owen, 1759. —: DCLC

—3rd ed. London: printed for J. Fuller, 1765. —: CtY; ViSL

—another ed. London: printed for W. Nicoll, 1769. —: NYPL

—4th ed. Dublin: printed for James Williams, 1770. LBL: MH

—5th ed. London: printed for W. Nicoll, 1770.[3] —: —

—6th ed. London: printed for W. Nicoll, 1772. LWML: NNNAM

1. The contents cover a great variety of subjects, including, for example, a summary of 'the late Marriage Act', and a list of children's names. See illustration on p. 75.
2. The frontispiece is entitled: 'Madam Johnson the accomplish'd Lady'.
3. The only known reference to this edition is given in *Pub.Adv.* (26 Dec. 1770), p. 1, which states: 'A very proper Christmas Box, or New Years Gift, for Servant-Maids. This day is published, The Fifth Edition, to which are added, some plain and very necessary Directions to Maid-Servants . . . The compiler, Madam Johnson, in order to make this useful Book come as cheap as possible to the Purchasers, has out of her Benevolence, fixed the Price at 1 s 6 d bound, tho' it contains double the Quantity that is usually sold for that Price . . .'.

JOHNSON, MARY (*fl.* 1753)

The young woman's companion; or the servant-maid's assistant; digested under several heads . . . viz. . . . a short essay on the benefits of learning . . . the compleat market woman . . . the compleat cook-maid, pastry-cook, and con-fectioner. etc.[1] London: printed for H. Jeffery, 1753.[2] [——] frontis. [——]

Cited: Oxford, p. 83

Copies: *BI*: —
      NA: —

1. The author described herself as 'for many years a superintendent of a lady of quality's family in the City of York'.
2. According to Oxford, p. 83, 'a second edition appeared in 1759 under the title of Madam Johnson's Present. It has many points of difference from the original'. The present compiler thinks it more likely that these are two separate books; see previous entry: JOHNSON, Mary, Madam Johnson's present.

JOHNSON, ROBERT WALLACE (*fl.* 1767-1793)

Some friendly cautions to the heads of families, . . . containing also ample directions to nurses who attend the sick and women in child-bed. etc.[1] [by a physician]. London: sold by D. Wilson, 1767. 111 p. 19 cm.

Cited: —

Copies: *BI*: EUL*; LWML[2]
      NA: CaBVaUW; DCLC; DNLM

—2nd ed. Brentford: printed for the author by P. Norbury, 1772. LWML: —

—3rd ed. with additions. Brentford: printed for the author by P. Norbury, 1793. LBL; LWML: DNLM

1. The second half of this work contains many diet recipes, including white caudle, mutton broth, boiled pigeon, blanc-manger, batter pudding and linseed-tea.
2. The LWML copy contains contemporary MS receipts.

JOHNSTON, [——] [Mrs] (*fl.* 1740?)

Mrs. Johnston's receipts for all sorts of pastry, creams, puddings, custards, preserves, marmalets . . . sauces, pickles and cookery, after the newest and most approved method.[1] Edinburgh: printed in the year [1740]. 3–117 p. 17 cm.

Cited: —

Copies: *BI*: ENLS*[2]
        NA: —

1. The first 92 pages of this work are identical to a book which was published under a different title with a different author a few years earlier; see under later entry: McLintock, [——] [Mrs], Mrs. McLintock's receipts for cookery and pastry-work. The identical contents end with 'Hunting pudding', and the last 25 pages (receipts 187–221) are additional and new. It is possible that Mrs Johnston was the same person as Mrs McLintock, and that 'Johnston' could be either a pseudonym or the name of her second husband. It is also possible that Mrs Johnston is the same person as the author of the following entry; see Johnston, Eliza, The accomplish'd servant-maid.
2. The ENLS copy is the only known copy of this work, but it is wanting pages 7–10. It is not cited in any of the leading bibliographies in this field and, hitherto, nobody has compared it with Mrs McLintock's work, which was undoubtedly the first Scottish cookery book.

JOHNSTON, Eliza (*fl.* 1747)

The accomplish'd servant-maid: or, the whole art of cookery made easy to the meanest capacity. etc. [——]: printed for [——]. 1747. [——] [——] 1 sh.

Cited: —

Copies: *BI*: —
        NA: NPV[1]

—3rd ed.[2] [——]: printed for the author, 1748. —: KMK

1. The present compiler regrets that it has not been possible to obtain details of place of publication, the printer or publisher, pagination, and size, from Vassar College, Pough-keepsie, NY, USA. If the place of publication is recorded as 'Edinburgh', it would help to establish a link, if any, between this Mrs Eliza Johnston, and the Mrs Johnston whose work is dealt with in the previous entry.
2. This edition is given in Rudolph, p. 34. The author calls herself: 'Mrs. Eliza Johnston, Upwards of Fifty Years Cook, or House-Keeper, to Three Noble Families'. The price is 1 sh. and there are 25 unnumbered leaves.

JONE (or JONES), [——] [Mrs]

The cottage cook; or, Mrs. Jone's [*sic*][1] cheap dishes; shewing the way to do much good with little money. London: printed for and sold by J. Marshall and R. White, [*c.*1797]. 16 p. [——]

Cited: —

Copies: *BI*: LBL[2]
        NA: NSyU

—another ed. London: printed for and sold by J. Evans and Son, [*c.*1797]. —: MH

—another ed. London: printed for and sold by J. and C. Evans, [c.1797].
—: ViU

—another ed. Dublin: printed for W. Watson, [c.1800]. ENLS: —

1. *NUCat.* ascribes the authorship to Hannah More.
2. The British Library copy has been lost or mislaid.

K

K., J.
   see MASSIALOT, François.

KELLET, SUSANNA; and ELIZABETH; and MARY (*fl.* 1780)

A complete collection of cookery receipts, (consisting of near four hundred,) which have been taught upwards of fifty years. etc. [by Susanna, Elizabeth, and Mary Kellet].[1] Newcastle upon Tyne: printed by T. Saint and sold by W. Charnley, Whitfield & Co., 1780. vi, xii, 192 p. 22 cm.

Cited: Bitting, p. 256

Copies: *BI*: LBL; LeU(B)*[2]; NPL
         NA: CaBVaUW; DCLC

1. This work is dedicated by these three cookery teachers (probably a mother and two daughters, *or* three sisters) to 'The Ladies who honoured our School with their attendance', and the dedication is followed by a list of subscribers. Only two of the many receipts are medicinal; one for rheumatism, the other an alleged cure for the bite of a mad dog.
2. The LeU(B) copy contains the bookplate of Thomas Bell, 1797.

KENT, COUNTESS OF
   see GREY (or DE GREY), Elizabeth, Countess of Kent.

KETTILBY, MARY (*fl.* 1714-1728?)

A collection of above three hundred receipts in cookery, physick and surgery; for the use of all good wives, tender mothers, and careful nurses. [by several hands].[1] London: printed for Richard Wilkin,[2] 1714. [In two volumes, with one title-page, with continuous pagination, and one price for the complete work].[3] Vol. 1. 121 p. 20 cm; Vol. 2. 123-218 p. 2 sh. 6 d.[4]

Cited: Bitting, p. 258; Oxford, p. 54

Copies: *BI*: ENLS*; LBL; LeU(B)
         NA: CSmH; MiD; NIC

—2nd ed.[5] London: printed for Mary Kettilby and sold by Richard Wilkin, 1719. [Vols. 1 and 2 bound together.] LWML; LeU(B); SFC(WF): InU; KMK; NYPL

A

COMPLETE COLLECTION

OF

COOKERY RECEIPTS,

(Confisting of near Four Hundred,)

Which have been Taught upwards of
Fifty Years, with great Reputation.

———————————————

BY

SUSANNA, ELIZABETH, and MARY
KELLET.

———————————————

NEWCASTLE UPON TYNE:
Printed by T. SAINT; and fold by W. CHARNLEY,
WHITFIELD and Co. and all the Book-
sellers in Town and Country.

MDCCLXXX.

The title-page of a north-country book of 1780. It is interesting to compare the typography with
that of the earlier title-page opposite. Neither is cluttered with a mass of detail, but the later book
uses a smaller, more discreet type-face.

A

COLLECTION

Of above Three Hundred

RECEIPTS

I N

Cookery,

Phyſick and Surgery;

For the Uſe of all
Good Wives, Tender Mothers,
and Careful Nurſes.

By ſeveral Hands.

LONDON,
Printed for RICHARD WILKIN, at the
King's Head in St. Paul's Church-yard.
MDCCXIV.

Although this title-page declares authorship to be vested in 'several hands', it is known that the author was Mary Kettilby. Note the emphasis given, typographically, to cookery as the main constituent of the book.

—3rd ed. London: printed for Mary Kettilby, 1724. [Vols. 1 and 2 bound together.] EUL; LBL; LeU(B): NYPL; ViSL

—4th ed. London: printed for Mary Kettilby and sold by R. Wilkin, 1728. [Vols. 1 and 2 bound together.] CUL; LWML; LeU(B): MH; MiD

—5th ed. London: printed for the executrix of Mary Kettilby, and sold by W. Parker, 1734. [Vols. 1 and 2 bound together.] LBL; LWML; LeU(B): CSmH; DCLC; NIC

—6th ed. London: printed for the executrix of Mary Kettilby, and sold by W. Parker, 1746. [Vols. 1 and 2 bound together.] LWML; LeU(B): DNLM; WU

—7th ed. London: printed for the executrix of Mary Kettilby, and sold by H. Lintot, 1749. [Vols. 1 and 2 bound together.] LWML: MH; NYPL

—7th ed. London: printed for the executrix of Mary Kettilby, and sold by R. Withy, 1759. [Vols. 1 and 2 bound together.] —: KMK

1. Although the title-page clearly states that this work was 'by several hands', there is little doubt, from evidence in later editions, that Mary Kettilby was the principal author. Her surname is often wrongly given as 'Kittelby' by bibliographers; e.g. Oxford, p. 54. She recommended her book to the clergy, 'especially those whose parishes are remote from other help'. A few of her recipes have odd names, such as 'Quire of Paper' (a pancake).
2. Several bibliographers, including Oxford, p. 54, have wrongly added 'd' to Wilkin's surname. The present compiler has never seen a copy with the form 'Wilkind'.
3. The 1st ed. was published as two separate volumes, but with only one title-page, and with continuous pagination. The 2nd and all subsequent editions were published as two volumes bound as one, but with each volume having its own title-page and its own pagination.
4. *Mon.Cat./1*, p. 10 (June 1714), confirms that the price was 2 sh. 6 d.
5. Hazlitt, p. 174,.wrongly dates the 2nd ed. as '1729'.

KIDDER, EDWARD (1666–1739)

E. Kidder's receipts of pastry and cookery, for the use of his scholars. Who teaches at his school in Queen Street near St. Thomas Apostles. On Mondays, Tuesdays & Wednesdays, in the afternoon. Also on Thursdays, Fridays & Saturdays, in the afternoon, at his school next to Furnivals Inn in Holborn. Ladies may be taught at their own houses. [London]: printed for [——], [c.1720].[1] 80 p. [or 40 unnumbered leaves][2] frontis.[3] pls. 19 cm.

Cited: Bitting, pp. 258–9; Oxford, p. 71.

Copies: *BI*: LBL; LGL; LeU(B)*
          NA: KMK; MB; NIC

—another ed. ['. . . school in Queen Street . . .' is changed to '. . . school in St. Martins le Grand . . .']. [London]: printed for [——], [c.1725]. LBL; LWML: DCLC; OrU

1. All the bibliographies and catalogues, with one exception, date both of Kidder's editions as 'ca. 1740', which is an error; see *Catalogue of Printed Books in the Wellcome Historical Medical Library: 1641–1850*, op. cit., vol. 3, p. 390, which shows that Kidder was born in 1666 and died in 1739. As his title-pages were advertising his cookery schools, there can be no doubt that his work was published in his lifetime, and the present compiler has judged the dates of the two editions to be much earlier. The John Crerar Library in Chicago holds a Kidder MS

E. Kidder's
RECEIPTS
OF
PASTRY
AND
COOKERY,
For the Use of his Scholars.

Kidder's handsome book was a remarkable production. Not only were the title-page (of which the upper part is shown above) and the frontispiece (see the frontispiece of this volume) engraved on copper, but so was the whole text, as the sample recipe below shows.

A Marron Pudding.

Boyl a quart of cream or milk with a stick of cinnamon a quarter'd nutmeg and large mace, then mix it with 8 eggs well beat; a little Salt, Sugar, Sack and orange flower water, strain it, then put to it, 3 grated biskets, an handfull of currants, as many raysons of the Sun, the marrow of 2 bones all to 4 large pieces: then gather it to a body over ye fire & put it in a dish having the brim thereof garnish-ed with puff past and rais'd in the oven: then lay on the 4 pieces of marrow, colour'd knots & pasts, slic'd citron and lemon peel.

of about 1730 which shows that his schools were then 'in little Lincoln Inn feilds [*sic*] . . . and Norris-street in St. James's market'. Assuming that he progressed as his schools became better known, it could also be assumed that he moved to better addresses. If so, allowing for five years for every move, then Queen Street in about 1720, St. Martin's le Grand in about 1725, and finally Lincoln's Inn Fields and Norris Street in about 1730, could be the bases for approximating the dates of his editions.

2. The whole book was engraved on copper plates. The verso page of every one of the full leaves is blank, except in the case of the frontispiece, where the recto page is blank. Out of 80 pages only 40 are used.

3. The frontispiece for the main entry is a portrait entitled 'Edw. Kidder Pastry-master', and is signed by 'Rob. Sheppard Sculp.', who also did the portrait for the other edition. In the latter, Kidder is shown in a magistrate's wig.

KING, WILLIAM (1650–1729)

The art of cookery. A poem. In imitation of Horace's ['] Art of Poetry [']. By the author of ['] A Tale of a Tub [']. etc.[1] London: printed, and are to be sold by the booksellers of London and Westminster, 1708.[2] 16 p. [——]

Cited: Oxford, p. 51

Copies: *BI*: —
     NA: KMK

1. For a life of the author; see: *DNB*, vol. 11 (1909), pp. 161–3, where it states: 'In February 1708 Lintot paid him 32 l. 5 s. for "The Art of Cookery". . . . It was published the following month without date. *Daily Courant* 13 March 1708.' Although the payment might have been for King's other work on the same subject in the same year (see next entry), it could have included the fee for this much shorter work as well. The poem is a satire on Dr Martin Lister's edition of the work of APICIUS (see that entry).
2. This entry is based on Rudolph, p. 17 (No. 57).

KING, WILLIAM (1650–1729)

The art of cookery, in imitation of Horace's ['] Art of Poetry [']. With some letters to Dr. Lister, and others: occasion'd principally by the title of a book publish'd by the Doctor, being the works of Apicius Coelius, . . . to which is added, Horace's ['] Art of Poetry ['], in Latin. . . . Humbly inscrib'd to the Honourable Beefsteak Club. [Anon.]. London: printed for Bernard Lintott, [1708].[1] 160 p. 19 cm.

Cited: Bitting, p. 260

Copies: *BI*: ENLS*; LWML; LeU(B)
     NA: MH; NYPL; ViU

—2nd ed. London: printed for Bernard Lintott, [1710].[2] LBL; LeU(B): CtY; ViWC

1. For proof of date; see under previous entry: KING, William, The art of cookery. A poem (note 1).
2. An engraved frontispiece by Van der Gucht was added to this edition; see Murphy, p. 24.

KIRKPATRICK, H. (*fl.* 1796)

An account of the manner in which potatoes are cultivated and preserved . . . in the counties of Lancaster and Chester, together with a description of a new

variety of the potatoe [*sic*]. etc.[1] Warrington: printed by W. Eyres, 1796. 46 p.
22 cm. 1 sh.[2]

Cited: —

Copies: *BI*: LBL*
       NA: CU; DNAL; MH

1. This work includes several recipes for potato dishes, such as 'North of England potatoe pie'
   and 'Potatoe pudding'.
2. *Scots Mag.*, vol. 59 (Mar. 1797), pp. 195-6, confirms that the price was 1 sh.

L

LA CHAPELLE, VINCENT (*fl.* 1733–1751)

The modern cook:[1] containing instructions for preparing and ordering publick
entertainments for the tables of princes, ambassadors, noblemen, and magis-
trates. etc.[2] London: printed for the author, and sold by Nicolas Prevost, 1733.
[In three volumes.][3] Vol. 1 viii, 328 p. frontis. pls. 20 cm; Vol. 2 xxii, 316 p. pls.
20 cm; Vol. 3 307 p. pls. 20 cm.

Cited: Bitting, p. 268; Oxford, p. 63

Copies: *BI*: LBL*
       NA: DCLC

—2nd ed. London: printed for Thomas Osborne, 1736. 3 Vols. [15 sh.][4]
  LeU(B): IaU

—3rd ed. London: printed for Thomas Osborne, 1736. 3 Vols. LWML: ICJ;
  KMK

—3rd ed. London: printed for Thomas Osborne, 1744. 3 Vols. DoCL; LBL:
  MiD; NIC; NYPL

—4th ed. London: printed for R. Manby, and H. S. Cox, 1751. 1 Vol. only.
  LeU(B): DCLC; NYPL

1. For the French editions under the title *Le Cuisinier Moderne* see Vicaire, pp. 868-9.
2. The author described himself (in 1736) as 'Late Chief Cook to the Right Honourable the Earl
   of Chesterfield: And now Chief Cook to his Highness the Prince of Orange'. This would
   appear to be in conflict with the following advertisement for his work in *Gents.Mag.*, vol. 4
   (Jan. 1734), p. 55, where he is called 'M. Vincent la Chapelle, Cook to the Count of Montijo'.
   It is not clear how he could work for a Dutch prince and a Spanish grandee at the same time. In
   1742 (on the title-page of a French edition) he ignored his service to Chesterfield and claimed
   to be Head Cook to the Prince of Orange only. See also Philip and Mary Hyman, La Chapelle
   and Massialot, *Petits Propos Culinaires*, vol. 2 (1979), pp. 44-54.
3. Oxford, p. 63, wrongly states that the 1st ed. was 'in two volumes'. He could not have
   consulted *Gents.Mag.*, vol. 4 (Jan. 1734), p. 55, loc. cit., which states that the work was 'sold by
   the author in 3 volumes'.
4. *Ann.Cat.*, p. 7, confirms that the price of this edition was 15 sh.

LADIES

The ladies annual journal:[1] or complete pocket book for the year 1771 . . . an elegant bill of fare for every month in the year. etc. London: printed for Elizabeth Stevens and J. Taylor, 1770.[2] [——] [——] 1 sh. neatly bound in red.

Cited: —

Copies: *BI*: —

      NA: —

—another ed. London: printed for [——], [1786]. —: NYPL

1. This work, as the title clearly indicates, is not a book but a diary. One main entry, with a few variants by other printers or publishers, will suffice, therefore, to exemplify a publication which scarcely altered in its layout whatever the year or whomsoever the printer. In the great majority of cases, apart from providing a blank page for each day of the year, these special diaries for women contained, in preliminary pages *or* interspersed between the months *or* in appendices, useful household information, mostly bills of fare for each month of the year, but also home cures, hints on beauty treatment, advice on social etiquette, and occasionally cookery recipes. Due to their personal nature, it is doubtful if many of them survived the lifetimes of their owners. They are rarely held by libraries or sought after by collectors.
2. This entry is based on an advertisement in the *Pub.Adv.*, (21 Dec. 1770), p. 1. The following are three other examples of the same sort of publication:
   (A) The ladies compleat pocket book. etc. London: printed for F. Newbery, 1752. 1 sh. Advertised in *Scots Mag.*, vol. 14 (Nov. 1752), p. 560. Other known references to the same publication include: the edition for 1761, advertised in *Scots Mag.*, vol. 22 (Dec. 1760), p. 672; the edition for 1769, held by LBL; and the edition for 1771 (printed for T. Carnan and F. Newbery, jun.), advertised in *Pub.Adv.* (4 Dec. 1770), which announced: 'the ladies complete pocket book has now been annually published for upwards of 20 years . . .'.
   (B) The ladies own memorandum book: or daily pocket journal for the year 1771. [by a lady]. London: printed for Robinson and Roberts; and for T. Slack at Newcastle, 1770. 1 sh. Advertised in *Pub.Adv.* (27 Nov. 1770), which announced: 'To be continued annually'. It included 'a large and new marketing table'. An earlier edition (*c.*1766) is in the New York Public Library, and has 154 pages.
   (C) The ladies pocket book, or daily register . . . for the year 1771. etc. London: printed for F. Newbery, 1770. 1 sh. Advertised in *Pub.Adv.* (1 Dec. 1770), p. 1, and it included 'the terms used in carving' and 'the art of making soups'.
   It is obvious that they were advertised for Christmas presents. At 1 sh. per copy they were quite expensive.

LADIES

The ladies companion: or modern secrets and curiosities . . . containing the art of painting . . . the face . . . the art of preserving . . . the hair . . . the art of preserving the teeth.[1] etc. London: printed and sold by A. Baldwin, [*c.*1760]. [——] 15 cm.

Cited: —

Copies: *BI*: —

      NA: CtY

1. The preface is signed 'T.B.'

LADIES

The ladies companion; or, the housekeeper's guide: being a magazine of such choice matters, as the housekeeper ought not to be without . . . with a great variety of other materials as will be found both necessary and valuable . . . the most certain and best method for the management of a good beer cellar: how to restore sour beer to its perfection; . . . also an extraordinary good way of preserving a constant stock of yeast. [by a gentlewoman].[1] London: printed for [———], 1756.[2] 80 p. [———]

Cited: Oxford, p. 87

Copies: *BI*: LWML*
        NA: —

1. The author fully described herself as 'a Gentlewoman, Who has been a Housekeeper to several Noble Families many Years'.
2. The LWML copy has the imprint cropped from the title-page, which has destroyed the printer's name and all that was below it, and made accurate measurement of the work impossible. The copy bears the signature of Dr A. W. Oxford on the flyleaf, but, strangely, the wording of the title-page varies from the entry he recorded in his bibliography; see Oxford, p. 87.

LADIES

The ladies' delight, or cook-maids best instructor. London: printed for Henry Woodgate and Samuel Brooks, [*c*.1770]. 116 p. 15 cm.

Cited: Oxford, p. 104

Copies: *BI*: —
        NA: MCR*

LADIES LIBRARY

see PERKINS, John.

LADY

see ACCOMPLISHED lady's delight.

LADY

see GLASSE, Hannah.

LADY'S COMPANION

see WHOLE duty of a woman.

LAIRD

The laird and farmer. A dialogue upon farming, trade, cookery, and their method of living in Scotland, balanc'd with that of England. In sixteen chapters. [by the author of The Familiar Catechism]. London: printed for the author, and sold by R. Griffiths, 1740. viii, 3–118 p. 20 cm. 1 sh.

Cited: —

Copies: *BI*: LBL*; MU(JR)
        NA: MH-BA; NNC

—another ed. [by a Native of the Country].[1] London: printed for the author, and sold by R. Griffiths, 1750. ENLS; LBL: —

1. *BMCat.* (1962), states that this edition is 'a duplicate with a new title-page'. This would explain the change of pseudonym from 'the author of The Family Catechism' to 'a Native of the Country'.

LAMB, PATRICK (*fl.* 1660–1731)

Royal cookery; or, the complete court-cook. Containing the choicest receipts in all the particular branches of cookery, now in use in the Queen's Palaces of St. James's, Kensington, Hampton-Court, and Windsor. etc.[1] London: printed for Abel Roper and sold by John Morphew, 1710. 127 p. pls. 20 cm.

Cited: Bitting, p. 270; Oxford, 52–3

Copies: *BI*: DTCL; ENLS*; LBL
      NA: DCLC; MH; NYPL

—1st ed.[2] London: printed for and sold by Maurice Atkins, 1710. —: NYPL

—2nd ed. with additions. London: printed for J. Nutt, [and] A. Roper, and sold by E. Nutt, 1716. ENLS; LBL; LeU(B): NYPL; PPL

—3rd ed. with additions. London: printed for E. and R. Nutt, and A. Roper, 1726. [6 sh.][3] DNLI; LBL; LeU(B): KMK; MiD; NIC

—3rd ed. with additions.[4] London: printed for E. and R. Nutt, and H. Lintot, 1731. CUL; LBL: CtY; MB

1. The author is described as 'near 50 Years Master-Cook to their late Majesties King Charles II, King James II, King William and Queen Mary, and to Her Present Majesty Queen Anne'.
2. Further references to the 1st ed. can be found in *Sotheby Cat.* (1 Aug. 1968), p. 16, and Pennell, p. 144.
3. *Mon.Cat./2* (vol. 1), p. 140 (Dec. 1725) confirms that the price of this edition was 6 sh.
4. *BMCat.* (1962), states that this 3rd ed. is a duplicate 'with a new title-page bearing the date 1731'.

LAMBERT, EDWARD (*fl.* 1744–1749?)

The art of confectionary. I. Shewing the various methods of preserving all sorts of fruit . . . II. Flowers and herbs . . . also how to make all sorts of biscakes [*sic*]. etc. London: printed for T. Taylor, [*c.*1744]. 61 p. 20 cm. 1 sh.[1]

Cited: Bitting, p. 271; Oxford, p. 81[2]

Copies: *BI*: LeU(B)*
      NA: DCLC

—another ed. London: printed for T. Payne, 1761.[3] LBL: DNAL; NYPL

—another ed. with additions.[4] [same main-title, but altered sub-titles]. London: printed for F. Newbery, [*c.*1767]. LBL: NYPL

1. *Gents.Mag.*, vol. 14 (Apr. 1744), p. 231, confirms that the price was 1 sh.
2. Oxford wrongly dates the edition he quotes as *c.*1750. He also gives the printer as F. Newbery, who was born in 1743, and began printing in 1767. It is, therefore, certain that Oxford's entry relates to the second of the additional editions.

3. Lambert was dead in or before 1749; see under earlier entry: BRADSHAW, Penelope, Bradshaw's valuable family jewel (note 1), where she acknowledged that Lambert who was a confectioner in Pall Mall, was the joint-author of that book. The 1761 and subsequent editions were, therefore, also published posthumously.

4. The 'additions' are given on the title-page of this edition as follows: 'To which is now added the ladies toilet or the art of preserving beauty'; and the author is called 'ingenious', which was the description he received as co-adjutor of Penelope Bradshaw.

LAMBERT, EDWARD

see BRADSHAW, Penelope, Bradshaw's valuable family jewel.

LEARNED DISSERTATION

see CAREY, Henry.

LÉMERY, LOUIS (1677-1743)

A treatise of foods, in general: First, the difference and choice which ought to be made of each sort in particular. Secondly, the good and ill effects produced by them. Thirdly, the principles wherewith they abound. And, Fourthly, the time, age and constitution they suit with. etc. Written in French[1] ... Now done into English by D[aniel] Hay.[2] London: printed for John Taylor, 1704. xx, 320 p. 20 cm.

Cited: Bitting, p. 281; Oxford, p. 48[3]

Copies: *BI*: EUL; LWML; LeU(B)*
      NA: DCLC; MH; NjP

—another ed. London: printed for John Taylor, 1704. LeU(B): —

—another ed. London: printed for Andrew Bell, 1706. —: DNLM; FU

—another ed. to which is added an introduction treating of foods in general. London: printed for T. Osborne, 1745. ENLS; LBL; LeU(B): —

—2nd ed. London: printed for T. Osborne, 1745. LWML; LeU(B): DCLC; MiD; NYPL

—3rd ed. London: printed for W. Innys, T. Longman, and T. Shewell, 1745. LWML: CaBVaUW; DCLC; KMK

1. The author is described as 'Regent-Doctor of the Faculty of Physick at Paris, and of the Academy Royal of Sciences'. For his biography see *Nouvelle Biographie Générale*, tome 30 (Paris, 1859), p. 603: Dr Louis Lémery was the son of Dr Nicolas Lémery; see under next entry.

2. For Dr D[aniel] Hay see *Catalogue of Printed Books in the Wellcome Historical Medical Library: 1641-1850*, op. cit., vol. 3, p. 226.

3. Oxford, p. 48, in a footnote, states: 'To this book is appended the imprimatur of the College of Physicians as well as translations of those given by the University of Paris and the Royal Academy of Sciences.'

LÉMERY, NICOLAS (1645-1715)

Curiosa arcana:[1] being curious secrets, artificial and natural. In three parts. Containing [1] secrets in hunting, fishing, ... directions to beautifie the face ...

to make perfumes . . . receipts in cookery and to make sweetmeats. [2] the art of moulding, and casting medals . . . [3] excellent secrets for beautifying. etc.[2] London: printed for J.N., [c.1711]. 354 p. frontis. pls. 18 cm. 5 sh.

Cited: —

Copies: *BI*: ENLS*; LBL; LeU(B)
       NA: CtY; DCLC; NYPL

1. This work has the secondary title: 'New curiosities in art, and nature'. It appears to be an English translation of the *Recueil de Curiositez Rares et Nouvelles*, Paris, 1674.
2. For a biography of Le Sieur Nicolas Lémery, Apothecary to the King of France, see *Nouvelle Biographie Générale*, op. cit., tome 30, pp. 598–603.

LESSIUS, Leonardus (1554–1623)

Hygiasticon: or, a treatise of the means of health and long life. Written originally in Latin by Leonard Lessius. Now rendered into English, by T[imothy] Smith. Whereunto is annexed, [Louis] Cornaro's treatise of the benefits of a sober life. etc. London: printed; and sold by Charles Hitch, 1742.[1] 126, 48 p. 19 cm.

Cited: Bitting, p. 286; Oxford, p. 20

Copies: *BI*: —
       NA: DCLC; MH

—another ed. London: printed for C. Hitch, and J. Leake, 1743. LBL: CtY; ViU
—another ed. London: printed for L. Hawes, W. Clarke and R. Collins, 1767. LBL: MoU

1. The first English translation of the original was published in 1613. Oxford, p. 20, gives the details of the 1634 ed., which was produced by the Printers to the University of Cambridge; and he mentions the 1743 ed., which was translated by 'Timothy Smith, Apothecary'.

LETTSOM, John Coakley (1744–1815)

The natural history of the tea-tree, with observations on the medical qualities of tea, and effects of tea-drinking. London: printed for Edward and Charles Dilly, 1772. viii, 64 p. pl. 18 cm.

Cited: —

Copies: *BI*: ENLS*[1]; LBL
       NA: DNAL; MH-A; WU

—another ed. Dublin: printed by R. Marchbank for J. Williams, T. Walker and C. Jenkins, 1772. LBL; LeU(B): —
—a new ed. London: printed by J. Nichols, for Charles Dilly, 1799. ENLS; LBL: CtY; DCLC

1. The copy held by the ENLS has a fine engraving of a tea plant between pages 8 and 9. In the 1799 ed., of which the ENLS also hold a copy, the same engraving, now colour-tinted, is properly placed where a frontispiece should be.

LISTER, Martin
see Apicius.

LISTER, MARTIN
    see KING, William.

LOCKE, JOHN (1632-1704)
Observations upon the growth and culture of vines and olives: the production of silk: the preservation of fruits. etc.[1] London: printed for W. Sandby, 1766. xv, 73 p. 17 cm.
Cited: Bitting, p. 291
Copies: *BI*: —
        NA: CtY; DCLC; MH

1. This entry is based on Bitting, p. 291.

LONDON
The London complete art of cookery; containing the most approved receipts ever exhibited to the public; selected with care from the newest editions of the best authors, French and English. Also the complete brewer. etc.[1] London: printed for William Lane, 1797.[2] 232 p. frontis. pls. 18 cm.
Cited: Oxford, p. 124
Copies: *BI*: —
        NA: KMK; NYPL; NcU

1. This is almost certainly a spurious and pirated version of a book first published in 1783, which went into its 8th ed. in 1796; see under earlier entry: FARLEY, John, The London art of cookery.
2. This entry is based on Rudolph, pp. 78-9. For a copy that is (or was) in the British Isles; see *B.&G.Cat.*, No. 27, p. 14.

M

M., W.
    see QUEEN'S closet opened.

MACBRIDE, DUNCAN (*fl.* 1793)
General instructions for the choice of wines and spiritious [*sic*] liquors. . . . an account of many disorders cured by the wine called toc-kay de Espagña, with letters relative to its extraordinary effects.[1] London: printed for J. Richardson, J. Debrett, and T. Murray, [1793].[2] vi-xii, 14-86, 16 p. 21 cm. 2 sh. 6 d.
Cited: —
Copies: *BI*: ENLS*; EUL; LBL
    NA: DCLC; ICJ

1. This work is in four parts, the first describing 'those wines which are best to be used at the tables of the opulent'.
2. The preface is dated 'January 24 1793'.

MACDONALD, Duncan[1] (*fl.* 1800)

The new London family cook: or, town and country housekeeper's guide . . . directions for marketing . . . pastry and confectionary . . . directions for carving . . . valuable family recipes in dyeing, perfumery, instructions for brewing . . . distilling, managing the dairy, and gardening . . . and an appendix. etc. London: printed and published by J. Robins and Co., [*c*.1800]. iv, 630 p. frontis. pls. 22 cm.

Cited: Bitting, p. 297; Oxford, pp. 129–30

Copies: *BI*: —
         NA: DCLC

—another ed.[2] London: printed for John Cundee, [*c*.1800]. LeU(B): —

1. The author is recorded as 'late Head Cook at the Bedford Tavern and Hotel, Covent Garden'.
2. There were further editions in the 19th century.

MACIVER, Susanna (*fl.* 1773–1790?)

Cookery and pastry. As taught and practised by Mrs. Maciver, teacher of those arts in Edinburgh.[1] Edinburgh: printed for the author; and sold by her, at her house, Stephen Law's close, back of the City-guard, 1773.[2] [——] [——] [2 sh. 6 d.]

Cited: Bitting, p. 299; Oxford, p. 106

Copies: *BI*: —
         NA: —

—another ed. Edinburgh: printed for the author, and sold by her, 1774. —: NYPL

—2nd ed. Edinburgh: printed for the author, and sold by her, 1777. AUL: MH

—3rd ed. Edinburgh: printed for the author, 1782. ENLS; LWML; LeU(B): NIC; NYPL

—4th ed. Edinburgh: printed for C. Elliot, and G. Robinson, 1784. ENLS[3]; GPL(M); LBL[4]: DCLC; OrU

—a new ed. Edinburgh: printed for C. Elliot [at Edinburgh] and for G. G. & J. Robinson [at London], 1787. CUL; ENLS[5]; OBL: NPV

—a new ed. with additions. London: printed for C. Elliot [at Edinburgh] and for T. Kay [at London], 1789. DoCL; GUL; LeU(B): KMK; NjP; OrU

—a new ed. with additions. Edinburgh: printed by D. Schaw and Co., 1800.[6] LBL: FTaSU

1. Mrs Susanna Maciver and her colleague Mrs Frazer ran one of the few schools of cookery for ladies in Edinburgh. After Mrs Maciver's death (*c*.1790), the school was continued by Mrs Frazer alone; see under earlier entry: FRAZER, [——] [Mrs], The practice of cookery, which is clearly based on Mrs Maciver's book. For further information see Alexander Law, *Education in Edinburgh in the Eighteenth Century* (London, 1965), p. 186.

2. This entry is based on Oxford, p. 106.
3. The ENLS copy of this edition is inscribed: 'Mary Steuart'.
4. The LBL copy has been lost or mislaid.
5. The ENLS copy of this edition is inscribed in pencil: 'John Chalmers 1795'.
6. Hazlitt, p. 178, wrongly gives the author as 'Mrs. Macivey'.

MACIVER, Susanna (fl. 1773–1790?)

A new and experimental treatise on cookery, pastry, etc. as taught and practised by Mrs. Maciver, teacher of those arts in Edinburgh. Edinburgh: printed for and sold by the author and by Drummond, Gray and Elliot, 1773.[1] [——] [——] 2 sh. 6 d.

Cited: —

Copies: *BI*: —
   NA: —

1. The only known reference to this title is given in *Scots Mag.*, vol. 35 (Dec. 1773), p. 654, which also gives the price. In the present compiler's opinion, this was a forward announcement for a book which never appeared under the advertised title. Mrs. Maciver could have been told that her book would achieve very poor sales with a main title which began with such daunting words as 'A new and experimental treatise', when her proposed subject was the homely one of cookery. It is more than probable, therefore, that she simply ordered a new title-page for the same contents, and sold her work as the 1st ed. of 'Cookery and pastry'. In short—this entry is a discarded title for the only book which Mrs Maciver ever wrote, with the price she had already fixed being retained for the 1st ed. of the previous entry, where it is given in square brackets. It is interesting to note that Mrs Maciver retained personal control of the sales of her book for several years.

MACKENZIE, James (1680?–1761)

The history of health, and the art of preserving it: or, an account of all that has been recommended by physicians and philosophers, towards the preservation of health, from the most remote antiquity to this time. etc.[1] Edinburgh: printed by W. Gordon, 1758.[2] xii, 436 p. 21 cm.

Cited: —

Copies: *BI*: ENLS*
   NA: ICJ; MH; NNAM

—another ed. Dublin: printed by George and Alexander Ewing, 1759. —: DCLC; ICJ

—2nd ed. Edinburgh: printed by William Gordon, 1759. ENLS: CSmH; DCLC

—3rd ed. with additions. Edinburgh: printed for William Gordon, 1760. ENLS: DCLC; NNNAM

—another ed. London: printed for [——], 1774. —: ScU

1. Included in the work are chapters on writers on food and British writers on health.
2. For the most recent reference to this work see *Sotheby Cat.* (6 Apr. 1970), p. 43.

McLINTOCK, [——] [Mrs] (fl. 1736)

Mrs. McLintock's receipts for cookery and pastry-work.[1] Glasgow: printed in the year 1736.[2] 62 p. 16 cm.

Cited: —

Copies: *BI*: GUL*

      NA: —

1. This is undoubtedly the first cookery book written and published in Scotland, and it has never been cited in any of the major bibliographies or catalogues dealing with cookery and household subjects. Indeed, the first published use of its contents was made by Virginia Maclean in *Much Entertainment: A Visual and Culinary Record of Johnson and Boswell's Tour of Scotland in 1773* (London and New York, 1973). The present compiler was, therefore, keen to take some trouble to discover the identity and occupation of Mrs McLintock, but, unfortunately, to no avail. A search was made for the printer, and the conclusion was reached that it could have been James Duncan of Gibson's Wynd in Saltmarket Street, Glasgow. A work entitled *A View of the City of Glasgow*, by James McUre alias Campbell (GUL, press-mark Mu.23-di), which was printed by Duncan in 1736, has type-faces and a general layout which very closely resemble those used for Mrs McLintock's work in the same year, but this is a conjecture which needs critical assessment from an expert in typography. The Glasgow directories for the period offer no clue to Mrs McLintock's residence; and few people with her surname appear at all until the second half of the 18th century. The only positive lead is revealed in a book which was published in Edinburgh about 1740; see under earlier entry: JOHNSTON, [——] [Mrs], Mrs Johnston's receipts; a work of 117 pages, of which the first 92 pages are identical to those in Mrs McLintock's book. This could mean that Mrs Johnston was a plagiarist, or that Mrs McLintock had assumed a pseudonym. It could also mean that Mrs McLintock was a widow who had remarried a Mr Johnston, probably a citizen of Edinburgh. Future research in the marriage and death registers for Glasgow and Edinburgh could help to establish the author's identity. Meanwhile, it remains a mystery.

2. Only two copies of this work have been located, both in GUL; one in the John Ferguson Collection (which is bound separately), and one in the William Euing Collection (which is bound with other works under the title *History of Adolphus*).

McVITIE, WILLIAM (*fl.* 1795)

Whisky: a poem.[1] Edinburgh: printed for [——], 1795. 4-15 p. 18 cm.

Cited: —

Copies: *BI*: ENLS*

      NA: —

1. The following quatrain appears on the title-page:

> 'O Whisky! Whisky! pest and nuisance,
> Scotia ne'er thy like did ken—
> While ither liquors ruin thousands,
> Thou destroys thy thousands ten!'

MAGISTRATE

see ACCOUNT of a meat and soup charity.

MARSHALL, ELIZABETH (*fl.* 1770-1790)

The young ladies' guide in the art of cookery: being a collection of useful receipts, published for the convenience of the ladies committed to her care.[1] Newcastle: printed for the author, by T. Saint, 1777. iv, 199 p. pls. 22 cm.

Cited: Bitting, p. 311; Oxford, p. 108

Copies: *BI*: LBL; LeU(B)*; NPL

      NA: DCLC

1. The preface is addressed 'To the Young Ladies who have done me the Honour of attending my School'. Miss Elizabeth (or Elisabeth) Marshall ran a pastry-school in Newcastle upon Tyne from about 1770 until she retired in 1790; see Dr F. J. G. Robinson's University of Newcastle Ph.D. thesis, op. cit., vol. 2, appendix 1.

MARTIN, Sarah (*fl.* 1795–1800?)

The new experienced English-housekeeper, . . . being an entire new collection of original receipts . . . in every branch of cookery, confectionary, etc.[1] Doncaster: printed for the authoress by D. Boys, 1795. 173 p. frontis. 21 cm. 4 sh.[2]

Cited: Bitting, p. 312; Oxford, p. 123

Copies: *BI*: GUL*; LBL; LeU(B)
      NA: DCLC[3]; MH; NYPL

—2nd ed. Doncaster: printed by D. Boys, 1800.[4] LePL; LeU(B): —

1. According to Mrs Sarah Martin, she was 'many years Housekeeper to the late Freeman Bower, Esq. of Bawtry.' Her work contains a list of subscribers mainly resident in Yorkshire, Northumberland, Lincolnshire, Cheshire, and Staffordshire.
2. The author thought that the price of her book should have been lower, because it was smaller than contemporary works of a similar nature. The reason her book was smaller was due to her attempt 'to avoid the repetition which is the sole cause of their prolixity'.
3. The Library of Congress copy contains 300 additional pages in manuscript; see: *NUCat*.
4. There was at least one further edition in the 19th century.

MASON, Charlotte[1] (*fl.* 1773–1800?)

The lady's assistant for regulating and supplying her table; containing one hundred and fifty select bills of fare . . . now first published from the manuscript collection of a professed housekeeper, who had upwards of thirty years experience in families of the first fashion. etc. [Anon.]. London: printed for J. Walter, 1773. iv, 408 p. 22 cm.

Cited: Bitting, pp. 313–14; Oxford, pp. 107–8

Copies: *BI*: ANLW
      NA: KMK

—2nd ed. corrected and enlarged. London: printed for J. Walter, 1775. LeU(B): KMK; NYPL

—3rd ed. London: printed for J. Walter, 1777.[2] LWML; LeU(B): MH; NNNAM; NIC

—4th ed. Dublin: printed for Robert Burton, 1778. DNLI; LWS: DCLC

—a new ed. corrected and enlarged. London: printed for J. Walter, 1786. LBL; LWML; LeU(B): KMK; MH

—6th ed. corrected and enlarged. London: printed for J. Walter, 1787. BPL; DoCL; LeU(B): FTaSU; NNNAM; NYPL

—7th ed. London: printed for J. Walter, 1793. —: WU

—a new ed. London: printed for J. Walter, [c.1800].[3] LBL: —

1. The author described herself as 'Mrs. Charlotte Mason', but she is listed as 'Mrs. Sarah Mason' by Vicaire, p. 572, and as 'Sarah Mason' in the *NUCat*.

THE
Court and Country Cook:
GIVING
New and Plain DIRECTIONS
How to Order all manner of
ENTERTAINMENTS,
And the beſt ſort of the
Moſt exquiſite *a-la-mode* RAGOO's.

Together with
NEW INSTRUCTIONS
FOR
CONFECTIONERS:
SHEWING
How to Preſerve all ſorts of FRUITS, as well
dry as liquid : Alſo,

How to make divers SUGAR-WORKS, and other
fine Pieces of Curioſity;

How to ſet out a DESERT, or Banquet of
SWEET-MEATS to the beſt advantage; And,

How to Prepare ſeveral ſorts of LIQUORS, that
are proper for every Seaſon of the Year.

A WORK more eſpecially neceſſary for Stewards,
Clerks of the Kitchen, Confectioners, Butlers, and
other Officers, and alſo of great uſe in private Families.

Faithfully tranſlated out of French into Engliſh by J. K.

London : Printed by *W. Onley*, for *A.* and *J. Churchill*, at
the Black Swan in *Pater-noſter-row*, and M. *Gillyflower*
in *Weſtminſter-hall*, 1702.

The titles of the two works by Massialot, the contents of which were soon to be visible in English books such as that of Patrick Lamb (page 88), are translated literally in this English version. One wonders whether there was in fact anyone who was both a court and country cook and a confectioner.

2. Printed at the same time as the 3rd ed. was 'an appendix to the lady's assistant, and complete system of cookery . . . with remarks on kitchen-poisons, and necessary cautions thereon'. Some copies of the 3rd ed. are bound with the appendix, others not. There are a few copies (e.g. DCLC) with the appendix alone. For a recent reference to a 3rd ed. bound with an appendix see *BABCat.*, No. BA/20, p. 33.

3. There was at least one further edition in the 19th century.

MASON, SIMON (b. 1701)

The good and bad effects of tea consider'd. Wherein are exhibited, the physical virtues of tea . . . to which are subjoined, some considerations on afternoon tea-drinking. etc.[1] London: printed for M. Cooper, 1745. 52 p. 23 cm. 1 sh.[2]

Cited: —

Copies: *BI*: EUL*; LBL
    NA: CtY-M; MH

1. The author was an apothecary.
2. *Gents.Mag.*, vol. 16 (Sept. 1745), p. 504, confirms that the price was 1 sh.

MASON, SIMON (b. 1701)

Practical observations in physick . . . to which are added rules and directions how to preserve good health and long life. etc. Birmingham: printed by T. Warren, 1757. xlix, 260 p. 21 cm.

Cited: —

Copies: *BI*: —
    NA: DNLM; MiU; NNNAM

MASSIALOT, FRANÇOIS (1660?-1733)

The court and country cook: . . . together with new instructions for confectioners . . . faithfully translated out of French into English by J. K.[1] [Anon.] in two parts. London: printed by W. Onley, for A. and J. Churchill, and M. Gillyflower, 1702. 276, 130, 20 p. frontis. pls. 20 cm.

Cited: Bitting, p. 538; Oxford, pp. 47-8

Copies: *BI*: LeU(B)*[2]
    NA: KMK; NPV; NYPL

1. This work is based on translations from two of the author's books: *Le Cuisinier roïal et bourgeois*, (Paris, 1691), and *Nouvelle instruction pour les confitures, les liqueurs, et les fruits* (Paris, 1692); see Vicaire, pp. 453-4. Vicaire ascribes the authorship of the former, but not the latter, to François Massialot. Oxford, p. 48, noted Vicaire's work and confirms that Massialot wrote both books.
2. The LeU(B) copy is inscribed: 'Mary Bentley her Booke, 1785'.

MEDICAL GENTLEMAN

see EASY way to prolong life.

AN
ECONOMICAL,
AND
NEW
Method of Cookery;

DESCRIBING UPWARDS OF
EIGHTY
Cheap, Wholefome, and Nourifhing Difhes,

CONSISTING OF
ROAST, BOILED, AND BAKED MEATS;
STEWS, FRIES,

And above Forty Soups;

A VARIETY OF
PUDDINGS, PIES, &c.
WITH NEW AND USEFUL
OBSERVATIONS
ON
Rice, Barley, Peafe, Oatmeal, and Milk,
AND THE NUMEROUS DISHES THEY AFFORD,
Adapted to
THE NECESSITY OF THE TIMES,
Equally in all Ranks of Society,

By ELIZA MELROE,

"Œconomy is the fource of Plenty."
"Bury not your Talent."

London: Printed and publifhed for the Author, by C. CHAPPLE, No. 66,
PALL-MALL; fold alfo by T. N. LONGMAN, Paternofter-Row;
and all other Bookfellers in Town and Country.
Price 2s. 6d. or fix for 10. 6d. if purchafed by Clubs of the labouring
Poor, or intended for their Ufe.

1798.
ENTERED AT STATIONER's-HALL.

Eliza Melroe composed her title-page in tune with the 'necessity of the times', as explained in the catalogue entry. Hence the emphasis on soups and cereal dishes.

MELROE, Eliza (*fl.* 1798)

An economical, and new method of cookery; describing upwards of eighty cheap, wholesome, and nourishing dishes . . . adapted to the necessity of the times, equally in all ranks of society. etc.[1] London: printed and published for the author, by C. Chapple, and sold by T. N. Longman, 1798. viii, 94 p. 20 cm. 2 sh. 6 d.[2]

Cited: Bitting, pp. 319–20; Oxford, p. 125

Copies: *BI*: DoCL; LBL*; LeU(B)
        NA: DCLC; MiD; NYPL

1. This pamphlet was one of several in the same vein which was produced as a response to the hardship caused in this period by both the shortage and high price of commodities.
2. *Scots Mag.*, vol. 60 (Apr. 1798), p. 271, confirms that the price was 2 sh. 6 d. 'or six for 10 sh. 6 d. if purchased by clubs of the labouring poor, or intended for their use'.

MENON, [——] (*fl.* 1740–1795)

The art of modern cookery displayed. Consisting of the most approved methods of cookery, pastry, and confectionary of the present time. Translated from ['] Les Soupers de la Cour, ou, La Cuisine Reformée [']; the last and most complete practice of cookery published in French. etc.[1] [Anon.]. London: printed for the translator,[2] and sold by R. Davis, 1767. [2 volumes bound together]. xvi, 286, 289–588 p. 21 cm. 6 sh.[3]

Cited: Bitting, p. 519; Oxford, pp. 95[4] and 101

Copies: *BI*: OBL*[5]
        NA: DCLC; MH; NNNAM

—2nd ed. [with changed title-page, but same contents: The professed cook: or, the modern art of cookery, pastry, and confectionary, made plain and easy. Consisting of the most approved methods in the French as well as English cookery. . . . Translated from ['] Les Soupers de la Cour ['] . . . And adapted to the London markets]. London: printed for R. Davis, and T. Caslon, 1769. LBL; LWML: DCLC; MCR

—3rd ed. revised and much enlarged. London: printed for W. Davis, 1776. LeU(B): KMK; MCR; NYPL

1. See Vicaire, p. 591, for the work by Menon published in France, of which this book is a translation. Vicaire does not give the Christian name of Menon, and searches for it elsewhere have proved unsuccessful.
2. The translator does not reveal his identity until the publication of the 3rd ed., when he describes himself as 'B. Clermont, who has been many years Clerk of the Kitchen in some of the first families of this kingdom, and lately to the Right Hon. the Earl of Abingdon'; see Rudolph, p. 61. In the 2nd ed. he describes himself not as 'translator', but as 'Editor': see Oxford, p. 101. According to J. Jean Hecht, *The Domestic Servant Class in Eighteenth-Century England*, op. cit., p. 43, his full name was Bernard Clermont.
3. *Scots Mag.*, vol. 29 (Feb. 1767), p. 92, confirms that the price was 6 sh.
4. Oxford, p. 95, gives only the main title and no further information, except the date of publication—'1766'—which is wrong. On p. 101 he gives a full entry for the 2nd ed., but does not realize that it is another edition of 'The art of modern cookery' with a changed title-page.
5. The Bodleian Library copy is inscribed: 'Sussana Walker her her [*sic*] Book'.

Five Hundred
NEW RECEIPTS

IN

Cookery,   Preserving,
Confectionary,   Conserving,
Pastry,   Pickling;

AND THE

Several Branches of these ARTS
necessary to be known by all good
HOUSEWIVES.

By *JOHN MIDDLETON*,
Cook to his Grace the late Duke of *Bolton*.

Revised and Recommended by
Mr. *HENRY HOWARD*.

THOMAS ASTLEY.

LONDON:
Printed for Tho. Astley, at the *Rose*
against the North Door of St. *Paul's*.
M DCC XXXIV.

This title-page, in which the emblem of the printer figures so largely, is the favourite of the
present compiler among all those of the eighteenth century.

MENON, [——] (*fl.* 1740–1795)

The French family cook: being a complete system of French cookery . . . instructions for making out bills of fare for the four seasons of the year . . . translated from the French.[1] [Anon.]. London: printed for J. Bell, 1793.[2] xxiv, 342 p. 21 cm.

Cited: Bitting, p. 554; Oxford, pp. 121–2

Copies: *BI*: CUL; LBL*; LeU(B)
　　　　NA: DCLC; NIC; NYPL

—4th ed. enlarged by S. Taylor.[3] [main title changed, but sub-titles not altered. The complete family cook; being a system of cookery]. London: printed [for ?] J. Annereau, 1796. LWML: —

1. This work is a translation of Menon's *La Cuisinière Bourgeoise* (Paris, 1746); see Vicaire, p. 589.
2. See under earlier entry: GLASSE, A., The accomplished family cook, for a pirated edition of this work, with, according to Oxford, p. 125, the same title-page, except for 'accomplished' in place of 'French'. Oxford also states that 'the book was probably a failure'.
3. By 1796 the war with France had given the British a xenophobic attitude towards that country, and it was more than expedient to change the main-title of the 4th ed. by removing the double reference to 'French', but the publisher's or printer's surname is blatantly French.

MIDDLETON, JOHN (*fl.* 1734)

Five hundred new receipts in cookery, confectionary, pastry, preserving, conserving, pickling; and the several branches of these arts necessary to be known by all good housewives.[1] Revised and recommended by Mr. Henry Howard.[2] London: printed for Thomas Astley, 1734. iv, 249 p. 20 cm.

Cited: Bitting, p. 324; Oxford, p. 64

Copies: *BI*: LBL; LeU(B)*[3]
　　　　NA: DCLC; KMK; NPV

1. The author described himself as 'Cook to his Grace the late Duke of Bolton'.
2. For two works by the reviser, see under earlier entries: HOWARD, Henry, The British cook's companion; and, idem, England's newest way in . . . cookery.
3. The LeU(B) copy contains the bookplate of 'Strickland Freeman, Esqr Fawley Court, Bucks. 1810'.

MODERN

A modern bill of fare for seven, as it was perform'd, by their own desire and approbation, in May, Anno Domini 1751, and compared with a bill of fare provided for King Henry the 8.th, and his Queen, the foreign ministers, Lord-Mayor, judges, etc.[1] London: printed for Mons. Potage Julien Verd la Petit Paté,[2] and sold by Mons. Carpenter, 1751. 8 p. 30 cm.

Cited: —

Copies: *BI*: OBL*
　　　　NA: ICJ; TxU

1. The following advertisement appears at the end of this booklet or pamphlet: 'To all Printers, Booksellers, Stationers, and others, this to give notice. That this is not enter'd in the

Hall-Book of the Company of Stationers, but it is earnestly requested that no-body will pirate it, as it is done for the benefit of several French cooks just imported, who want shirts to their ruffles.' See under earlier entry: EXPLANATION.

2. The corporate pseudonym is obviously a joke. From the advertisement given in note 1 it is clear that the compilers of this small work were Frenchmen, yet the spelling and construction of the French in the pseudonym is chaotic. 'Verd', the outmoded form of 'vert', was used to mean 'bawdy' as well as the usual 'green'; and '*patte*' is used to mean 'a dog's dinner'. In its crude form, the nearest translation for the pseudonym is 'Mr. Soup with Shredded Salad and Game Pie', but with double-meanings, such as 'bawdy', it could be a risqué play on the cooks' surnames.

MODERN

The modern method of regulating and forming a table, explained and displayed. Containing a great variety of dinners laid out in the most elegant taste, from two courses of five and five, to twenty-one and twenty-one dishes; finely represented on one hundred and fifty-two copper plates.[1] etc. [by several eminent cooks]. [London]: printed for J. Hughes, and S. Crowder, [c.1760]. vi, 171 p. pls. 34 cm.

Cited: Bitting, p. 579; Oxford, pp. 80-1

Copies: *BI*: LeU(B)*
       NA: DCLC; MH

1. The first work to be published entirely devoted to the ways of setting a dining-table, with specimen menus for each setting.

MOFFET, THOMAS

see MOUFET, Thomas.

MONTAGUE, PEREGRINE (*fl.* 1768?)

The family pocket-book: or, fountain of true and useful knowledge . . . of the tea-tree . . . the young housekeeper's guide to cooking . . . preserving and making all sorts of wine . . . compiled after thirty years experience. etc.[1] London: printed by Henry Coote, and sold by George Paul, [c.1768]. viii, 9-162 p. frontis. pls. 17 cm. 1 sh. stitched 1 sh. 6 d. bound in neat red leather.

Cited: —

Copies: *BI*: LBL; LeU(B)*
       NA: CaBVaUW; CtY

1. Coinciding with the present compiler's visit to the University of British Columbia, Vancouver, in July 1976, was an exhibition of cookery books in the Woodward Biomedical Library. One of the items had the following caption: 'Peregrine Montague, gent., of Grange-Abbey in Oxfordshire compiled—"after 30 years experience"—*The family pocket-book: or, Fountain of true and useful knowledge.* The subject matter covers an enormous range from veterinary science and the management of race-horses through hair-dressing, dentistry and gardening to cookery. Thirty pages encompass *The Young house-keeper's pocket companion in the art of cookery.* Compendiums of a similar nature, containing advice to the layman, continued to be published into the 20th century, and are now becoming fashionable again. They are the lineal descendants of the old books of "secrets".'

MOORE, Isabella[1] (*fl.* 1772)

The useful and entertaining family miscellany: containing the complete English housekeeper's companion . . . in which are added the genuine receipts for compounding Mr. Ward's principal medicines. Also every-one his own physician . . . likewise, the fair one's pleasing songster. etc. London: printed for John Smith, 1772. vii, 110 p. pls. 20 cm.

Cited: —

Copies: *BI*: LMWL; LeU(B)*
      NA: —

1. The author described herself as 'Mrs Isabella Moore who was twenty years a worthy and frugal housekeeper in a private gentleman's family at Duffield, near Derby'.

MORE, Hannah

see Jone (or Jones), [——] [Mrs].

MORE, Sir Jonas (*fl.* 1703)

Englands interest: or the gentleman and farmers friend. Shewing . . . how to make cyder . . . directions for brewing the finest malt-liquors . . . the husbandry of bees. etc.[1] 2nd ed. with large additions. London: printed by J. How, 1703. 166 p. pls. 15 cm.

Cited: —

Copies: *BI*: LBL*
      NA: CLU-C; DFo; MH

—3rd ed. with additions. London: printed by J. How, 1705. LBL: CtY; ICJ; MH

—4th ed. London: printed by J. How, 1707. —: ICJ; ICN; MH

—another ed. London: printed and sold by E. Tracy, 1712. BULA: —

—another ed. London: printed for A. Bettesworth, 1721. LBL: CtY; DNAL; MH

1. This work contains receipts for making wines, including cherry, currant, gooseberry, and mulberry.

MORRIS, Mary

see Harrison, Sarah.

MOSELEY, Benjamin (1742–1819)

Observations on the properties and effects of coffee. London: printed for the author and sold by John Stockdale, 1785. 38 p. [——]

Cited: —

Copies: *BI*: —
      NA: DNLM

—2nd ed. with additions. [New title. A treatise concerning the properties and effects of coffee.] London: printed for the author, and sold by John Stockdale, 1785. LBL: CtY-M; OCl

—3rd ed. with additions. London: printed for the author, and sold by John Stockdale, 1785. LBL: MiU; PPL

—4th ed. London: printed for T. Cadell, 1789. —: MiU

—5th ed. with considerable additions. London: printed for J. Sewell, 1792. LBL; MPL: MH; MiU; NNNAM

—1st American ed. Philadelphia: printed by Samuel Smith, 1796. —: DCLC; NNNAM; PPL

MOUFET, THOMAS[1] (1553–1604)

Health's improvement: or, rules comprizing and discovering the nature, method and manner of preparing all sorts of foods used in this nation. Written by that ever famous Thomas Moffet, Doctor in Physick. Corrected and enlarged by Christopher Bennet, Doctor in Physick, and Fellow of the College of Physicians in London. To which is now prefix'd, a short view of the author's life and writings, by Mr. [William] Oldys, and an introduction by R[obert] James, M.D. London: printed for T. Osborne, 1746.[2] xxxii, 398 p. 17 cm. 3 sh. 6 d.[3]

Cited: Oxford, pp. 27–8

Copies: *BI*: ERCP*; LBL; LeU(B)
    NA: DCLC; KMK; PPL

1. Thomas Moffet or Muffet, or Muffett, or Moufet, or Mouffet (1553–1604), was a prominent London physician, MP for Wilton in 1597, father of 'Little Miss Muffet' of nursery-rhyme fame, and compiler of a MS on food; see *DNB*, vol. 13 (1909), pp. 548–50 (under Moffet); and Crahan, p. 54 (under Muffett). The spelling of his surname has caused some confusion among bibliographers and cataloguers, but as his very great and literate contemporary, Mr Will Shaxper, spelled his own surname in a dozen or more ways, the use of five was not remarkable. In an age when many English surnames were gradually hardening into their final forms, there was nothing holy about spelling. It is probable that his true surname was Moffat or Moffet, with the 'o' being pronounced 'u' as in 'cumpton' for Compton and 'montgumery' for Montgomery. The most frequently used versions seem to be Moufet and Moffet.
2. See Wing *STC*, vol. 2 (1948), p. 443, for the 1st ed. See also A. H. T. Robb-Smith, MD, 'Doctors at Table', *Journal of the American Medical Association*, vol. 224 (1973), pp. 28–34, in which appears the following extract: 'Dr. Thomas Mouffet, a successful Elizabethan physician with paracelsian leanings, left a number of unfinished manuscripts at his death in 1604, amongst them one entitled *Healths Improvement* . . ., which was edited in 1655 by his younger colleague Christopher Bennet.'
3. *Gents.Mag.*, vol. 16 (May 1746), p. 276, confirms that the price was 3 sh. 6 d.

MOXON, ELIZABETH (*fl.* 1741–1800)

English housewifry [*sic*]. Exemplified in above four hundred receits [*sic*], never before printed; . . . A book necessary for mistresses of families, higher and lower women servants, and confined to things substantial and splendid, and calculated for the preservation of health. etc.[1] Leeds: printed by J. Lister, and sold by J. Swale at Leeds, J. Lord at Wakefield, and the author at Pontefract, [*c*.1741]. 209 p. pls. 21 cm.

Cited: Bitting, pp. 333-4; Oxford, p. 78

Copies: *BI*: LePL*
   NA: DNAL; KMK; WU

—2nd ed. corrected.[2] Leeds: printed by James Lister and sold by John Swale; and by S. Birt at London, [*c*.1743]. LePL: KMK

—3rd ed.[2] Leedes [*sic*]: printed by James Lister and sold by John Swale, [*c*.1746]. ENLS; LePL; LeU(B): —

—4th ed. Leedes: printed by James Lister and sold by John Swale, [*c*.1749]. DoCL; LBL; LePL: —

—5th ed. Leedes: printed; and sold by S. Birt at London, and E. Swale and J. Lister at Leedes, [*c*.1752]. LePL; MPL: DCLC; NYPL

—6th ed. Leedes: printed for S. Howgate and J. Wilson, 1755. GUL; LWML: —

—7th ed. Leedes: printed for [———], 1758. BPL: —

—supplement. English housewifry [*sic*] improved; or, a supplement to Moxon's cookery, containing upwards of sixty modern and valuable receipts in pastry, preserving, made dishes, made wines, etc. Collected by a Person of Judgment. Leedes: printed by Griffith Wright, for George Copperthwaite, 1758. [Hereafter, when it is bound with the original, it is known as 'Part 2', and the original as 'Part 1'.][3]

—8th ed. corrected. Leedes: printed by Griffith Wright, for George Copperthwaite, 1758. [Parts 1 and 2 bound together.] LBL; LePL; LeU(B): ICJ; MCR; MnU

—9th ed. corrected. Leedes: printed by Griffith Wright, for George Copperthwaite, 1764. [Parts 1 and 2 bound together.] LWS: DCLC; MiD; NYPL

—another ed. The compleat family cook. Hull: printed by J. Rawson and Son, 1766.[4] —: DCLC

—10th ed. corrected. Leeds: printed by Griffith Wright, for George Copperthwaite, 1769. [Parts 1 and 2 in one vol.] ENLS; LePL; LeU(B): CtY; MH

—11th ed. corrected. Leeds: printed by Griffith Wright, for George Copperthwaite, 1775. [Parts 1 and 2 in one vol.] LePL; LeU(B): DCLC; MB; NPV

—12th ed. [———]: printed for [———], 1778.[5] —: —

—12th ed. corrected. Leeds: printed by T. Wright, for W. Fawdington, 1785. [Parts 1 and 2 in one vol.] LeU(B): CU

—13th ed. London: printed for W. Osborne, T. Griffin and H. Mozley, 1789. [Parts 1 and 2 in one vol.] —: CtY; IEN; NNNAM

—13th ed. corrected. Leeds: printed by Thomas Wright, for J. Binns and William Fawdington, 1790. [Parts 1 and 2 in one vol.] LBL; LeU(B): NYPL; OrU; ViWC

—a new ed. London: printed for [———], 1798. LeU(B): —

—14th ed. corrected. London: printed and sold by Andrew Hambleton and H. and G. Mozley, 1800.[6] LeU(B): —

1. Elizabeth (or Elisabeth) Moxon, who lived in Pontefract, launched the 1st ed. of her book on a subscription basis. For further information on her see Elizabeth Parr, 'Early Leeds Printers, Publishers and Booksellers', University of Leeds M.Phil. thesis, 1973, pp. 54-5, 163.
2. In the 2nd and 3rd eds. the author's Christian name is spelt 'Elisabeth'.
3. According to Oxford, p. 78, this supplement was bound and sold as a separate work in 1758, and was first conjoined with the original work when the 8th ed. was published the same year.
4. This edition is certainly a spurious and pirated version of Part 1 of Mrs Moxon's work; see under earlier entry: COMPLEAT, The compleat family cook.
5. Oxford, p. 78, says that this edition 'seems to be spurious'.
6. Again, Oxford, ibid., loc. cit., is suspicious, and says this edition 'by Elizabeth Moxon, and Others' is spurious.

MUFFET, THOMAS
see MOUFET, Thomas.

MY FRIEND
see POISON detected.

N

NATIVE OF THE COUNTRY
see LAIRD and farmer.

NELSON, JAMES (1710-1794)
An essay on the government of children under three general heads: viz. health, manners and education. etc.[1] London: printed for R. and J. Dodsley, 1753.[2] viii, 420 p. 20 cm.

Cited: —

Copies: *BI*: LWML*
     NA: CtY-M; DCLC; ICU

—2nd ed. London: printed for R. and J. Dodsley, 1756. LBL: CtY; ICJ; ICN

—another ed. Dublin: printed for W. Williamson, 1763. LBL: ICJ; NYPL; ViSL

—3rd ed. London: printed for R. and J. Dodsley, 1763. LBL; LWML: CaOTP; CtY-M

1. The diet of children is comprehensively covered in the section on health.
2. The brothers Robert and James Dodsley were booksellers and publishers with wide interests, and were soon to launch (in 1758) the first issue of *The Annual Register* (which is still published today) with the celebrated Edmund Burke as its editor; see Ralph Straus, *Robert Dodsley* (London, 1910).

NEW

A new and complete book of cookery: Containing upwards of two hundred and fifty choice and experienc'd receipts.[1] Liverpool: printed by J. Sadler, 1742. v, 124 p. 18 cm.

Cited: —

Copies: *BI*: —
     NA: NIC*[2]

1. The only known British reference to this work is given in *B.&G.Cat.*, No. 37, p. 9.
2. The NIC copy is inscribed 'Irene Osgood' on the title-page.

NEW

A new collection of the most easy and approved methods of preparing baths, essences, pomatums . . . with receipts for cosmetics of every kind. etc.[1] London: printed for Robert Turner, 1787. 104 p. 17 cm.

Cited: —

Copies: *BI*: LBL*; LWML
     NA: —

1. Although a main title has been omitted from this work, and the sub-titles have been very slightly altered, this is either a pirated version or an anonymous edition of a book first published in English in 1772; see under earlier entry: BUC'HOZ, Pierre Joseph, The toilet of Flora.

NEW

The new handmaid to arts, sciences and agriculture, containing monthly observations in the orchard, kitchen and flower garden; . . . the whole art of painting . . . with many other things worthy of note. etc. London: printed for and sold by W. Clements, and J. Sadler, 1790. 3–118 p. 18 cm.

Cited: —

Copies: *BI*: —
     NA: DCLC; NYPL

NOTT, JOHN (*fl.* 1723–1733)

The cook's and confectioner's dictionary: or, the accomplish'd housewife's companion. Containing . . . the choicest receipts in all the several branches of cookery . . . all manner of pastry-works . . . the way of making all English potable liquors . . . directions for ordering an entertainment, or bills of fare for all seasons of the year. etc.[1] London: printed for C. Rivington, 1723. [316 p.] frontis. pls. 21 cm. 6 sh.

Cited: Bitting, p. 346; Oxford, pp. 56–7

Copies: *BI*: LBL*; LeU(B)
     NA: KMK; MCR; NYPL

—2nd ed. with additions. London: printed by H. P. for Charles Rivington, 1724. LBL; LeU(B): DCLC; OClW; PBL

—3rd ed. with additions. London: printed by H. P. for Charles Rivington, 1726. LBL: MWelC; NYPL; PP

—4th ed. improved. London: printed for Charles Rivington, 1733. GPL(M); LeU(B); MPL: NIC

1. The author described himself in the 4th ed. as 'John Nott, late Cook to the Dukes of Somerset, Ormond and Bolton, Lords Lansdown and Ashburnham'. In the introduction he discusses the curious and elaborate practical jokes which were played at banquets in the past. See also the Introduction by Elizabeth David to the 1980 reprint of his book, listed on page 157.

NOUR EDDIN, ALRASCHIN
see ARMSTRONG, John.

NUTT, FREDERIC (*fl.* 1789–1819?)
The complete confectioner; or, the whole art of confectionary. etc. [Anon].[1] London: printed for the author, and sold by J. Mathews, 1789. v–xxiv, 212 p. pls.[2] 16 cm. 10 sh. 6 d.

Cited: Bitting, p. 347; Oxford, p. 117

Copies: *BI*: AUL; ENLS*; LBL
    NA: NYPL

—2nd ed.[3] London: printed for the author, and sold by J. Mathews, 1790. LBL; LWS; LeU(B): MiD; NYPL; ViWC

1. The author did not identify himself until the 4th ed. was published in 1807, when he said he was 'Frederic Nutt, late an apprentice to Messrs. Negri and Witten [confectioners] of Berkeley Square'.
2. Plate X, opposite p. 8, shows a very early type of piping syringe, called 'the syringe mould for shaping biscuits'.
3. Several editions were published in the 19th century.

O

OLD
The old man's guide to health and longer life: with rules for diet, exercise and physick; for preserving a good constitution, and preventing disorders in a bad one.[1] London: printed for M. Cooper and J. Jolliffe, [*c*.1748]. 54 p. 20 cm. 1 sh. 6 d.

Cited: —

Copies: *BI*: LeU(B)*
    NA: —

—2nd ed.[2] London: printed for M. Cooper, [*c*.1750]. —: DNLM; NNNAM

1. This is almost certainly an anonymous 1st ed. of a previously cited work; see under earlier entry: HILL, John, The old man's guide.

2. This 2nd ed. is identical to the 2nd ed. given as the main entry for a previously cited work, except that this book was published anonymously; see under earlier entry: HILL, John, The old man's guide. It is possible that the bookseller (or booksellers) has an arrangement with the author whereby he kept the profits from the books which carried his name, while his distributor (or distributors) kept the profits from the identical but anonymous edition. Too little is known about the financial aspect of publishing books, magazines, and newspapers in the 18th century, unless they were sold by subscription.

OLD TRADER
see FEMALE glossary.

OLDYS, WILLIAM
see MOUFET, Thomas.

ONE THOUSAND
see VALUABLE secrets.

P

P., T.
see ACCOMPLISH'D lady's delight in preserving.

P., T.
see PERCY, Thomas.

PAHUD DE VALANGIN, FRANÇOIS JOSEPH (*fl.* 1768)
A treatise on diet, or the management of human life. etc.[1] London: printed for the author, by J. & W. Oliver, 1768. x, 342 p. 21 cm.
Cited: —
Copies: *BI*: LBL*; LWML
    NA: —

1. This book is addressed 'To the inhabitants of London' and is 'an inquiry into the causes of diseases in this Metropolis'. The second of the six sections of the work (pp. 76-152) is devoted to food.

PARMENTIER, ANTOINE AUGUSTIN (1737-1813)
Observations on such nutritive vegetables as may be substituted in the place of ordinary food, in times of scarcity. etc.[1] London: printed for J. Murray, 1783.[2] viii, 80 p. 21 cm.

A
TREATISE
ON
TOBACCO, | COFFEE, *and*
TEA, | CHOCOLATE.

IN WHICH

I. The Advantages and Difadvantages attending the Ufe of thefe Commodities, are not only impartially confidered, upon the Principles of *Medicine* and *Chymiftry*, but alfo afcertained by *Obfervation* and *Experience*.

II. Full and diftinct Directions laid down for knowing in what Cafes, and for what particular Conftitutions, thefe Subftances are either beneficial, or hurtful.

III. The *Chinefe* or *Afiatic Tea*, fhewn to be the fame with the *European Chamelæagnus*, or *Myrtus Brabantica*.

The Whole Illuftrated with COPPER PLATES, *exhibiting the* Tea Utenfils *of the* Chinefe *and* Perfians.

Written originally by SIMON PAULI;
AND
Now Tranflated by Dr. *JAMES*.

Ante omnia fcire convenit Naturam Corporis; quia alii graciles, alii obefi funt, alii calidi, alii frigidiores, alii humidi, alii ficciores, alios adftricta, alios refoluta, alvus exercet. Celfus, *Lib.* 1. *Cap.* 3.

LONDON:
Printed for T. OSBORNE, in *Gray's Inn*; J. HILDYARD, at *York*; M. BRYSON, at *Newcaftle*; and J. LEAKE, at *Bath*.

M,DCC,XLVI.

Simon Pauli lays emphasis on the impartiality of his treatise on coffee, tea, etc. The merits and demerits of these beverages were extensively discussed in the eighteenth century.

Cited: —

Copies: *BI*: LBL*; LWML; MPL
     NA: CaBVaUW; DCLC; MH

1. Four years before this work was published, a piece on the author appeared in *Scots Mag.*, vol. 41 (Oct. 1779), pp. 519–20, which included: 'A method to make potato bread without the admixture of flour, by M. Parmentier of the College of Pharmacy, Paris', followed by a long and detailed receipt which took up nearly two pages. For a life of the author see *Nouvelle Biographie Générale*, op. cit., tome 39, pp. 232–4.
2. For the works in French by the author see Vicaire, p. 656.

PARTRIDGE, Ann (*fl.* 1780?)

The new and complete universal cook; or, young woman's best guide in the whole art of cookery . . . together with the whole art of pastry . . . to which are added many particulars.[1] London: printed for Alex. Hogg, [*c*.1780]. 70 p. frontis.[2] [——] 6 d.

Cited: Oxford, p. 111

Copies: *BI*: LBL[3]
     NA: —

1. The author described herself as 'Mrs. Ann Partridge, of Great George-Street, Westminster'.
2. The frontispiece (but nothing else) is identical to one used in another work printed for the same bookseller; see under later entry: PRICE, Elizabeth, The new, universal, and complete confectioner.
3. The British Library copy has been destroyed [Letter from BL Ref. Division to present compiler, dated 26 July 1977].

PASTRY-COOK

The pastry-cook's vade-mecum: or, a pocket-companion for cooks, house-keepers, country gentlewomen . . . also, the art of distilling and surgery.[1] London: printed for Abel Roper, 1705. 100 p. 16 cm.

Cited: Bitting, p. 589; Oxford, p. 49

Copies: *BI*: LBL*
     NA: DCLC

1. The preface states: 'As for the receipts relating to cookery and pastry-work, they must be own'd to be very useful, since they contain all that may contribute not only to the preservation, but even also to the recovery of health: a good kitchin [*sic*] having certainly a better influence upon our constitutions, than an apothecary's shop.'

PAULI, or PAULLI, Simon (1603–1680)

A treatise on tobacco, tea, coffee and chocolate. . . . the advantages and disadvantages . . . attending the use of these commodities. etc. [translated by Dr. James].[1] London: printed for T. Osborne (at London), for J. Hildyard (at York), for M. Bryson (at Newcastle upon Tyne), and for J. Leake (at Bath), 1746. 171 p. pls. 20 cm. 2 sh.[2]

Cited: —

Copies: *BI*: GUL; LWML; LeU(B)*
     NA: CtY; DCLC

1. Dr Robert James, who was educated at Lichfield Grammar School and St. John's College, Oxford, was a friend of Dr Samuel Johnson, and a physician to King George III. He also wrote an introduction to the 1746 edition of Dr Thomas Moufet's book; see under earlier entry: Moufet, Thomas, Health's improvement. See also *DNB*, vol. 10 (1908), pp. 657–8, under James.

2. *Gents.Mag.*, vol. 16 (Mar. 1746), p. 223, confirms that the price was 2 sh. Paulli was a Danish physician.

PECKHAM, Ann (*fl.* 1767–1790?)

The complete English cook; or, prudent housewife. Being an entire new collection of the most genteel, yet least expensive receipts in every branch of cookery and good housewifery . . . together with directions for placing dishes on tables of entertainment. etc.[1] Leeds: printed by Griffith Wright, and sold by the author, and J. Ogle, 1767.[2] iii–iv, 5–201 p. pls. 17 cm. 2 sh.

Cited: Bitting, p. 360; Oxford, pp. 95–6

Copies: *BI*: CUL; EUL*; LBL
     NA: NYPL

—2nd ed. Leeds: printed by Griffith Wright, 1771. —: MiD

—2nd ed. Leeds: printed (by assignment from the author) for Griffith Wright and John Binns, 1773. LeU(B): KMK

—3rd ed. to which is added a supplement. Leeds: printed for Griffith Wright and John Binns, [*c.*1775]. LBL; LWML; LePL: DCLC; ICJ; NYPL

—4th ed. to which is added a supplement. Leeds: printed for Thomas Wright, John Binns, and William Fawdington, [*c.*1790]. LePL; LeU(B): —

—another ed. Leeds: printed for Thomas Wright, and T. Wilson; and for R. Spence (at York), [*c.*1790]. LeU(B): —

1. The title-page (with minor exceptions in the last sub-titles) is identical to the one used for an entirely different work, which was published a few years before; see under earlier entry: Brooks, Catharine, The complete English cook. To plagiarize the title only was an odd and rare thing to do.

2. The author was described as 'Ann Peckham of Leeds, who is well known to have been for forty years past one of the most noted cooks in the County of York'. For further information see Elizabeth Parr's University of Leeds M.Phil. thesis, op. cit., p. 71. The copy of Ann Peckham's 1st ed. inspected by the present compiler at EUL is bound with a copy of a previously cited work; see under earlier entry: Johnson, Robert Wallace, Some friendly cautions to the heads of families.

PEGGE, Samuel (1704–1796)

The forme of cury;[1] a roll of ancient English cookery, compiled about A.D. 1390, by the Master-Cooks of King Richard II, presented afterwards to Queen Elizabeth, by Edward, Lord Stafford, and now in the possession of Gustavus Brander, Esq. . . . a manuscript of the editor of the same age and subject is subjoined. [by an Antiquary].[2] London: printed by J. Nichols, Printer to the Society of Antiquaries, 1780.[3] iv, xxxvi, 188 p. frontis. 22 cm.

Cited: Bitting, p. 361; Oxford, pp. 108–9

Copies: *BI*: LBL; OBL*[4]
    NA: MHi; MiD; NYPL

—another ed. London: printed by J. Nichols, 1780. LBL: KMK[5]: NIC

1. 'Cury' is the old English word for 'cookery', and the main title is a Chaucerian way of saying 'The art of cookery'. The whole work is written in a forthright, at times even violent, language; 'Take hares and hew them to gobbets . . .', and 'Take conies [rabbits] and smite them to pieces; seeth them in grease . . .' are but two examples. Oxford, p. 108, wrongly cites the main title as '*A* forme of cury'.
2. The editor of this work identified himself by having his portrait as a frontispiece. His pseudonym, 'An Antiquary', was probably chosen as an allusion to his membership of the Society of Antiquaries, but he used it for the 1st ed. only; in the 2nd he used no pseudonym, but kept the portrait as identification. For a life of Dr Samuel Pegge (who is known as 'the elder' to distinguish him from his son and namesake); see *DNB*, vol. 15 (1909), pp. 678–80.
3. John Nichols made a point of stating that he was the 'Printer to the Society of Antiquaries'; and ten years later the Society commissioned a work in the same field, which covered cookery receipts from the time of Edward III to the reign of William and Mary; see under earlier entry: COLLECTION, A collection of ordinances.
4. The copy inspected by the present compiler is in the Douce Collection in the Bodleian Library, and Francis Douce has inscribed the following note: 'This book belonged to Mr. Henderson, the celebrated actor.'
5. The copy held by Kansas State University Library is autographed by Gustavus Brander, who actually owned the MS of the original work; see Rudolph, p. 64.

PENKETHMAN, JOHN (*fl.* 1638)

A collection of several authentick accounts of the history and price of wheat, bread, malt, from the coming in of William the Conqueror to Michaelmas, 1745. etc.[1] London: printed for W. Warden, and sold by C. Davis, 1748. 79 p. [pl.][2] 22 cm.

Cited: —

Copies: *BI*: LBL*
    NA: CtY; MH-BA; NYPL

—another ed. London: printed for R. Davis, 1765.[3] ENLS; LBL: CSmH; CtY; MH-BA

1. This work has an additional title-page: Artachthos: or a new book declaring the assize or weight of bread. Stark, p. 14, spells assize as 'assise'.
2. Stark, p. 14, loc. cit., says that this edition contained a plate, but the British Library copy, which the present compiler inspected, had no plates; which could mean that any plate or plates have been removed.
3. This edition has a slight alteration in the title, and a frontispiece has been added.

PENNINGTON, THE HON. MRS (or, in one citation, PENNINGTON, Lady Margaret)

see PENNINGTON, [Mrs]—[next entry].

PENNINGTON, [MRS][1] (*fl.* 1774?)

The royal cook; or, the modern etiquette of the table, displayed with accuracy, elegance and taste, being a full and exact descriptions of the manner of dressing and serving up royal dinners at St. James's, Buckingham-House, Kew, and Gunnersbury[2] . . . directions for going to market . . . pickling, preserving, brewing . . . an important treasure of Domestic Medicine . . . the improvement of female oeconomy, and the preservation of that inestimaale [*sic*] blessing, health. etc. London: printed for Richard Snagg, [*c*.1774].[3] 142 p. pls. 18 cm. 1 sh. 6 d.

Cited: Bitting, p. 364

Copies: *BI*: —
     NA: DCLC*

1. This work is invariably listed under 'Pennington, The Hon. Mrs.', with no indication of her Christian name.
2. Bitting, p. 364, says that part of the contents of Mrs Pennington's book are identical to those contained in an anonymous work published in 1778; see under earlier entry: FRUGAL, The frugal house-keeper, which frankly admits in the title-page to the use of receipts from Pierre Joseph Buc'hoz's 'The toilet of Flora'. It is possible, therefore, that whoever compiled 'The frugal house-keeper' also wrote 'The royal cook', reusing parts of the former for the latter *and* borrowing the name of a long-dead titled woman for a pseudonym. It is also possible that a near relation of the titled lady used a MS which had genuinely been compiled by her, supplemented the MS with other material and published it under her name as a posthumous tribute to her. Apart from these conjectures, the present compiler has no solution to the mystery of the identity of 'The Hon. Mrs. Pennington'.
3. Bitting, p. 364, and Simon, p. 110, both give inaccurate assessments for the date of publication; the former says '*c*.1787', the latter says '*c*.1780'. The work was published in, or perhaps slightly before, 1774; see an advertisement for the book in *Scots Mag.*, vol. 36 (July 1774), p. 374, which is accorded the following, rather quaint, editorial comment: 'Well said, Title-page! M.' The author is referred to as 'The Hon. Mrs. Pennington, of Kensington', but, although it does not supply conclusive evidence, *Mortimer's London Directory* for 1773, 1774, and 1775 gives no Hon. Mrs Pennington at all, and no plain Mrs Pennington for Kensington. The mystery remains.

PERCY, HENRY ALGERNON, 5th Earl of Northumberland (1478-1527)

The regulations and establishment of the houshold [*sic*] of Henry Algernon Percy, the fifth earl of Northumberland, at his castles of Wresill and Lekinfield in Yorkshire, etc.[1] London: printed for [———], 1770. vi-xxvi, iii-x, 464 p. 22 cm.

Cited: —

Copies: *BI*: ENLS[2]; LBL
     NA: CtY; KMK; NYPL[3]

1. Edited with notes by T. P., i.e. The Rt. Rev. Dr Thomas Percy, Bishop of Dromore.
2. The ENLS copy is inscribed: 'By Command of The Duke of Northumberland this Book is presented to the Advocates' Library by The Editor Thomas Percy.'
3. The NYPL copy was originally presented to Dr Samuel Johnson, and is so inscribed.

PERCY, THOMAS

see PERCY, Henry Algernon, 5th Earl of Northumberland.

PERKINS, JOHN (*fl.* 1790-1796)

The ladies library: or, encyclopedia of female knowledge, in every branch of domestic economy: comprehending, in alphabetical arrangement, distinct treatises on every practical subject, necessary for servants and mistresses of families. I. A most extensive system of cookery. II. A complete body of domestic medicine. III. The preservation of beauty, and prevention of deformity. etc. [Anon.].[1] In two volumes. London: printed for J. Ridgway, 1790. Vol. 1. xv, 407 p. frontis. pls. 21 cm. Vol. 2. 512 p. pls. 21 cm.

Cited: Oxford, p. 119

Copies: *BI*: —
        NA: DCLC; PU

—4th ed. with additions. [with changed title-page: Every-woman her own housekeeper]. London: printed for J. Ridgway, 1796. [2 Volumes]. —: MCR; MH; NNNAM

1. Strictly speaking this work is the compilation of unnamed editors, but all the recipes were written by the late John Perkins, a cook. The frontispiece is of William Buchan, MD.

PERSON OF JUDGMENT
see MOXON, Elizabeth.

PHILLIPS, SARAH (*fl.* 1758)
The ladies handmaid: or, a compleat system of cookery; on the principals [*sic*] of elegance and frugality ... together with instructions for carving and bills of fare for every month in the year, embellished with a variety of curious copperplates. etc. London: printed for J. Coote, 1758. 4–472 p. frontis.[1] pls. 20 cm.

Cited: Bitting, p. 370

Copies: *BI*: LWS; LeU(B)*
        NA: DCLC; NNNAM; NYPL

1. The frontispiece is a portrait of Mrs Sarah Phillips.

PHILOTHEOS PHYSIOLOGUS
see TRYON, Thomas.

PHYSICIAN
see JOHNSON, Robert Wallace.

PHYSICIAN
see POISON detected.

PHYSICIAN
see QUÉLUS (or DE QUÉLUS), D.

PHYSICIAN
see SEDGWICK, James.

PHYSICIAN
see SHACKLEFORD, Ann.

POISON
Poison detected: or frightful truths; and alarming to the British metropolis. . . .
a treatise on bread; and the abuses practised in making that food, . . . shewing
also the virtues of good bread and the manner of making it. etc. [by my friend a
physician]. London: printed for Messrs. Dodsley, 1757. 3–75 p. 21 cm.
1 sh. 6 d.

Cited: —

Copies: *BI*: ENLS*
        NA: CtY; DCLC; NNC

POOLE, T. (*fl.* 1783)
A treatise on strong beer, ale, etc. fully explaining the art of brewing, etc.[1]
London: printed for the author and sold by J. Debrett, 1783. 91 p. 21 cm.

Cited: —

Copies: *BI*: LBL*
        NA: CtY

1. According to *BMCat.* (1963), the author was butler to Sir W. Aston.

POWELL, B. (*fl.* 1771?–1800?)
The guide to preferment: or: Powell's complete book of cookery. Containing
the newest and best receipts in cookery . . . likewise the best methods of
marketing . . . to prevent being cheated. etc.[1] London: printed by W. Bailey,
[*c.*1771]. xii, 9–184 p. frontis. 18 cm. 1 sh. 6 d.

Cited: Bitting, p. 379; Oxford, p. 130

Copies: *BI*: CUL; LeU(B)*[2]
        NA: DCLC

—another ed. The young men and maid's guide to preferment. London:
printed by W. Bailey, [*c.*1800].[3] —: —

1. For a work with the same main title and some similar sub-titles, but with different contents;
   see under earlier entry: FARLEY, [———] [Mr], The guide to preferment.
2. The LeU(B) copy is inscribed: 'Ellin Walshman Cook Book anno Domini 1771', and on the
   opposite page: 'Ellin Walshman Her own Book 1772' with this verse:
                    'Steal not this Book
                    'For fear of sheame
                    'for hear you see
                    'the owner's Name.'
3. The only known reference to the later edition is given in *B.&G.Cat.*, No. 37, p. 14.

POWNALL, THOMAS[1] (1722–1805)
The great advantage of eating pure and genuine bread, comprehending the
heart of the wheat, with all its flour. Showing how this may be a means of

promoting health and plenty, preserving infants from the grave, by destroying the temptation to the use of allum [*sic*] and other ingredients in our present wheaten bread.[2] London: printed for and sold at Mrs Woodfall's, 1773. [——] [——]

Cited: —

Copies: *BI*: —
   NA: —

1. The author, who was sometime Governor of the Colony of Massachusetts Bay, also wrote *Considerations on the Scarcity and High Prices of Bread-corn and Bread* (Cambridge, 1795).
2. This entry is based on Simon, p. 117.

PRACTICAL

The practical distiller: or, a brief treatise of practical distillation. In which the doctrine of fermentation is methodically explain'd in a new method with . . . a treatise of making artificial wines from several fruits of the British production.[1] etc. London: printed for B. Lintot, 1734. 58 p. pl.[2] 19 cm. 1 sh.

Cited:—

Copies: *BI*: ENLS*
   NA: —

1. In the appendix on p. 30 it is stated: 'The receipts are taken from the best manuscripts, such as have been long used in (and approved by) families of good account.'
2. The plate is of a new engine still.

PRENTISS, JOHN (*fl.* 1794)

The compleat toilet, or ladies companion. A collection of the most simple and approved methods of preparing baths, essences, pomatums, powders, perfumes and sweet-scented waters; with receipts for cosmetics of every kind that can smooth and brighten the skin. etc.[1] A new ed. New York: printed for [——], 1794.[2] [——] [——]

Cited: —

Copies: *BI*: —
   NA: —

1. Apart from a complete change of wording for the main title, all the sub-titles are identical to a book first published in English in 1772; see under earlier entry: BUC'HOZ, Pierre Joseph, The toilet of Flora. It would appear to be a pirated edition and, it would seem, not the first of its kind; see under earlier entry: NEW, A new collection.
2. For the only known reference to this work see Evans, vol. 9 (1793-4), p. 358.

PRESENT FOR A SERVANT-MAID
see HAYWOOD, Eliza Fowler.

PRICE, ELIZABETH (*fl.* 1760?)

The new book of cookery; or, every woman a perfect cook; containing the greatest variety of approved receipts in all the branches of cookery and confectionary . . . to which are added, the best instructions for marketing . . . also

directions for clear starching, and the ladies' toilet, or, art of preserving beauty;
likewise a collection of phisical [*sic*] receipts. etc.[1] A new eection [*sic*] for the
present year, with great additions. etc. London: printed for the authoress and
sold by Alex. Hogg, [*c*.1760]. iv, 13–371 p. frontis. 18 cm. 1 sh.[2]

Cited: Oxford, pp. 109–10

Copies: *BI*: LWML*
         NA: DCLC; DNLM; NYPL

—a new ed. with great additions.[3] London: printed for the authoress, and sold
by Alex. Hogg, [*c*.1765]. LeU(B): —

1. The author described herself as 'Mrs. Eliz. Price, of Berkeley Square, assisted by others who
   have made the art of cookery their constant study'.
2. The price is also given in the preface to the author's other work; see next entry: PRICE,
   Elizabeth, The new, universal, and complete confectioner (note 2).
3. The LeU(B) copy (which is wanting a frontispiece) is inscribed: 'Thos. Whisler Magdalen
   Norfolk', and is embossed on the cover: 'Maria Whisler 1795'.

PRICE, ELIZABETH (*fl.* 1760?)

The new, universal, and complete confectioner; or young woman's best guide,
in the whole art of cookery. . . . including various modern and original receipts
for making lemonade, orgeat,[1] orangeade. etc.[2] London: printed for Alex.
Hogg, [*c*.1760]. 5–94 p. frontis.[3] 17 cm. 1 sh. 6 d.[4]

Cited: Bitting, p. 382; Oxford, p. 110[5]

Copies: *BI*: ENLS*; LeU(B)
         NA: DCLC

—another ed. London: printed by S. Couchman for Alex. Hogg, [*c*.1780]. —:
DCLC

—another ed. the whole revised, corrected and improved. London: printed for
Alex. Hogg, [*c*.1780]. LeU(B): DCLC; NYPL

—[? another ed.] The whole art of confectionary, by Eliz. Glasse [i.e. Elizabeth
Price]. [London]: printed for [——], [——].[6] —: —

1. 'Orgeat' is a cooling drink made from barley or almonds and orange-flower water.
2. In her preface the author says: 'This day is published (price only 1 s.) Mrs. Price's New Book
   of Cookery, embellished with a beautiful frontispiece'; see under previous entry: PRICE,
   Elizabeth, The new book of cookery. Here is an advertisement which gives evidence for the
   price of the author's other, second work, but no clue to the date of 'this day' (in the same way
   in which she gave no clue to 'the present year' in the new edition of her second work).
3. The frontispiece (but nothing else) is identical to one used in another work sold by Alex.
   Hogg; see under earlier entry: PARTRIDGE, Ann, The new and complete universal cook.
4. Oxford, p. 110, gives the same price for the edition printed by S. Couchman and sold by Alex.
   Hogg *c*.1780.
5. Oxford, ibid., loc. cit., gives the same approximate year of publication (1780) for both Mrs
   Price's books, which seems unlikely.
6. The only known reference for this 'edition' is a footnote in Oxford, ibid., loc. cit., which states:
   '*The whole art of confectionary*, by Mrs. Eliz. Glasse, with no publisher's name and a preface
   signed Elizabeth Price, but copied from H. Glasse, seems another edition issued for
   fraudulent purposes. It is, however, a much larger book.' As the last sentence clearly means
   that Oxford had seen this spurious work, it is a pity he did not say more about the basis for his

opinion that it was an edition of one of her acknowledged books. He seems to contradict his more plausible assertion that Mrs Price was intent on deceiving the public by borrowing Hannah Glasse's surname and copying her work.

PRIMITIVE

Primitive cookery: or the kitchen garden display'd. Containing a collection of receipts for preparing a great variety of cheap, healthful and palatable dishes, without either fish, flesh or fowl; with a bill of fare of seventy dishes that will not cost above two-pence each. etc. 2nd ed. with considerable additions.[1] London: printed for J. Williams, 1767. viii, 82 p. 18 cm. 1 sh.[2]

Cited: Oxford, p. 97

Copies: *BI*: LBL*; LeU(B); MU(JR)
     NA: ViU

1. No copy of this vegetarian work in its original form has been located. As the 2nd ed. 'with considerable additions' is a fairly small book, the 1st ed. was probably a pamphlet or tract.
2. *Scots Mag.*, vol. 29 (Feb. 1767), pp. 91–2, confirms that the price was 1 sh.

PROFESSED COOK

    see MENON, [——], The art of modern cookery

Q

QUEEN

The Queen's[1] closet opened. Being incomparable secrets in physick, surgery, preserving, candying and cookery, after the newest mode now practised by the most experienced persons of the times. etc. 11th ed. corrected with additions.[2] London: printed for J. Phillips, H. Rhodes and J. Taylor, 1710. 240 p. 16 cm.

Cited: Oxford, p. 26

Copies: *BI*: LBL; LeU(B)*[3]
    NA: CSmH; KMK; NNNAM

—11th ed. enlarged. London: printed for W. Taylor, 1713. [2 sh.].[4] —: NYPL

1. The Queen alluded to was Henrietta Maria, the French wife of Charles I. When the book was first published in London for Nathaniel Brook in 1655, Oliver Cromwell was Lord Protector of England, and the Queen was in exile in her native land. As Cromwell was wholly intolerant of anything Royalist and also kept a tight control on publishing, it is a wonder that the appearance of this work and a further edition the following year was tolerated. Oxford, p. 26, gives full details of the 1st ed. and the dates of all subsequent editions.
2. *BMCat.* lists this work under 'M., W.'
3. The LeU(B) copy is bound with 'The Compleat Cook'.
4. *Mon.Cat./1*, p. 29 (Aug. 1714), confirms that the price of this edition was 2 sh.

THE
Queen's Closet
OPENED.

BEING

Incomparable Secrets in PHYSICK,
SURGERY, PRESERVING,
CANDYING, and

COOKERY.

After the newest Mode now practised in *England*,

By the most experienc'd Persons of the Times.

The **Eleventh Edition**, *Corrected, with many* New *and* Large ADDITIONS *throughout the whole*

Vivit post Funera Virtus.

LONDON:

Printed for *J. Phillips*, at the *King's-Arms* in
St. *Paul's* Church-yard; *H. Rhodes* at the *Star*,
the corner of *Bride-lane* in *Fleet-street*; and
J. Taylor, at the *Ship* in *Pater-noster-Row*,
MDCCX. X

This title-page, although dated 1710, really belongs to the latter part of the seventeenth century and is shown as an example of the design from which more modern title-pages evolved in the eighteenth century.

QUÉLUS (or DE QUÉLUS), D. (*fl.* 1724-1730)

The natural history of chocolate. Being a distinct and particular account of the cocao-tree . . . with the best ways of making chocolate. etc. [translated from the last edition of the French by a physician].[1] London: printed for J. Roberts, 1724. [in two parts] viii, 37, 38-95 p. 19 cm. 1 sh. 6 d.

Cited: —

Copies: *BI*: ENLS; LBL*
    NA: DNLM; NjR; PBL

—2nd ed. London: printed for John Roberts, 1730. LBL; LeU(B): MH-BA; NIC

1. *BMCat.* (1966), lists this work under 'Chélus, D. de'. The present compiler has taken some trouble to identify this author, but to no avail.

R

R., C.

    see HOUSE-KEEPER'S guide.

RAFFALD, ELIZABETH (1733-1781)

The experienced English house-keeper, for the use and ease of ladies, house-keepers, cooks, etc. . . . Consisting of near 800 original receipts, most of which never appeared in print. etc.[1] Manchester: printed by J. Harrop, for the author, and sold by Eliz. Raffald, Confectioner, near the Exchange, Manchester, 1769.[2] iii, 362, xi p. frontis. pls. 20 cm.

Cited: Bitting, p. 387; Oxford, pp. 98-9

Copies: *BI*: CUL; ENLS*; LWML
    NA: KMK; NIC; NYPL

—2nd ed. London: printed for the author, 1771. ESBL; LeU(B): InSL

—supplement. an appendix to the experienced English housekeeper. London: printed for the author, and sold by R. Baldwin, 1771. 48 p. 20 cm. MU(JR): MB*

—2nd ed. with appendix. London: printed for the author, and sold by R. Baldwin, 1771. [6 sh.].[3] LBL: DCLC; MB

—3rd ed. Dublin: printed for [——], 1772. —: IU

—3rd ed. London: printed for the author, and sold by R. Baldwin, 1773. DoCL; LBL; LeU(B): MBSi; NYPL; WU

—4th ed. London: printed for the author, and sold by R. Baldwin, 1775. LBL; RUL: DCLC

—5th ed. London: printed for the author, and sold by R. Baldwin, 1776. LBL; LWML; LeU(B): MH; NYPL

The EXPERIENCED
Englifh Houfe-keeper,

For the Ufe and Eafe of

Ladies, Houfe-keepers, Cooks, &c.

Wrote purely from PRACTICE,

And dedicated to the

Hon. Lady ELIZABETH WARBURTON,

Whom the Author lately ferved as Houfe-keeper.

Confifting of near 800 Original Receipts, moft of which never
appeared in Print.

PART FIRST, Lemon Pickle, Browning for all Sorts of Made
Difhes, Soups, Fifh, plain Meat, Game, Made Difhes both hot
and cold, Pyes, Puddings, &c,

PART SECOND, All Kind of Confectionary, particularly the
Gold and Silver Web for covering of Sweetmeats, and a Defert
of Spun Sugar, with Directions to fet out a Table in the moft
elegant Manner and in the modern Tafte, Floating Iflands, Fifh
Ponds, Tranfparent Puddings, Trifles, Whips, &c.

PART THIRD, Pickling, Potting, and Collaring, Wines, Vinegars, Catchups, Diftilling, with two moft valuable Receipts,
one for refining Malt Liquors, the other for curing Acid Wines,
and a correct Lift of every Thing in Seafon in every Month of
the Year.

By ELIZABETH RAFFALD.

MANCHESTER:

Printed by *J. Harrop*, for the Author, and fold by Meffrs. *Fletcher*
and *Anderfon*, in *St. Paul's* Church-yard, *London*; and by
Eliz. Raffald, Confectioner, near the *Exchange, Manchefter*, 1769.

The Book to be figned by the Author's own Hand-writing, and
entered at Stationers Hall.

—6th ed. London: printed for the author, and sold by R. Baldwin, 1778. LeU(B): —

—6th ed. Dublin: printed by J. Williams, 1778. DNLI: CSmH

—7th ed. London: printed for the author, and sold by R. Baldwin, 1780. LBL; OBL: MiD; PHi

—8th ed. London: printed for R. Baldwin, 1782. CUL; LBL; LeU(B): CaBVaUW; CtY

—a new ed. London: printed for R. Baldwin, 1784. —: ICRL

—9th ed. London: printed for R. Baldwin, 1784. LWML; LeU(B): CaOTUTF; MCR; MiEM

—10th ed. London: printed for R. Baldwin, 1786. LBL; LGL; LWML: KMK; MB; OHi

—a new ed. London: printed for A. Millar, W. Law, and R. Cater, 1787. LeU(B): —

—a new ed. London: printed for A. Millar, W. Law, and R. Cater, 1788. LeU(B); ShCL: —

—a new ed. London: printed for the booksellers, 1789. BPL; LWML: —

—a new ed. with additions. London: printed for A. Millar, W. Law, and R. Cater, 1789. —: DCLC; ICJ; MH

—a new ed. London: printed for A. Millar, W. Law, and R. Cater, 1791. BPL: —

—a new ed. London: printed for A. Millar, W. Law, and R. Cater, 1793. BPL; LWML; LWS: PP

—11th ed. London: printed for R. Baldwin, 1794. LWML; LeU(B): MiD

—a new ed. London: printed for [———], 1794.[4] —: —

—a new ed. London: printed for A. Millar, W. Law, and R. Cater, 1795. LBL; LeU(B); OBL: KMK

—a new ed. London: printed for A. Millar, W. Law, and R. Cater; and for Wilson, Spence and Mawman (at York), 1796. LeU(B): KMK; MOSV; ViWC

—a new ed. to which is added a treatise on brewing. London: printed for the booksellers, 1798. ANLW; LeU(B): —

—another ed. Manchester: printed for G. Bancks, 1798.[5] —: —

—12th ed. London: printed for R. Baldwin, 1799. LeU(B); MPL: MWA

—a new ed. London: printed for A. Millar, W. Law, and R. Cater, 1799. LBL: —

—another ed.[6] Manchester: printed for G. Bancks, [c.1799]. —: —

—a new ed.[7] London: printed for H. and G. Mozley, 1800. LeU(B): —

1. Elizabeth Raffald (1733–81) was, after Hannah Glasse, the most celebrated English cookery writer of the 18th century, and therefore deserves more than passing notice. She was the daughter of John Whittaker of Doncaster, and was for fifteen years employed as housekeeper to Lady Elizabeth Warburton of Arley Hall, Cheshire, to whom she dedicated her book. In 1763 she married her employer's gardener, John Raffald, and by him had fifteen daughters. In 1764 she became a confectioner in Manchester, and shortly afterwards established a cookery

school for young ladies, which she ran in her shop. Then, in 1769, just after she published her book, she temporarily took over the licence of the Bull's Head in Market Place, Manchester, before taking over the King's Head in Chapel Street, Salford, in 1770; both were old and famous inns. In 1771 she helped to found Salford's first newspaper, *Prescott's Journal*, and to become the adviser to, and part-owner of, *Harrap's Mercury*. She also found time to compile the first Manchester Directory, which appeared in 1772. It is said that she sold all the rights in her book to a London publisher for £600. For further information; see *DNB*, vol. 16 (1909), pp. 602-3; Charles P. Hampson, *Salford through the Ages* (Manchester, 1930), pp. 192-3; and Mary Aylett and Olive Ordish, *First Catch your Hare*, op. cit., pp. 126-38.

2. Commenting on the work of Catharine Brooks, Oxford, p. 94, writes: 'Two other editions, undated, are called "The Experienced English Housekeeper", and were probably issued after the appearance of Mrs. Raffald's book with that title in order to deceive. One was published at Manchester.' The present compiler believes that in this case Oxford was wrong in making such a charge, as Mrs Brooks almost certainly published an edition of her work with a changed title about three years before Mrs Raffald issued her book with an identical title; see under earlier entry: BROOKS, Catharine, The complete English cook. The contents of the two works are quite different. Mrs Raffald, for instance, gave no medical receipts.

3. This edition was advertised in Elizabeth Raffald's own compilation: *The Manchester Directory for the year 1772*, with the price of '6 sh. bound'.

4. The only known reference to this edition is given in *Christie's Cat.* (3 Nov. 1971), p. 10.

5. This is a spurious edition according to *The Manchester Press before 1801*, op. cit., p. 26.

6. Ibid., p. 28, states that this edition is also spurious.

7. Further editions were published in the 19th century; see *BMCat.* (1963).

ROBERTSON, HANNAH (*fl.* 1724-1806)

The young ladies school of arts; containing a great variety of practical receipts. etc.[1] Edinburgh: printed by Wal. Ruddiman, jun., for Mrs. Robertson, 1766.[2] xxiv, 215 p. 18 cm.

Cited: Bitting, p. 400; Oxford, pp. 96-7

Copies: *BI*: —
        NA: NNNAM; ViWC*

—2nd ed. with large additions. Edinburgh: printed by Wal[ter] Ruddiman, jun., for Mrs. Robertson, 1767. ENLS*[3]: DCLC; MiEM

—4th ed. Edinburgh: printed for R. Spence, 1777.[4] BPL: —

—4th ed. with large additions. York: printed at the New Printing Office, for Mrs. Robertson, 1777. LeU(B): —

—a new ed. Edinburgh, printed for Robert Jameson, 1777. GPL(M); LWML; LeU(B): —

—4th ed. with large additions. York: printed for R. Spence, 1784.[5] GUL; LBL: MiEM

1. For a life of the author see her autobiography *The Life of Mrs. Robertson* (Edinburgh, 1792). In it she claimed to be the granddaughter of Charles II.

2. The dedications vary from edition to edition. In the 1st ed. she dedicated her work to 'The Countess of Fyfe [*sic*]', and dated it 'Perth 15 July 1766'; see Crahan, p. 64.

3. The 2nd ed. is dedicated to 'The Right Honourable The Countess of Northesk'. Oxford, p. 97, says that this edition is dedicated to 'Mrs. Lockhart of Craighouse'. It is not known if the 1st ed. had plates; the American sources give no indication one way or the other. The 2nd ed. has 5 plates (of flowers), but the ENLS copy is wanting 2 of them.

4. The 4th eds. and the new edition are all dedicated to 'Mrs. Lockhart of Craighouse'.

5. There were further editions in the 19th century. In the 10th ed. (Edinburgh, 1806; ENLS), 'a narrative of the author's life' was added.

ROBERTSON, Joseph (1726–1802)

An essay on culinary poisons. Containing cautions relative to the use of laurel-leaves, hemlock, mushrooms, copper-vessels. etc. [Anon.]. London: printed for G. Kearsley, 1781. 8–45 p. 19 cm. 1 sh.

Cited: —

Copies: *BI*: ENLS*; LBL
      NA: CtY; MH

ROZEA, Jassintour (*fl.* 1753–1756)

The compleat cook, market woman, and dairy maid.[1] London: printed for W. Heard, at the Philobiblian Library; J. Warcus, and R. Richards, 1756.[2] 160 p. 20 cm. 1 sh.

Cited: —

Copies: *BI*: LWML*
      NA: DCLC[3]

1. The author described himself as 'Principal Cook to the late Charles Seymour, Duke of Somerset', and gave the following dedication: 'Dear Nelly, learn with Care the Cook'ry Art, And mind the easy Precepts I impart'. The name Jassintour Rozea is obviously an anagrammatic pseudonym, but attempts by the present compiler to solve its meaning have come to nought. It can be rearranged to produce 'Jeus Zoroastrian', but the French 'jeu' for 'game' is 'jeux' and not 'jeus' in the plural, and although 'Zoroastrian Games' could be freely given as 'Fire-worshipping Games', it is stretching licence too far to interpret 'fire-worship' as 'cookery'. The presence of 'j' and 'z' in the anagram suggest that the most likely solution is a French name or short phrase, and it is certain that the author spoke and wrote in French. In the introduction (p. 5) of his other work (see next entry), he wrote: 'I have served under the best masters, *French*, *Italian*, and *English*; and my first instructor is now one of the *French* King's principal cooks. I still maintain a correspondence, both foreign and domestic, with the most eminent of my profession. It is from this source, and twenty years practice, I have drawn the substance of this work. The rules that are here established have been approved of by people of the first rank in the kingdom, in whose families I have had the honour to be employed; as the Dukes of *Somerset*, *Montrose*, and *Roxburgh*, the Lords *Hervey*, *Edgecombe*, and the Earl of *Hopetoun*, with whom I am at present [1753].'
2. It is possible that this work and the author's other work (see next entry) are identical, or very similar, the only change being the title-page. Unfortunately, it is not possible to bring the LWML copy of this work to Edinburgh for a thorough comparison with the ENLS copy of the earlier work.
3. The DCLC copy is bound with a previously cited work; see HEALTH, Health's preservative.

ROZEA, Jassintour (*fl.* 1753–1756)

The gift of Comus;[1] or, practical cookery.[2] Number 1 and Number 2 bound together.[3] Edinburgh: printed by Hamilton, Balfour and Neill, 1753. 3–160 p. 19 cm. 1 sh. [2 sh.][4]

Cited: —

Copies: *BI*: ENLS*
      NA: —

THE
COMPLEAT COOK,
MARKET WOMAN,
AND
DAIRY MAID.

By *JASSINTOUR ROZEA*,

Principal Cook to the late

CHARLES SEYMOUR Duke of SOMERSET.

Dear Nelly, *learn with Care the Cook'ry Art,*
And mind the easy Precepts I impart.

L O N D O N:

Printed for *W. Heard,* at the *Philobiblian* Library,
in *Piccadilly* ; *J. Warcus,* at the *Indian Queen,* in
the *Poultry;* and *R. Richards* near *Barnard's-Inn,*
Holborn. 1756.

(Price 1s.)

A pleasing mid-century title-page. The verse, unlike the passage from Milton used by Mrs
Shackleford eleven years later (page 130), is unattributed.

1. This title was probably inspired by the work of a French chef—François Marin, *Les dons de Comus, ou les délices de la table* (Paris, 1739).
2. The receipts in this work are very detailed, and the author, having worked in both Scotland and England, took the trouble to explain how terms differed in those countries; for example (on p. 71): 'A broth of beef . . . in the first place, you must have a sauce-pan and cover, which in *Scotland* is called a goblet-pan; and what the *English* calls a stewpan, they name it a sauce-pan. The above is meant, that my readers in *Scotland* may remember this distinction.'
3. The following advertisement appeared in *Scots Mag.*, vol. 15 (Jan. 1753), p. 56: 'The gift of Comus; or, practical cookery. By Jassintour Rozea. No. 1 1 sh. This book is to consist of 12 numbers.' In fact, only Nos. 1 and 2 were published; the first on 9 Jan. 1753 (which was sold for the author by George Rig, Grocer, and Thomas Trotter, Merchant [both of Edinburgh], and from 13 Feb. 1753 was made available from Hamilton and Balfour, and other Edinburgh booksellers), and the second on 22 Mar. 1753 (which was published by Hamilton and Balfour). Copies of each number were bound and sold, and these are described as excessively rare (see Murphy, p. 40), and copies of both numbers, bound together by Hamilton, Balfour, and Neill, were also sold, and these are even rarer. For further information on the publishing history of the work see Warren James McDougall, 'Gavin Hamilton, John Balfour and Patrick Neill; A Study of Publishing in Edinburgh in the 18th Century', University of Edinburgh Ph.D. thesis, 1975, pp. 268-9.
4. The price for each number was 1 sh., and this is what is shown on the title-page of no. 1. When nos. 1 and 2 were bound together the title-page for no. 2 was omitted, although that too cost 1 sh. In short: the copies containing two numbers, which were worth 2 sh., appeared from the solitary title-page to cost 1 sh. There can be little doubt, however, that booksellers sold such joint copies for their true price, 2 sh.; see Dr Warren J. McDougall's University of Edinburgh Ph.D. thesis, op. cit., loc. cit.

RUSSELL, ELIZABETH (*fl.* 1800)

The complete family cook: . . . instructions for making out bills of fare . . . to furnish a table with few or any number of dishes at the most moderate possible expence. etc. London: printed for the author and sold by William Jee, 1800. xxiv, 342 p. 21 cm. 6 sh.

Cited: —

Copies: *BI*: LeU(B)*
     NA: —

S

S., E.

see SMITH, Eliza.

SALMON, WILLIAM (1644-1713)

The family-dictionary: or, houshold [*sic*] companion, containing . . . directions for cookery . . . the way of making of perfumes . . . virtues and uses of most unusual herbs and plants . . . preparation of several choice medicines. etc.[1] 3rd ed. enlarged. London: printed for H. Rhodes, 1705. 380 p. 20 cm.

Cited: Bitting, p. 416; Oxford, pp. 45–6

Copies: *BI*: LeU(B)*2
       NA: DCLC; KMK

—4th ed. London: printed for H. Rhodes, 1710. LBL; LeU(B); MPL: —

—4th ed. with additions. London: printed for A. Bettesworth and C. Hitch, 1734. [6 sh.].3 LeU(B): —

1. In the 1st ed. (1695), the author published his work under the initials 'J. H.'; in the 2nd ed. (1696), he disclosed his true identity; and in this edition he also called himself a 'Professor of Physick', although he was known to be a quack doctor. For a sketch of his life see *DNB*, vol. 18 (1909), pp. 698–9.
2. The LeU(B) copy is inscribed: 'John Weston of Balliol College', and 'John Tucker Nov 2nd 1745'.
3. *Lond.Mag.* (Sept. 1734), p. 500, confirms that the price of the 4th ed. of 1734 was 6 sh.

SAUNDERS, SARAH (*fl.* 1781?–1792?)

The fountain of knowledge; or, complete family guide. etc.1 London: printed by T. Sabine, [*c.*1781]. 3–136 p. frontis.2 [——]

Cited: —

Copies: *BI*: —
       NA: NYPL3

—6th ed. London: printed for [——], [*c.*1792]. LBL: —

1. The main title of this book is the same as the first sub-title (and the main title of another edition) of a previously cited work; see BRITISH, The British legacy. This is probably a coincidence, and not an indication of plagiarism.
2. The frontispiece shows Mrs Sarah Saunders with four of her seventeen children; see Stark, p. 117.
3. The NYPL copy is imperfect.

SCHNEBBELIE, JACOB CHRISTOPHER

   see HENDERSON, William Augustus.

SEDGWICK, JAMES (*fl.* 1725–1727)

A new treatise on liquors: wherein the use and abuse of wine, malt-drinks, water, etc. are particularly consider'd . . . with the proper manner of using them, hot or cold, either as physick, diet or both: containing plain and easy rules for the preservation of health, and the attainment of long life. The whole being a full determination of all that hath lately been publish'd on those subjects; tho' chiefly contrary to the opinions of Dr. Cheyne, Dr. Rouse, Dr. Short, Lommius, Van der Heyden, Dr. Hancocke, Mr. Smith and others. London: printed for Charles Rivington, 1725. 462 p. 19 cm. 5 sh.1

Cited: —

Copies: *BI*: LBL*; LGL
       NA: —

1. *Mon.Cat./2* (vol. 1), p. 86, (Aug. 1725), confirms that the price was 5 sh.

SEDGWICK, James (*fl.* 1725-1727)

Vinum Britannicum: or, an essay on the properties and effects of malt liquors. etc. [by a physician in the country].[1] London: printed for D. Midwinter and M. Bryson, 1727. v, 52 p. 19 cm.

Cited: —

Copies: *BI*: LBL*; LWML
      NA: —

1. *BMCat.* (1965), lists this work under 'British wine'.

SERVANT

The servant-maid's assistant.[1] [——]: printed for [——], 1753. [——] [——] 2 sh.

Cited: —

Copies: *BI*: —
      NA: —

1. The only known reference to this work is given in *Scots Mag.*, vol. 15 (June 1753), p. 312. The title of this work is identical to the first sub-title of a previously cited book, which was published in the same year; see JOHNSON, Mary, The young woman's companion. With so little information, no conclusions can be drawn.

SERVANT

The servant's plea: or, a defence of that present just and equitable practice, of giving servants, labourers and others, encouragement according to their merit: occasion'd by a late attempt to reduce servant's wages to a certain standard without a due regard to what they now deserve. etc.[1] London: printed for J. Roberts, [*c.*1732]. [——] [——] 6 d.

Cited: —

Copies: *BI*: —
      NA: —

1. The only known reference to this work is given in *Gents.Mag.*, vol. 2 (July 1732), p. 884.

SEVERAL EMINENT COOKS
   see MODERN method.

SEVERAL HANDS
   see KETTILBY, Mary.

SEVERAL VERY EMINENT AND INGENIOUS GENTLEMEN
   see COMPLETE family piece.

THE
Modern Art of Cookery
IMPROVED;
OR,

Elegant, Cheap, and Eafy Methods, of preparing
moft of the Dishes now in Vogue;

In the Compofition whereof

Both HEALTH and PLEASURE have been confulted,

BY,

Mrs. ANN SHACKLEFORD, of *Winchefter*.

TO WHICH IS ADDED,

An APPENDIX:

Containing a Differtation on the different Kinds of
Food, their Nature, Quality, and various Ufes.

By a PHYCISIAN.

AND

A MARKETING MANUAL,

And other ufeful PARTICULARS.

By the EDITOR.

She turns, on hofpitable thoughts intent,
What choice to chufe for delicacy beft;
What order, fo contriv'd as not to mix
Taftes, not well join'd, inelegant, but bring
Tafte after Tafte, upheld with kindlieft change.

MILTON.

LONDON:

Printed for J. NEWBERY, at the Bible and Sun, in
St. Paul's Church-Yard; and F. NEWBERY, in
Pater-nofter-Row. 1767.

Mrs Shackleford's title-page is craftily worded. Her art of cookery is not merely modern, but improved. In her work 'both health and pleasure have been consulted'. And the quotation from Milton applies a flattering gloss of literary culture.

SHACKLEFORD, Ann (*fl.* 1767-1771)

The modern art of cookery improved; or, elegant, cheap, and easy methods of preparing most of the dishes now in vogue . . . To which is added, an appendix; containing a dissertation on the different kinds of food, their nature, quality, and various uses. by a physician and a marketing manual. etc.[1] London: printed for J. Newbery and F. Newbery, 1767. xxiv, 284 p. 17 cm. 3 sh.[2]

Cited: Bitting, p. 430; Oxford, p. 95

Copies: *BI*: LeU(B)*
    NA: DCLC; NYPL

—another ed. Dublin: printed for [——], [*c.*1770]. LBL[3]: —

—another ed. London: printed for T. Carnan and F. Newbery jun., 1771.[4] —: —

1. Little is known about the author. On the title-page she simply called herself: 'Mrs. Ann Shackleford of Winchester'.
2. *Scots Mag.*, vol. 29 (Aug. 1767), p. 430, confirms that the price was 3 sh.
3. The British Library copy of this edition has been destroyed. [Letter from BL Ref. Division to present compiler, dated 26 July 1977.]
4. The only known reference to this edition is given in an advertisement in *Pub.Adv.* (23 Jan. 1771), p. 4, which also gives the price.

SHIRLEY, John

    see Accomplished ladies rich closet.

SHORT, Thomas (1690?-1772)

Discourses on tea, sugar, milk, made-wines, spirits, punch, tobacco etc. with plain and useful rules for gouty people.[1] London: printed for T. Longman and A. Millar, 1750. iii-vi, 424 p. 20 cm.

Cited: —

Copies: *BI*: ERCP*; LBL; LGL
    NA: DCLC; KMK; PPC

1. For a life of the author see *DNB*, vol. 18 (1909), pp. 154-5. He was regarded as the foremost writer on beverages in the 18th century.

SHORT, Thomas (1690?-1772)

A dissertation upon tea, explaining its nature and properties . . . the natural history of tea; . . . a discourse on the virtues of sage and water, and an enquiry into the reasons why the same food is not equally agreeable to all constitutions. London: printed by W. Bowyer for Fletcher Gyles, 1730. 119 p. 25 cm. 2 sh. 6 d.[1]

Cited: —

Copies: *BI*: ENLS*; LBL; LWML
    NA: CtY; MH; NYPL

—2nd ed. London: printed for D. Browne, 1753. LBL: MnU

1. *RB* (Jan. 1730), p. 20, confirms that the price was 2 sh. 6 d.

SIMMONS, AMELIA (*fl.* 1796)

American cookery, or the art of dressing viands, fish, poultry and vegetables, and the best modes of making pastes, puffs, pies, tarts, puddings, custards and preserves, and all kinds of cakes, from the imperial plumb [*sic*] to plain cake. Adapted to this country, and all grades of life.[1] Hartford [Conn.]: printed by Hudson and Goodwin, for the author, 1796. 47 p. [——] 2 sh. 3 d.[2]

Cited: Bitting, p. 435

Copies: *BI*: —
          NA: CtZHS; MB; MWA

—2nd ed. Albany [New York]: printed by Charles R. and George Webster, for the authoress, 1796. —: MWA; NYPL

—another ed. Hartford [Conn.]: printed for Simeon Butler (at Northampton), 1798.[3] —: MWA; NYPL

1. The author described herself as 'Amelia Simmons, an American orphan'. Little seems to be known about her, although she produced the first American cookery book, with native recipes and terms. Cookery books had been printed in America from at least 1742, when William Parks of Williamsburg, Virginia, published an edition of Eliza Smith's The Compleat Housewife (see under later entry), but these works had been written by British writers for a British market, with no thought of the special interests of Americans. Amelia Simmons compiled the first genuinely native American cookbook, which owed nothing to British influences, and which was never (as far as research has shown) reprinted in the British Isles, or even sold in the British Isles, which may account for the absence of a copy in any of the major British libraries. It was advertised in *The Connecticut Journal* (8 June 1796), as 'just published and to be sold by Isaac Beers, price 2/3'; see Lowenstein, p. 5. For a detailed analysis of the author's work see Mary Tolford Wilson, 'Amelia Simmons Fills a Need: *American Cookery*, 1796', *William and Mary Quarterly*, 3rd Series, vol. 14 (1957), pp. 16–30.
2. The price is given in *The Connecticut Journal*, op. cit., loc. cit., and it is interesting to note that British currency is used, although the USA was well established as a republic.
3. For further information on this edition see Crahan, p. 70.

SKEAT, J. (*fl.* 1769?–1772)

The art of cookery and pastery [*sic*] made easy and familiar, in upwards of two hundred different receipts and bills of fare . . . To which is added, a variety of tables for forms of entertainment, and an exact representation of the tables at the Guild-Feasts of Norwich and Lynn.[1] London: printed for the author and sold by him at his house next door to the Maid's Head, in St. Simon's; and by J. Crouse, at Norwich, [*c.*1769]. 6–48 p. pls. 24 cm. 2 sh. 6 d.

Cited: Oxford, pp. 99–100

Copies: *BI*: ENLS*; LBL
          NA: —

—another ed. London: printed for [——], 1772.[2] —: —

1. The author simply called himself a 'Cook'. His work contains some fine folding tables, depicting the number of dishes served for the various removes [or courses] at banquets of the time.
2. The only known reference to this edition is in Lewer, p. 223.

SMITH, A. [Mrs] (*fl.* 1781–1787)

A new book of cookery; or, every woman a perfect cook; containing a very great variety of approved receipts in all the branches of cookery and confectionary. etc.[1] London: printed for [——], 1781. 219 p. 18 cm.

Cited: —

Copies: *BI*: LeU(B)*[2]

    NA: MCR

—another ed. London: printed for [——], 1787.[3] —: MH

1. The author is described as 'Mrs. A. Smith, of Stafford' and is almost certainly the same person as Mrs Alice Smith; see next entry. But for two slight differences, the title is identical to that used for a previously cited work; see under earlier entry: PRICE, Elizabeth, The new book of cookery, which is a much longer work. It is possible that Mrs Smith was one of those who assisted Mrs Price (who freely acknowledged having received help), and who later decided to write a cookery book of her own.
2. The LeU(B) copy is inscribed: 'Ann Ward Her Book August 27th 1788 London'.
3. For the only known British references to this edition see *Sotheby Cat.* (3 May 1972), p. 20, and ibid. (9 Apr. 1973), p. 30.

SMITH, ALICE (*fl.* 1758–1760)

The art of cookery: or, the compleat house-wife. etc.[1] London: printed for the author, 1758. 132 p. 18 cm.

Cited: —

Copies: *BI*: —

    NA: NYPL

—another ed. Edinburgh: printed for [——], 1760. [1 sh.][2] —: —

1. The author is simply described as 'Mrs. Alice Smith'. She was probably the same person as Mrs A. Smith of Stafford; see previous entry.
2. The only known reference to this edition is given in *Scots Mag.*, vol. 22 (Oct. 1760), p. 557.

SMITH, ELIZA (*fl.* 1727–1732)

The compleat housewife; or, accomplished gentlewoman's companion: being a collection of upwards of five hundred of the most approved receipts in cookery, pastry, confectionary, preserving, pickles, cakes, creams, jellies, made wines, cordials. With copper plates curiously engraven for the regular disposition or placing the various dishes and courses. And also bills of fare for every month of the year. To which is added, a collection of near two hundred family receipts of medicines. etc. [by E—— S——].[1] London: printed for J. Pemberton, 1727. 326 p. pls. 20 cm. 5 sh. 6 d.[2]

Cited: Bitting, p. 438; Oxford, pp. 60-1

Copies: *BI*: LWML; LeU(B)*

    NA: ICJ; NYPL

—2nd ed. London: printed for J. Pemberton, 1728. LeU(B): —

—another ed. London: printed for J. and J. Pemberton, [*c.*1728]. LWML: KMK

—3rd ed. corrected and improved. London: printed for J. Pemberton, 1729.
LBL; LeU(B): MCR

—4th ed. corrected and improved. London: printed for J. Pemberton, 1730.
CUL; LWML; LeU(B): DCLC

—5th ed. with additions. London: printed for J. Pemberton, 1733. GUL: —

—6th ed. with very large additions. London: printed for J. Pemberton, 1734.
DoCL; LBL; LeU(B): ICN; NIC; ViSL

—7th ed. with very large additions. London: printed for J. and J. Pemberton,
1736. —: NPV

—8th ed. London: printed for J. and J. Pemberton, 1737. DoCL; SFC (WF): IaU

—9th ed. with very large additions. London: printed for J. and J. Pemberton,
1739. LWML: KMK; MCR; MiD

—10th ed. London: printed for J. and H. Pemberton, 1741. ENLS; LBL;
LeU(B): CLSU

—[1st American ed.] collected from the 5th ed.[3] Williamsburg [Virginia]:
printed and sold by William Parks, 1742. —: CSmH; MWA; ViWC

—11th ed. with very large additions. London: printed for J. and H. Pemberton,
1742. LBL: ViWC

—12th ed. with large additions. London: printed for J. and H. Pemberton,
1744. LeU(B): KMK; NNNAM; OrU

—13th ed. London: printed for J. and H. Pemberton, 1746. —: —

—14th ed. to which is added a collection of above three hundred family receipts
in medicine. London: printed for R. Ware, S. Birt, and T. Longman, 1750.
AUL; LeU(B): ViWc

—[2nd American ed.] collected from the 6th ed. To which is also added, every
man his own doctor: or, the poor planter's physician. Williamsburg
[Virginia]: printed for and sold by William Hunter, 1752.[4] —: —

—15th ed. with additions. London: printed for R. Ware, S. Birt, and T. Longman, 1753. LBL; LeU(B): CtY; NIC; NYPL

—16th ed. London: printed for C. Hitch and L. Hawes, 1758. LWML: CtY

—[another American ed.] New York: printed for Hugh Gaine, 1761.[5] —: —

—[another American ed.] New York: reprinted for Hugh Gaine, 1764.[6] —: —

—17th ed. with additions. London: printed for J. Buckland, 1766. ANLW[7];
LeU(B): DCLC; NBu

—18th ed. with additions. London: printed for J. Buckland and J. F. Rivington,
1773. LBL; LWML: MiD; MoU; NYPL

1. Although the 1st ed. was published under her initials only, she gave her name in subsequent
editions. After Hannah Glasse and, perhaps, Elizabeth Raffald, Eliza Smith is one of the best
known of 18th-century cookery writers, and it was her work which, in 1742, became the first
cookbook to be published in America. Unlike Glasse and Raffald, very little is known about
her, except that in one of her prefaces she wrote: '. . . what I here present the World with, is the
Product of my own Experience, and that for the Space of thirty Years and upwards . . . I have
been constantly employed in fashionable and noble Families . . .'; quoted by Genevieve Yost,
'The Compleat Housewife or Accomplish'd Gentlewoman's Companion: a Bibliographical

Study', *The William and Mary Quarterly*, 2nd Series, vol. 18 (1938), pp. 418–35 (quote on p. 426). In his foreword to the facsimile edition (London, 1968) of the 15th ed. of 1753, Lord Montagu of Beaulieu wrote: 'When I was first shown "The Compleat Housewife" I was fascinated to find that several of the recipes contained were identical to those in manuscript form in my books. Although it is not known in which great houses Mrs. E. Smith worked, it is more than probable that some of these dishes were originally created in one of my ancestor's kitchens.' Some of these dishes were, however, curious: such as 'To mumble rabbets and chickens'; 'To make a Poloe'; 'To make a Pulpatoon of Pigeons'; and 'To make a Tureiner'. The medical recipes are rather disgusting. Mrs Smith died about 1732, because the title-page of the 5th ed. of 1733 states that 'near fifty receipts' were 'communicated just before the author's death'.

2. *Mon.Cat./2* (vol. 2), p. 63 (June 1727), confirms that the price was 5 sh. 6 d.
3. For the publishing history of this 1st American ed. see Genevieve Yost, 'The Compleat Housewife . . .', op. cit., pp. 419–24, which has (on p. 418) a facsimile of the title-page, across the top of which is an owner's inscription: 'Joseph Billups Jr his Book price 7/6', and on the flyleaf (p. 423): '. . . Bot [*sic*] of a Pedlar [*sic*] at Mathews Court House, July 12, 1812 price 7/6.'
4. William Parks, who reprinted the 5th ed. in 1742 as the 1st American ed., died in 1750, and his printing office was purchased by his assistant William Hunter, who on 29 May 1752 published the following advertisement in the *Virginia Gazette*: 'Just Imported, and to be Sold at the Printing Office in Williamsburg, A Great Variety of new Books, a Catalogue of which will be published next Week: Where likewise may be had, Just Published, *The compleat Housewife . . .* by E. Smith. Collected from sixth Edition. To which is also added, *Every Man his Own Doctor: or, The Poor Planter's Physician.*' The last addition had been a popular pamphlet in its own right, and was a 47-page work by J. Tennent, which William Parks had printed and published, and had gone into a 2nd ed. in 1734 and a 3rd ed. in 1737, each priced at '1 sh.'. The 2nd American ed. of 1752 was therefore a combination of Mrs Smith's 6th ed. and J. Tennent's 4th ed. of *Every Man his Own Doctor . . .* (which had been printed by William Hunter in 1751); ibid., pp. 423 and 430. See also Evans, vol. 3 (1751–64), p. 44.
5. Hugh Gaine was a publisher, not a printer, and doubts have been raised about the inclusion in bibliographies of two editions of Eliza Smith's work which are listed as being printed 'by' Gaine, when the word should be 'for' Gaine: ibid, p. 303, and Genevieve Yost, 'The Compleat Housewife . . .', op. cit., p. 431. The following advertisement appeared in the *New York Mercury* (20 July 1761), supplement: 'This Day is publish'd and to be sold by HUGH GAINE. *The Complete Housewife . . .* the Sixteenth Edition [1758], with Additions.'; ibid., p. 431. See also Hugh Gaine, *Journals of Hugh Gaine*, ed. by Paul Leicester Ford (New York, 1902), vol. 1, p. 107.
6. The following advertisement appeared in the *New York Mercury* (30 Jan. 1764), p. 3: 'The following books are just publish'd and are to be sold at Hugh Gaine's book-store [in Hanover Square, New York City] . . . The Compleat Housewife . . .'; and the same advertisement appeared in the same paper on 27 February 1764; see Genevieve Yost, 'The Compleat Housewife . . .', op. cit., pp. 431–2; and Evans, vol. 3 (1751–64), p. 406.
7. The ANLW copy has the following inscription: 'Mary Morgan her book Sep 24 1770'.

SMITH, GEORGE (*fl.* 1725–1766)

A compleat body of distilling; explaining the mysteries of that science, in a most easy and familiar manner; containing an exact and accurate method of making all the compound cordial-waters now in use, with a particular account of their several virtues . . . adapted no less to the use of private families, than of apothecaries and distillers. [in two parts]. London: printed for Bernard Lintot, 1725. 89, 93–150 p. 20 cm. 2 sh. 6 d.[1]

Cited: —

Copies: *BI*: ENLS*; LBL; LWML
   NA: CLU-C; CU-A

—2nd ed. London: printed for Henry Lintot, 1731. —: DCLC; MH; NIC

—another ed. London: printed for Henry Lintot, 1734. —: —

—3rd ed. London: printed for Henry Lintot, 1737. —: DNAL

—3rd ed. London: printed for Henry Lintot, 1738. LBL; LGL; LWML: CtYM; PV

—another ed. London: printed for Henry Lintot, 1738. LBL: —

—a new ed. London: printed for Henry Lintot, 1749. LWML: CtY; MH; WU

—another ed. London: printed for L. Hawes, W. Clarke, and R. Collins, 1766. LBL; LeU(B): NYPL

1. *Mon.Cat./2* (vol. 1), p. 87 (Aug. 1725), confirms that the price was 2 sh. 6 d.

SMITH, GEORGE (*fl.* 1725–1766)

The nature of fermentation explain'd; with the method of opening the body of any grain or vegetable subject, so as to obtain from it a spirituous liquor . . . to which is added, a collection of several compound cordial waters . . . by way of appendix to the ['] compleat body of distilling [']. [1] London: printed for Bernard Lintot, 1729. 56 p. 20 cm. 1 sh. [2]

Cited: —

Copies: *BI*: ENLS; LBL*
         NA: DCLC; ICJ; NYPL

1. As indicated, this is a separate work, but it forms an appendix to the author's first publication four years earlier; see previous entry: SMITH, George, A compleat body of distilling.
2. *Mon.Cat./2* (vol. 2), p. 10 (Sept. 1729), confirms that the price was 1 sh.

SMITH, MARY (*fl.* 1772–1799)

The complete housekeeper and professed cook, . . . containing . . . upwards of 700 practical and approved receipts. etc. [1] Newcastle: printed for the author, by T. Slack, 1772. v, 10–392 p. pls. 23 cm.

Cited: Bitting, pp. 439–40; Oxford, p. 106

Copies: *BI*: LBL; LeU(B)*; NPL
         NA: DCLC; MCR; NYPL

—a new ed. with considerable additions and improvements. Newcastle: printed for S. Hodgson; and for G. G. J. and J. Robinson [at London], 1772. [2] —: —

—a new ed. with considerable additions. Newcastle: printed for S. Hodgson; and for G. G. J. and J. Robinson [at London], 1786. LeU(B); NPL: DCLC; KMK; NYPL

—another ed. Newcastle: printed for S. Hodgson, 1799. [3] —: —

1. The author described herself as 'Mary Smith, late House-Keeper to Sir Walter Blackett, Bart. and formerly in the Service of the Right Hon. Lord Anson, Sir Thomas Sebright, Bart. and other Families of Distinction, as House-Keeper and Cook'.
2. The only known reference to this edition is given by Oxford, p. 106, where the title-page is quoted in full. Oxford has no comments on the work, except a short footnote in which he says: 'According to Ellwanger the first edition was 1772.'

3. The only known reference to this edition is given by Richard Welford, *Early Newcastle Typography: 1639–1800*, op. cit., p. 140.

SMITH, ROBERT (*fl.* 1723–1725)

Court cookery: or, the compleat English cook. Containing the choicest and newest receipts. etc.[1] London: printed for T. Wotton, 1723. [in two parts].[2] 112, 82 p. 20 cm. 3 sh. 6 d.[3]

Cited: Bitting, p. 440; Oxford, pp. 55–6

Copies: *BI*: LBL; LeU(B)*
         NA: ICJ; NYPL; WU

—another ed. Dublin; printed for Pat. Dugan and W. Smith, 1724. DNLI; LeU(B): —

—2nd ed. with large additions. London: printed for T. Wotton, 1725. LWML; LeU(B): DCLC; MiEM; PBL

1. The author described himself as 'Cook (under Mr. Lamb) to King William; as also to the Dukes of Buckingham, Ormond, D'Aumont (the French Ambassador) and others of the Nobility and Gentry'. In his preface he stated: 'It is true, there are several Books of Cookery already extant, but most of 'em very defective and erroneous, and others filled with old Receipts, that are impracticable at this Time.' He went on to denounce the work of his former chief, Patrick Lamb, and attacked him for pirating other people's receipts; see under earlier entry: LAMB, Patrick, Royal cookery.
2. This work is in two parts; the first devoted to cookery, the second to confectionary.
3. *Mon.Cat./2* (vol. 1), p. 8 (Nov. 1724), confirms that the price was 3 sh. 6 d.

SMITH, TIMOTHY

see LESSIUS, Leonardus.

SMITH, WILLIAM (*fl.* 1776)

A sure guide in sickness and health, in the choice of food, and use of medicines. etc.[1] London: printed for and sold by J. Bew and J. Walter, 1776. iii, 356 p. 21 cm. 6 sh.[2]

Cited: —

Copies: *BI*: LBL*
         NA: DNLM; NIC; PPC

1. Although the emphasis in this work is on medical matters, it contains some very interesting information on food.
2. *Scots Mag.*, vol. 38 (Nov. 1776), pp. 607–8, confirms that the price was 6 sh.

SOCIETY OF ANTIQUARIES

see COLLECTION of ordinances.

SPENCER, E. (*fl.* 1782–1784)

The modern cook; and frugal housewife's compleat guide to every branch in displaying her table to the greatest advantage, viz.: The judgement of meat at market; with directions for roasting, boiling, hashing, sewing [*sic*], boiling [*sic*], frying, fricasseying, and baking; also for making puddings, custards, cakes, cheese cakes, pies, tarts, ragouts, soups, creams, jellies, syllabubs, wines, &c. &c. And several select papers by a lady of distinction, lately deceased, of new and infallible rules to be observed in pickling, preserving, brewing, &c.[1] Newcastle upon Tyne: printed by and for T. Saint, 1782. vi, 7–152 p. [——]

Cited: —

Copies: *BI*: —
　　　　NA: DNLM

—2nd ed. Newcastle upon Tyne: printed by and for T. Saint, 1784.[2] —: —

1. The author described himself as 'E. Spencer, Late Principal Cook to a Capital Tavern in London'.
2. The only known reference to this edition is given in *B.&G.Cat.*, No. 27, p. 8.

STAFFORD, HUGH (*fl.* 1753)

A treatise on cyder-making, . . . to which is prefixed a dissertation on cyder and cyder-fruit. London: printed for E. Cave, 1753. v, 68 p. pls. 23 cm. 2 sh.

Cited: —

Copies: *BI*: LBL*
　　　　NA: PHi

—2nd ed. with additions. London: printed for D. Henry, and R. Cave, 1755. LBL: OCl

STONE, JAMES (*fl.* 1770?)

The complete baker; or, a method of effectually raising a bushel of flour with a teaspoonful of barm. etc. Salisbury: printed for the author, [*c.*1770]. iii, 9 p. 18 cm. 1 sh.[1]

Cited: —

Copies: *BI*: LBL*; MU(JR)
　　　　NA: CtY; ICJ

1. *Scots Mag.*, vol. 33 (Feb. 1771), p. 93, confirms that the price of this pamphlet was 1 sh.

SUGGESTIONS

Suggestions offered to the consideration of the public, and in particular to the more opulent classes of the community, for the purpose of reducing the consumption of bread corn. etc. London: printed by His Majesty's printers, [*c.*1799] 19 p. 21 cm.

Cited: Oxford, p. 125

Copies: *BI*: —
　　　　NA: MH-BA

—2nd ed. corrected and enlarged. London: printed by His Majesty's printers, [*c.*1800]. —: CtY; MH-BA

SUMMER

The summer's amusement[s]; or, the young ladies companion. Containing above one hundred and fifty of the choicest modern receipts. etc.[1] Newcastle: printed for the author, by W. Cuthbert, 1746.[2] vii, 70 p. [——]

Cited: —

Copies: *BI*: NPL

      NA: NYPL

1. There is no doubt that this is an anonymous edition of a previously cited entry; see under DOUGLASS, C., The summer's amusements.
2. This entry is based on Stark, p. 14, who says that the NYPL copy has 'numerous ms. receipts bound in at the end of the volume'.

SWIFT, JONATHAN (1667-1745)

Directions to servants in general; and in particular to the butler, cook, footman, coachman, groom, house-steward and land-steward, porter, dairy-maid, chamber-maid, nurse, laundress, house-keeper, tutoress or governess. etc.[1] London: printed for R. Dodsley, and M. Cooper, 1745. 93 p. 22 cm. 1 sh. 6 d.[2]

Cited: —

Copies: *BI*: LBL; LeU(B)*

      NA: CtY; IU; MH

—another ed. Dublin: printed by George Faulkner, 1745. —: NjP

—another ed. Dublin: printed by George Faulkner, 1746. —: CtY

—another ed. London: printed for C. Hitch, Davis and R. Dodsley, 1749. —: PU

—another ed. Glasgow: printed in the year 1765. ENLS: —

—another ed. Perth: printed by Robert Morison, 1766. LBL: —

—a new ed. London: printed for T. Osborne, 1766. —: NIC

—a new ed. London: printed for J. Nunn, 1798. —: ICU

1. The author Jonathan Swift (1667-1745), who was appointed Dean of St. Patrick's, Dublin, in 1713, is regarded as one of the greatest satirists in English of all time. He is, of course, best remembered for *Gulliver's Travels*, but some of his other books have also become classics, including *A Tale of a Tub*. It is odd, therefore, that William King should claim in 1708 on the title-page of his satirical poem on Dr Martin Lister's edition of the cookery book by the Roman writer APICIUS that it was by the author of *A Tale of a Tub*. There is sound evidence to show that King was paid £32 5 sh. by Bernard Lintot for writing the satirical poem and the longer work on the same subject, and yet he indirectly asserts that the poem was by Swift; see under earlier entry: KING, William, The art of cookery. A poem. It is another of those mysteries which bears no solution. In his *Directions to Servants*, which was published in the last year of his life, Swift was mildly satirical. For a biographical sketch of Swift see *DNB*, vol. 19 (1909), pp. 204-27.
2. *Scots Mag.*, vol. 7 (Nov. 1745), p. 544, confirms that the price was 1 sh. 6 d.

SWITZER, STEPHEN[1] (1682?-1745)

The practical kitchen gardiner [*sic*]: or, a new and entire system of directions for his employment in the melonry,[2] kitchen-garden, and potagery,[3] in the

several seasons of the year. etc.[4] London: printed for Tho. Woodward, 1727.
xx, 424 p. 19 cm.

Cited: —

Copies: *BI*: LBL; LeU(B)*
   NA: CU; DCLC; WU

1. For a life of the author see *DNB*, vol. 19 (1909), pp. 241–2. Switzer wrote several books on gardening and agriculture; see *BMCat.* (1964).
2. A 'melonry' is an orchard.
3. A 'potagery' is a cookery-garden, for supplying herbs and small vegetables.
4. This work gives an insight into the range of vegetables and herbs grown in the 18th century.

SYLVAN, Agricola
 see Farmer (first entry).

T

TAYLOR, E. (*fl.* 1769–1795)
The lady's, housewife's, and cookmaid's assistant: or, the art of cookery explained and adapted to the meanest capacity. etc. Berwick upon Tweed: printed by H. Taylor, for R. Taylor, Bookseller, 1769.[1] iii–xii, 276 p. 18 cm.

Cited: Bitting, p. 457; Oxford, p. 100

Copies: *BI*: ENLS*; LBL; LeU(B)
   NA: CLSU; DCLC; NYPL

—2nd ed. Berwick upon Tweed: printed for R. Taylor, 1778. LeU(B): —

—3rd ed. enlarged and improved. Berwick upon Tweed: printed and sold by John Taylor, 1795. LeU(B): —

1. The list of subscribers in this work shows that it received a lot of support from people living in East Lothian.

TAYLOR, S.
 see Menon, [——], The complete family cook.

TENNENT, J.
 see Smith, Eliza.

THACKER, John (*fl.* 1742–1765?)
The art of cookery. Containing above six hundred and fifty of the most approv'd receipts . . . Also, a bill of fare for every month in the year, with an alphabetical index to the whole. etc.[1] Newcastle upon Tyne: printed by I. Thompson and Company, 1758. 322 p. 21 cm.

Cited: Bitting, p. 458; Oxford, p. 88

Copies: *BI*: LBL; LeU(B)*; NPL
    NA: DCLC; NIC

—2nd ed. London: printed for J. Richardson, 1762. —: DCLC

—another ed. [———]: printed for [———], [*c*.1765]. LeU(B): —

1. The author described himself as 'Cook to the Honourable and Reverend the Dean and Chapter in Durham'. Although he apologized for adding yet another cookery book for sale, he justified his work (in the preface) on the ground that those available were 'far short of being generally useful, especially in these Northern Parts, where the Seasons occasion such Alterations in the Bills of Fare for each Month, from those calculated for the Southern Parts'. In 1742 John Thacker opened a cookery school in Durham; see Dr F. J. G. Robinson's University of Newcastle Ph.D. thesis, op. cit., vol. 1, p. 221.

TOWN

The town and country cook; or, young woman's best guide in the whole art of cookery . . . together with the whole art of pastry . . . to which are added many particulars.[1] London: printed for W. Lane, [*c*.1780]. 84 p. frontis.[2] 17 cm. 6 d.

Cited: Oxford, p. 91[3]

Copies: *BI*: —
    NA: DCLC; NYPL

1. Although the main title only is different, this work is either an anonymous edition or a pirated version of a previously cited book; see under earlier entry: PARTRIDGE, Ann, The new and complete universal cook.
2. The frontispiece is identical to one which has been used in two previously cited books; see under earlier entries: PARTRIDGE, Ann, The new and complete universal cook, and PRICE, Elizabeth, The new, universal, and complete confectioner; see notes at the end of entries for these three works in Oxford, pp. 91, 110, and 111.
3. Oxford has assessed the approximate date of publication as '1760', and the copy listed in *B.&G.Cat.*, No. 37, p. 13, has been dated 'ca. 1780'. It is much more likely that the book was published in or about the same year as the works named in note 2; i.e. *c*.1780.

TOWNSHEND, JOHN (*fl*. 1773)

The universal cook;[1] or, lady's complete assistant . . . together with a great variety of original receipts . . . and others communicated to him by his friends who are celebrated in the culinary art. etc.[2] London: printed for S. Bladon, 1773. 308 p. 17 cm.

Cited: Bitting, pp. 463–4

Copies: *BI*: —
    NA: DCLC

1. According to Bitting, this work (but not the sub-titles) is identical to a book published in 1792, which has been previously cited; see under earlier entry: COLLINGWOOD, Francis, and WOOLLAMS, John, The universal cook. Bitting also says that this work is very rare.
2. John Townshend described himself as 'Late Master of the Greyhound Tavern, Greenwich, and Cook to his Grace the Duke of Manchester'.

TRADER IN FISH

see BEST and most approved method.

TREATISE

A treatise on the use and abuse of the second, commonly called, the steward's table, in the families of the first rank. etc.[1] [by a coachman]. London: printed for the author, and sold by Mr. Carter, [c.1758]. 70 p. frontis. 20 cm. 1 sh. 6 d.

Cited: —

Copies: *BI*: LBL*
         NA: CtY; MH; MnU

1. This work is an attack on the nobility and gentry for their disregard of the welfare of their staff, and the way in which the occupants of the 'second table' were used to keep other servants under strict control. As Dr J. Jean Hecht has explained in her work: *The Domestic Servant Class in Eighteenth-Century England*, op. cit., p. 35, '. . . in large establishments, upper servants dined together at the second table, while the lower servants sat at the third', and ibid., p. 51, 'Of the inferior [or lower] manservants—those who wore livery—the coachman ranked highest.' Hence the significance of the pseudonym, which implied that the protest was from the senior member of lower order of servants, who sat at the head of the third table, not only against his masters but also those who held power over him on the second (or steward's) table. The class divisions between servants were as rigid and as important as the class divisions within and between the upper, middling, and 'employing' sections of society, and this work gives a valuable insight into the way in which large establishments were run and the hierarchies which governed their existence.

TRUSLER, JOHN (1735-1820)

The honours of the table, or, rules for behaviour during meals; with the whole art of carving . . . by the author of [']Principles of Politeness[']. etc. [Anon.].[1] London: printed for the author, at the Literary-Press, 1788. 120 p. pls. 16 cm. 2 sh. 6 d.[2]

Cited: Bitting, p. 466; Oxford, p. 117

Copies: *BI*: LBL; LWML; LeU(B)*
         NA: DCLC; KMK; MiD

—2nd ed. London: printed for the author, at the Literary-Press, 1791. ANLW; LGL; LeU(B): DCLC; MB; NPV

—another ed. Dublin: printed by W. Sleator, 1791.[3] —: CtY; MH; NYPL

1. For a life of Dr John Trusler see *DNB*, vol. 19 (1909), pp. 1195-6, where he is described as an 'eccentric divine, literary compiler, and medical empiric'. He was extremely interested in the wages and conditions of servants; see J. Jean Hecht, *The Domestic Servant Class in Eighteenth-Century England*, op. cit., *passim*. He was also keen on recording the household customs of his time; hence his work on the 'honours of the table'.
2. *Scots Mag.*, vol. 51 (Nov. 1789), p. 544, confirms that the price was 2 sh. 6 d.
3. There were further editions in the 19th century; see *BMCat.* (1964).

TRYON, THOMAS[1] (1634-1703)

The good house-wife made a doctor. etc.[2] [Another edition.][3] London: printed for G. Conyers, 1702. 285 p. [———]

Cited: Oxford, p. 43[4]

Copies: *BI*: —
         NA: —

1. The author wrote most of his books under the pseudonym 'Philotheos Physiologus' (meaning, presumably, God-loving Student of natural phenomena), and often called himself 'Student in Physic', although he was a hatter by trade. He became a Pythagorean (or vegetarian), who won popularity in the 18th century. Benjamin Franklin, who was much impressed by his work, was a 'Tryonist' for a time, and he used Tryon's economies in *Poor Richard's Almanac*; see Crahan, p. 72. See also *DNB*, vol. 19 (1909), pp. 1201–3; and the article by A. H. T. Robb-Smith, MD, 'Doctors at Table', *JAMA*, vol. 224, op. cit., p. 30.

2. This entry is based on Simon, p. 139.

3. For earlier editions of this work see Wing *STC*, vol. 3 (1951), p. 398, and Sir William Osler, Bt., *Bibliotheca Osleriana* (London, 1969), pp. 494–5, and Oxford, p. 43. The date of the 1st ed. is not known; another or 2nd ed. was published in 1692.

4. Oxford gives no entry for this work, except the title and dates of publication of the first two editions. He lists ten of the works of Tryon, who he says wrote under the pseudonym 'Phylotheus [*sic*] Physiologus', which must be a misprint. The first two books written by Tryon were *Healths Grand Preservative* (1682), and *A Treatise of Cleanliness in Meats and Drinks* (1682).

TRYON, Thomas (1634–1703)

The way to get wealth; or, an easie way to make wine of gooseberries, currans [*sic*], raspberries . . . [and] the duty of all sorts of servant maids. etc. [Anon.]. London: printed for G. Conyers, 1702. 76 p. 15 cm. 1 sh. 6 d.[1]

Cited: Bitting, p. 467; Oxford, p. 43

Copies: *BI*: LBL*
     NA: CLU-C; DCLC

—2nd ed. enlarged. London: printed for G. Conyers, 1706. LBL; LWS; LeU(B): DCLC

1. *Bib.Ann.*, vol. 2 (1701–3), p. 81, confirms that the price was 1 sh. 6 d.

TUSSER, Thomas (1524?–1580)

Tusser redivivus: being part of Mr. Thomas Tusser's [']Five Hundred Points of Husbandry['];[1] . . . To which are added notes and observations explaining many obsolete terms. etc. [12 parts . . . bound in 1 Volume].[2] [Another edition].[3] London: printed and sold by John Morphew, 1710. [——] pls. 19 cm.

Cited: Bitting, p. 468

Copies: *BI*: ENLS*[4]
     NA: DCLC; IU; MH-A

—another ed. London: printed for M. Cooper, and sold by John Duncan, 1744. [3 sh. 6 d.][5] ENLS; LeU(B): DCLC

1. In a note to the 1638 ed., Stark, p. 8, states: 'First published London, 1573, as an enlargement of his: *A hundreth good pointes of husbandrie* (London, 1557).' The same edition has a full entry in Murphy, p. 44—[*Five Hundred points of good Husbandry . . . besides the Booke of Huswifery*, London: printed by I[ohn ?] O[kes ?] for the Company of Stationers, 1638]—with the following note: 'Tusser's homely and aphoristic verses were of great value in their day; since then they have earned the praise of Davy, who styled their author "the British Varro," of Southey, and of Scott. The last named held this book, for evidence of "rigid and minute attention to every department of domestic economy," comparable only to Swift's "Directions to Servants." [see under earlier entry: SWIFT, Jonathan, Directions to servants] Tusser . . . wrote in the tongue of ploughmen for ploughmen's understanding; he was rewarded, for his

book's deserved popularity caused it frequently to be reprinted, though its author died in a debtors' prison.' For a life of Thomas Tusser see *DNB*, vol. 19 (1909), pp. 1306-8.

2. This book was issued in twelve monthly parts, and bound as one volume when all the parts had been collected. For this reason it is classed by collectors as 'very rare'. Each of the twelve parts has a separate title and pagination.

3. For the various editions of this work, which was last reprinted in 1931 (under the title *Thomas Tusser*, edited by Dorothy Hartley), see *BMCat.* (1964).

4. The ENLS copy is inscribed: 'Andrew Lumisden'.

5. *Scots Mag.*, vol. 5 (Dec. 1743), p. 576, confirms that the price of the 1744 edition was 3 sh. 6 d.

TWAMLEY, JOSIAH (*fl.* 1784)

Dairying exemplified, or the business of cheese-making: laid down from approved rules . . . also the most approved method of making butter. etc.[1] Warwick: printed for the author by J. Sharp, 1784. vi, [8]-180 p. 21 cm.

Cited: —

Copies: *BI*: LBL*; OBL
        NA: CU; ICJ; MH

—2nd ed. corrected and improved. Warwick: printed for the author by J. Sharp, 1787. [2 sh.] LBL: CtY; DNAL; NYPL

—another ed. [American ed.] Providence [Rhode Island]: printed by and for Carter and Wilkinson, 1797. —: DCLC; MWA

1. A valuable work for housewives, for the information it gave them on cheese and butter making.

TWEED, JOHN

see CONCISE observations.

TWO

Two new and curious essays: . . . concerning the best methods of pruning fruit-trees . . . [and] a discourse concerning . . . the various ways of preparing and dressing potatoes for the table.[1] London: printed for W. Bickerton, C. Corbet and R. Chandler, 1732. iv, 64 p. 19 cm.

Cited: —

Copies: *BI*: LBL*; LRAS; LRHS(L)
        NA: MdBJ

—another ed. London: printed for Richard Chandler, 1733.[2] CUL; LRHS(L): —

1. This work is included for its section on potatoes.
2. This edition is an appendix to Cowell, John, The curious fruit and flower gardener.

U

UNIVERSAL

The universal family book; or, a necessary and profitable companion, for all degrees of people of either sex; containing, choice physical and chirurgical treatises, for the cure of most distempers, directions for cookery, etc. The art of perfuming, to make waxwork, the art of brewing, and the compleat gardiner [*sic*], with directions to destroy all vermin.[1] London: printed for D. Midwinter, and T. Leigh, 1703. 206 p. 16 cm.

Cited: —

Copies: *BI*: —

    NA: CLU-C; DFo

1. The only known British reference to this work is given in *Bib.Ann.*, vol. 2 (1701–2), p. 65.

UNIVERSAL

The universal library, or compleat summary of science. Containing above sixty select treatises. . . . With divers secrets, experiments and curiosities therein.[1] In two volumes.[2] London: printed for George Sawbridge, 1712. [——] pls. [——]

Cited: Oxford, p. 181.

Copies: *BI*: LBL[3]

    NA: CtY; DNLM; MH

—2nd ed. with additions. London: printed for T. Warner, 1722. —: DCLC; FU

—another ed. London: printed for J. Robinson, 1747 —: CU; MH-BA; NYPL

1. The preface is signed 'H. Curzon'.
2. Vol. 1 is devoted to theology, cookery, and diet; and Vol. 2 to animals. The cookery section is in Vol. 1, pp. 553–68; and the author acknowledged that it was based upon the following previously cited works; see under earlier entries: ACCOMPLISH'D, The accomplish'd lady's delight in preserving; HOWARD, Henry, England's newest way . . . of cookery; and LAMB, Patrick, Royal cookery; and upon two uncited works which were printed in the 17th century: MAY, Robert, The accomplisht cook, printed by R. W. for Nath. Brooke, 1660 (see Oxford, p. 30); and WOLLEY (or WOOLLEY), Hannah, The queen-like closet, printed for R. Lowndes, 1670 (ibid., p. 35).
3. The British Library copy has been lost or mislaid, and this entry has therefore been based on the *BMCat.*, and checked against the entry in Oxford, p. 181.

USEFUL

Useful hints on a variety of subjects. etc. Newcastle upon Tyne: printed for M. Angus, 1791. vi, 89 p. [——]

Cited: —

Copies: *BI*: LBL[1]

    NA: —

1. This entry is based on the *BMCat.*, but the copy in the British Library to which that listing refers has been lost or mislaid. The present compiler has not, therefore, been able to judge

if this work is suitable for inclusion in this short-title catalogue. It is included because works with a general title of this sort *usually* contained cookery or household information.

USEFUL

Useful suggestions favourable to the comfort of the labouring people and of decent housekeepers.[1] London: printed for the author, by Henry Fry, 1795. 16 p. 21 cm.

Cited: Oxford, p. 125 (footnote)

Copies: *BI*: —
   NA: CtY; MdBJ; PU

1. Although no copy is listed for any of the major libraries in the British Isles, one was offered for sale in London about 1934; see *B.&G.Cat.*, No. 37, p. 35, which states: 'The object of this tract is to popularise potatoe [*sic*] soup, barley, broth, &c. as substitutes for bread.'

V

VALANGIN, François Joseph Pahud de
 see Pahud de Valangin, François Joseph.

VALUABLE

Valuable secrets concerning arts and trades: or approved directions from the best artists . . . containing upwards of one thousand . . . receipts. etc.[1] London: printed by Will. Hay, printer and bookseller to the Society of Artists of Great Britain, 1775. xxxiv, 312 p. 17 cm.

Cited: Oxford, p. 108

Copies: *BI*: LBL*
   NA: DCLC; MH; PP

—another ed. Dublin: printed by James Williams, 1778. LeU(B): MH; MH-BA; PPL

—2nd ed. London: printed by W. Hay, 1780. —: CtY

—another ed. London: printed for [——], 1781. LBL: —

—1st American ed. One thousand valuable secrets. Philadelphia: Printed for B. Davis and T. Stephens, 1795. —: MH; MWA

—2nd American ed. Norwich [Connecticut]: printed by T. Hubbard, 1795. —: DCLC; MWA; NIC

—3rd American ed. Boston: printed by J. Bumstead, 1798. —: DCLC; ICU; NYPL

1. Although this work covers a wide variety of subjects, the whole of Chapter 14 is devoted to 'the art of confectionary', and other chapters deal with wines, vinegars, etc.

VERRAL, WILLIAM (*fl.* 1759)

A complete system of cookery. In which is set forth, a variety of genuine receipts, collected from several years experience under the celebrated Mr. de St. Clouet, sometime since Cook to his Grace the Duke of Newcastle. . . . Together with an introductory preface, shewing how every dish is brought to table, and in what manner the meanest capacity shall never err in doing what his bill of fare contains. To which is added, a true character of Mons. de St. Clouet.[1] London: printed for the author, and sold by him; as also by Edward Verral, bookseller, in Lewes; and by John Rivington (in London), 1759. xxxiii, 240 p. 21 cm. 4 sh.[2]

Cited: Bitting, p. 477; Oxford, p. 89

Copies: *BI*: LBL*[3]; LWML; LeU(B)
      NA: KMK; MCR; MiD

1. The author described himself as 'William Verral, Master of the White-Hart Inn in Lewes, Sussex'.
2. *Scots Mag.*, vol. 21 (Oct. 1759), p. 559, and *Gents.Mag.*, vol. 29 (Nov. 1759), p. 541, both confirm that the price was 4 sh.
3. The British Library holds two copies of this work. The first (press-mark 1037.g.21) is inscribed: 'Elizabeth Chapman Her Cookery Book 1760.' The second (press-mark c.28.f.13) contains copious MS notes by Thomas Gray, the poet. The whole work, with a new title, has been reprinted; see William Verral, *The Cook's Paradise* (London, 1948), with an introduction by R. L. Mégroz, and with Thomas Gray's cookery notes in holograph. Little is said about M. de St. Clouet, except that he had also been cook to 'Marshal Richelieu'.

W

W., J. [Philo-Chym. & Med.]
    see BEAUTIES treasury.

WARD, MARIA (*fl.* 1766?)

The complete cook-maid, or housewife's assistant: containing plain and easy instructions for preparing and dressing every branch of cookery, according to the most genteel, yet least expensive practice; . . . The whole adapted to the meanest capacity, and intended to make young persons perfect in the whole art of cookery.[1] London: printed for the authoress, [*c.*1766]. 127 p. frontis. [——]

Cited: —

Copies: *BI*: —
      NA: —

1. For the only known reference to this work see Crahan, p. 74, who owns a copy which he believes is a unique example. The preface is dated 'November 7, 1766'.

Antiquitates Culinariæ;

or

CURIOUS TRACTS

relating to the Culinary affairs

of the

OLD ENGLISH,

With a preliminary discourse, Notes, and Illustrations,

By

The Reverend Richard Warner,

OF SWAY,

near Lymington, Hants.

Πολλῷ τοί πλέονασ λιμοῦ κόροσ ὤλεσεν ανδρασ.

Non in Caro nidore voluptas
*Summa, **sed** in tæipso est; tu pulmentaria quære*
Sudando.

LONDON,

Printed for R. Blamire, Strand.

1791.

The Reverend William Warner's book represented one of the first signs of scholarship being applied to the history of early English cookery, a development which occurred in the last three decades of the eighteenth century. The typography of his title-page is particularly complex and pleasing.

WARNER, RICHARD (1763–1857)

Antiquitates culinariæ; or, curious tracts relating to the culinary affairs of the Old English, with a preliminary discourse, notes, and illustrations.[1] London: printed for R. Blamire, 1791. 137 p. frontis. pls. 31 cm.

Cited: Bitting, p. 485; Oxford, p. 120

Copies: *BI*: ENLS; LBL;[2] OBL*
    NA: KMK; MiD; NYPL

1. The main content of the book is a printed version of The forme of cury, on which see the entry under PEGGE, Samuel; but there is other interesting and early material included. The two coloured plates may be the earliest in English books on cookery. One of them, the 'Peacock Feast', had to be withdrawn after publication, as it infringed copyright. At the time he wrote this work, the Revd. Richard Warner was the Rector of Sway, near Lymington, in Hampshire. For his life see *DNB*, vol. 20 (1909), pp. 856–9.
2. The British Library copy has been annotated (probably by the author).

WATKINS, GEORGE (*fl.* 1760–1773)

The compleat brewer; or, the art and mystery of brewing, etc. London: for J. Cooke, 1760. xvi, 239 p. 17 cm. 3 sh.

Cited: —

Copies: *BI*: —
    NA: ICJ; NYPL*; PPL

—another ed. The compleat English Brewer. London: printed for J. Cooke, 1767. CUL; LBL; OBL: ICJ; NYPL

—another ed. London: printed for J. Cooke, 1773. LBL: ICJ; NYPL

WAY

The way to health and long life:[1] or, a discourse of temperance shewing how every man may know his own constitution and complection [*sic*]. As also discovering the nature, method, and manner of preparing all foods used in this nation . . . likewise that every man or woman may be their own doctor . . . [and that] temperence is the best physick. London: printed for G. Conyers, 1726. 72 p. 15 cm.

Cited: —

Copies: *BI*: LeU(B)*
    NA: DNLM; KU

—another ed. London: printed by and sold by Andrew Sowle, 1726. LWS; LeU(B): —

1. Simon, pp. 150–1, says that this work is sometimes wrongly attributed to Thomas Tryon, but it is more than possible that this is a later edition of one of his works, *The Way to Health, Long Life and Happiness*, published 1683, 1691, and 1697 (see Oxford, p. 43, who gives these details only); and the publisher of this work, G. Conyers, is the same person who published two previously cited books; see under earlier entries: TRYON, Thomas, The good house-wife; and idem, The way to get wealth. Furthermore, the themes of this work above are temperance and vegetarianism, which were the favourite topics (almost obsessions) of Thomas Tryon.

WHEATLAND, Thomas (*fl.* 1731)
A manual for servants.[1] [——]: printed for [——], 1731. [——] [——]
Cited: —
Copies: *BI*: —
      NA: —

1. The only known reference to this work is given in *Gents.Mag.*, vol. 1 (Nov. 1731), p. 502.

WHOLE

The whole duty of a woman: or a guide to the female sex, from the age of sixteen
to sixty, &c. Being directions, how women of all qualities and conditions, ought
to behave themselves in the various circumstances of this life, for their
obtaining not only present, but future happiness. I. Directions how to obtain
the divine and moral vertues [*sic*] of piety, meekness, modesty, chastity,
humility, compassion, temperence, and affability, with their advantages, and
how to avoid the opposite vices. II. The duty of virgins, directing them what
they ought to do, and what to avoid for gaining all the accomplishments
required in that state. With the whole art of love. . . . Also choice receipts in
physick, and chirurgery. With the whole art of cookery, preserving, candying,
beautifying, &c.[1] [by a lady]. 3rd edition. London: printed for J. Guillim, 1701.
184 p. 17 cm.
Cited: Oxford, pp. 46–7.
Copies: *BI*: LBL*
      NA: DCLC; MnU

—4th ed. London: printed for [——], 1707. LBL: —
—5th ed. London: printed for J. Gwillim, 1712. LBL: NNC
—8th ed. London: printed for A. Bettesworth and C. Hitch, 1735. —: DCLC
—6th ed. London: printed for J. Gwillim, 1718. —: CLU-C

1. Although this work has the same main title and some similar sub-titles to the next
entry, it is an entirely different work. Both works have preliminary chapters on moral
conduct, but this work does not devote as much space to cookery as the next book.

WHOLE

The whole duty of a woman:[1] or, an infallible guide to the fair sex; containing
rules, directions, and observations, for their conduct and behaviour through all
ages and circumstances of life, as virgins, wives, or widows. With directions,
how to obtain all useful and fashionable accomplishments suitable to the sex. In
which are comprised all parts of good housewifery, particularly rules and
receipts in every kind of cookery. . . . Also rules and receipts for making all the
choicest cordials for the closet; brewing beers, ales, &c. Making all sorts of
English wines, cyder, mum, mead, metheglin,[2] vinegar, verjuice,[3] catchup, &c.
With some fine perfumes, pomatums, cosmeticks and other beautifiers. [by
a lady]. London: printed for T. Read, 1737. iv, 692 p. pls. 19 cm.
Cited: Oxford, pp. 69–70

Copies: *BI*: LBL*; LeU(B)
    NA: NPV; NYPL

—2nd ed. [Title-page only changed. The lady's companion.] London: printed for T. Read, 1740. LBL: KMK; NYPL; PPL

—4th ed. with additions. London: printed for T. Read, 1743. ANLW; LBL: —

—5th ed. London: printed for T. Read, and R. Baldwin, 1751. [In 2 volumes.] LWML; LeU(B): MOSV; MiD

—6th ed. with additions. London: printed for J. Hodges, and R. Baldwin, 1753. [2 sh.][4] LeU(B): DCLC; MB

1. This work is not only different from the previous entry, but also quite different from yet another book with the same main title by William Kenrick, which was published in America as a purely devotional work, and went into several editions.
2. 'Metheglin' is spiced mead.
3. 'Verjuice' is a tart liquor made from crab-apples or sour grapes, and is used in cooking.
4. *Scots Mag.*, vol. 15 (Feb. 1753), p. 104, confirms that the price was 2 sh. for the 6th ed.

WHOLE ART OF CONFECTIONARY

see PRICE, Elizabeth, The new, universal, and complete confectioner [under pseudonym 'GLASSE, Elizabeth'].

WILKINSON, [——] [Mrs] (*fl.* 1757)

The compleat servant maid. etc.[1] [London]: printed for J. Cooke, 1757. [——] [——] 1 sh.[2]

Cited: —

Copies: *BI*: —
    NA: —

1. For the last known reference to this work; see *Sotheby Cat.* (4 Mar. 1968), p. 19. Apart from one small spelling difference ['compleat' instead of 'complete'], this work has the same main title, the same publisher, and the same price as a previously cited book; see under earlier entry: BARKER, Anne, The complete servant maid; and the former could be another edition of the latter.
2. *Scots Mag.*, vol. 19 (Nov. 1757), p. 616, confirms that the price was 1 sh.

WILLIAMS, T. (*fl.* 1797)

The accomplished housekeeper, and universal cook, containing all the various branches of cookery; directions for roasting, boiling and made dishes, also for frying, broiling, stewing, mincing, and hashing. . . . With a catalogue of the various articles in season every month in the year.[1] London: printed for J. Scatcherd, 1797. xvi, 274 p. pls. 19 cm. 3 sh.

Cited: Bitting, pp. 498–9; Oxford, pp. 123–4

Copies: *BI*: LBL; LeU(B)*
    NA: DCLC; NYPL

1. The book was written 'By T. Williams, and the Principal Cooks at the London and Crown and Anchor Taverns'. The unnamed 'Principal Cooks' were the authors of a previously cited work; see under earlier entry: COLLINGWOOD, Francis, and WOOLLAMS, John, The universal cook, and city and country housekeeper; of which book the above work is certainly an abridgement. Collingwood and Woollams were described on the title-page of their unabridged book as 'Principal Cooks at the Crown and Anchor Tavern in the Strand, late from the London Tavern', when it was published in 1792.

WILLICH, ANTHONY FLORIAN MADINGER (*fl.* 1799–1802)

Lectures on diet and regimen:[1] being a systematic enquiry into the most rational means of preserving health and prolonging life. etc.[2] London: printed for T. N. Longman, 1799. xxiv, 643 p. 21 cm.

Cited: —

Copies: *BI*: ERCP*; LBL
          NA: CaBVaUW; DNLM; PPC

—2nd ed. enlarged. London: printed for T. N. Longman, and O. Rees, 1799.
    LBL: CaBVaUW; DNLM; PU

—3rd ed. corrected. London: printed by A. Strahan for T. N. Longman, 1800.
    LBL: DNLM; MoU; NjP

—another [American] ed. Boston: printed by Manning and Loring, for J. Nancrede, 1800.[3] —: DCLC; MiU; NIC

1. Chapter V (pp. 265–393) is devoted to food and drink.
2. The author also wrote *The Domestic Encyclopedia* (London, 1802).
3. A further edition appeared in the 19th century.

WILMER, BRADFORD (*fl.* 1781)

Observations on the poisonous vegetables which are either indigenous in Great-Britain, or cultivated for ornament. London: printed for T. Longman, 1781. xv, 103 p. 20 cm.

Cited: —

Copies: *BI*: LBL*; LRSM; LWML
          NA: DNLM; KU; WU-M

WILSON, MARIA

see GLASSE, Hannah, The compleat confectioner.

WILSON, MARY (*fl.* 1770?)

The ladies complete cookery. etc. London: printed for the authoress, and sold by J. Roson, [*c.*1770].[1] 188 p. 17 cm.

Cited: —

Copies: *BI*: CUL
          NA: NYPL

1. Stark, p. 12, gives no approximate date of publication for the NYPL copy, but the CUL shelf-catalogue (press-mark S446.d.77.1) states 'ca. 1770'.

WIMPEY, JOSEPH (1739-1808)

An essay on the present high price of provisions . . . particularly corn, butcher's meat, cheese and butter. etc.[1] London: printed for T. Davies, 1772. 68 p. 21 cm. 1 sh. 6 d.[2]

Cited: —

Copies: *BI*: ENLS*; LBL
       NA: CtY; PU

1. This work is in a similar vein to a previously cited book; see under earlier entry: ESSAY, An essay on tea, sugar, . . .; which was published in 1777.
2. *Scots Mag.*, vol. 34 (Aug. 1772), p. 436, confirms that the price was 1 sh. 6 d.

WINTHORP, JOHN

see ENUMERATION of the principal vegetables.

WOLLEY (or WOOLLEY or WOOLEY), HANNAH

see ACCOMPLISH'D lady's delight in preserving.

WOOLLAMS, JOHN

see COLLINGWOOD, Francis.
see also WILLIAMS, T.

WORLIDGE, JOHN (*fl.* 1669-1698)

Dictionarium rusticum & urbanicum: or, a dictionary of all sorts of country affairs, handicrafts, trading and merchandizing. etc.[1] [Anon.].[2] London: printed for J. Nicholson, 1704. [843 p.] pls. 20 cm.

Cited: Oxford, pp. 54-5

Copies: *BI*: LBL; LeU(B)*
       NA: NYPL

—another ed. London: printed for A. & J. Churchill, and John Taylor, 1704. ENLS[3]; LBL; LWML: MB

—2nd ed. revised, corrected and improved. [title-page only changed. Dictionarium rusticum, urbanicum & botanicum]. London: printed for J. Nicholson, W. Taylor, and W. Churchill, 1717. ERCP; LBL; LeU(B): DCLC

—3rd ed. revised, corrected and improved. London: printed for James and John Knapton, 1726. [In 2 volumes.][4] CUL; ENLS; LBL: —

—4th ed. revised. London: printed for L. Hawes, W. Clarke and R. Collins, 1765. —: MB

1. This work includes receipts for 'common drinks and eatables', and has a section on country housewifery.
2. Although Oxford (p. 55, note) says the authorship of this work was at one time attributed to Nathan Bailey (see earlier entry: BAILEY, Nathan, Dictionarium domesticum), it has more recently, with some certainty, been ascribed to John Worlidge; see Samuel Halkett and

John Laing (edd.), *Dictionary of Anonymous and Pseudonymous English Literature*, vol. 2 (Edinburgh, 1926), p. 60. Writing under his initials only, J[ohn] W[orlidge] first came to the public's notice with Vinetum Britannicum: or, a treatise of cider, and such other wines and drinks that are extracted from all manner of fruits growing in this kingdom. [By J. W., Gent., London: printed by J. C. for Tho. Dring and Tho. Burrel, 1676]. This last work has occasionally been confused with a previously cited book; see under earlier entry: SEDGWICK, James, Vinum Britannicum.

2. The ENLS copy of this edition contains the bookplate of 'Mr. Ambrose Holbech, of Mollington in the County of Warwick, 1702', and it is inscribed 'A. Holbech'. As the edition was published in 1704, the bookplate must be a part of an order given two years earlier. It is an example of how bookplates (unlike dated inscriptions) are often misleading as evidence, especially when attempting to give an approximate year of publication to an undated work.

4. It would appear that although the 1st ed. was in two parts, *but* bound as one volume, there are examples of the parts being bound and sold separately; see Stark, p. 12. The 3rd ed. was intended for sale as two volumes.

WRIGHT, JOHN (*fl.* 1798)

An essay on wines, and especially on port wine.[1] London: printed for J. Barker, 1795. [——] [——]

Cited: —

Copies: *BI*: —
   NA: —

1. The only known reference to this work is Simon, p. 153.

Y

YOUNG

The young lady's companion in cookery, and pastry, preserving, pickling, candying, &c. Containing the newest and best receipts for making all sorts of broths, gravies, soups, ragoo's [*sic*], hashes, &c. Dressing several sorts of meats, collering, potting, and making force-meats, &c. Also making of cakes, creams, jellies, ... Likewise preserving and candying angelico, apples, cherries, ... And the best method of pickling melons, cucumbers, barberries, mushrooms, purflame[1] [*sic*], &c. [by a gentlewoman].[2] London: printed for A. Bettesworth and C. Hitch, 1734. 204 p. 17 cm. 2 sh.[3]

Cited: Bitting, pp. 619–20; Oxford, pp. 64–5

Copies: *BI*: —
   NA: DCLC; KMK; PBL

1. This is a printer's error for 'purslaine', a salad herb which was used as a vegetable or pickled as a condiment.
2. The author fully described herself as 'a gentlewoman who formerly kept a boarding school'.
3. *Gents.Mag.*, vol. 4 (May 1734), p. 280, confirms that the price was 2 sh.

YOUNG

The young wifes guide.[1] [——]: printed for [——], 1764. [——] [——] 1 sh. 6 d.

Cited: —

Copies: *BI*: —
       NA: —

1. The only known reference to this work is given in *Lond.Mag.* (Mar. 1764), p. 168. As the present compiler has not been able to locate a copy of this work, its suitability for inclusion has been judged by the title alone.

FACSIMILES, REPRINTS AND TRANSLATIONS OF WORKS INCLUDED IN THIS CATALOGUE

APICIUS

The Roman cookery book a critical translation of the Art of cooking by Apicius by Barbara Flower and Elisabeth Rosenbaum, Harrap, London, 1958. 240 pages.

BRADLEY, RICHARD

The country housewife and lady's director in the management of a house. 6th edition with additions [being Parts 1 and 2 in one volume]. London: printed for D. Browne, 1736. Reprinted with the addition of an extensive introduction by Caroline Davidson, and a glossary. Prospect Books, London, 1980. 496 pages.

BUC'HOZ, PIERRE JOSEPH

The toilet of Flora; or, a collection of the most simple and approved methods of preparing baths, essences, pomatums . . . and sweet-scented waters. etc. a new edition, improved. London: printed for J. Murray and W. Nicoll, 1779. Reprinted by the Herb Lovers Book Club, Milford, Connecticut, 1939. 151 pages.

CARTER, SUSANNAH

The frugal housewife or complete woman cook. Another edition. London: printed for F. Newbery; and Boston: reprinted and sold by Edes and Gill [c.1772]. Reprinted with an introduction and illustrations by Jean McKibbon, Dolphin Books, New York, 1976. 134 pages.

COOK, ANN

Professed cookery . . . together with a plan of housekeeping. 3rd ed. Newcastle: printed for the author, 1760. Reprinted as Ann Cook and friend. An edition of 'A plan of housekeeping' taken from the third edition of 1760 of Professed cookery, together with receipts selected from the same work. With an introduction and notes by Regula Burnet, Oxford University Press, London, 1936. xxxv, 161 pages.

EVELYN, JOHN

Acetaria. A discourse of sallets. 1st edition. London: printed for B. Tooke 1699. Reprinted by the Women's Auxiliary Brooklyn Botanic Gardens, Brooklyn, 1937. 20, 148 pages. 1000 copies reprinted.

FARMER

The farmer's wife; or the complete country housewife . . . to which is added the art of breeding and managing song birds. etc. London: printed for Alex. Hogg, *c.*1780. Reprinted by the Longship Press, Nantucket, Massachusetts, 1976. 136 pages.

GLASSE, Hannah

The art of cookery, made plain and easy. A new edition. London: printed for T. Longman, 1796. Reprinted with a new introduction by Fanny Cradock. S. R. publishers, Wakefield and Shoe String Press, U.S.A. 1971. viii, 419 pages.

GLASSE, Hannah

The servant's directory, or house-keeper's companion. 4th edition, improved. Dublin: printed by James Potts, 1762. Reprinted by Huntington Laboratories, Huntington, Indiana, 1971. 64 pages.

RAFFALD, Elizabeth

The experienced English housekeeper, for the use and ease of ladies, housekeepers, cooks. 8th edition. London: printed for R. Baldwin, 1782. Reprinted by E. and W. Books (Publishers) Ltd. 1970 and Redwood Press for Paul Minet reprints. 1972. iii, 384 pages.

NOTT, John

The cook's and confectioner's dictionary: or, the accomplish'd housewife's companion. Containing . . . the choicest receipts in all the several branches of cookery . . . all manner of pastry-works . . . the way of making all English potable liquors . . . directions for ordering an entertainment, or bills of fare for all seasons of the year. etc. 3rd ed. with additions. London: printed by H. P. for Charles Rivington, 1726. Reprinted by Lawrence Rivington (a descendant of Charles Rivington), London, 1980. No pagination but about 400 pages.

SIMMONS, Amelia

American cookery, or, the art of dressing viands, fish, poultry and vegetables, and the best modes of making pastes, puffs, pies, tarts, puddings, custards and preserves and all kinds of cakes. Hartford: printed by Hudson and Goodwin for the author, 1796. Reprinted for the Prospect Press, 1937. 69 pages. 185 copies printed.

—another issue. Oxford University Press, New York. 1958.

—another issue. Michigan. 1965.

SMITH, Eliza

The compleat housewife: or, accomplish'd gentlewoman's companion. 15th edition. London: printed for R. Ware, S. Birt and T. Longman, 1753. Reprinted with a foreword by Lord Montagu of Beaulieu, and the addition of a glossary compiled by C. H. Hudson, Literary Services and Production Ltd., London, 1968. ix, 396 pages.

TRUSLER, John

The honours of the table. London: printed for the author, at the Literary Press, 1788. Reprinted as The art of carving with biographical notes by S.M. [Stanley Morison] and an appreciation by S.C.R. [Sydney Castle Roberts], Cambridge University Press, 1931. xi, 75 pages. 100 copies.

—a reissue Cambridge University Press, 1932.

VERRAL, William

The cook's paradise. Being William Verral's complete system of cookery. London: printed by the author and sold by him 1759. Reprinted with Thomas Gray's cookery notes in holograph. With an introduction and appendices by R. L. Megroz, Sylvan Press, London, 1948. 139 pages.

WARNER, Richard

Antiquitates culinariae; or, curious tracts relating to the culinary affairs of the old English, with a preliminary discourse, notes and illustrations. London: printed for R. Blamire, 1791. Reprinted by Prospect Books, London, 1981. 204 pages, coloured pls.

SELECT BIBLIOGRAPHY OF
WORKS CONSULTED

All the sources consulted were either printed or typed, and they are divided into two main groups. The first, PRIMARY SOURCES, are subdivided into four sections: (A) Newspapers and Periodicals; (B) Works written in the eighteenth century; (C) Works of Reference; and (D) Select Typescripts. The second, SECONDARY SOURCES, are subdivided into three sections: (A) Books; (B) Articles; and (C) Theses.

1. PRIMARY SOURCES

A. *Newspapers and Periodicals*

The dates shown against works without an asterisk indicate the years within which research-sampling was carried out. The dates shown against works with an asterisk indicate the full duration of the magazine's existence, within one series.

Caledonian Mercury, 1736–1800
Connecticut Journal, 1796
Edinburgh Advertiser, 1764–1800
Edinburgh Evening Courant, 1719–1800
Gentleman's Magazine,* Series 1, 103 vols., London, 1731–1833
Newcastle Journal, 1753
Public Advertiser, 1734–76
Scots Magazine,* Series 1, 79 vols., Edinburgh, 1739–1817

B. *Works written in the eighteenth century*

This section includes eighteenth-century manuscripts which have been edited and published for the first time in the twentieth century; reprints of eighteenth-century works; and books published in the eighteenth century which have been referred to in 'Notes' to main entries.

Armstrong, John, *Miscellanies*, 2 vols., London, 1770.

Baillie, Lady Grisell, *The Household Book of Lady Grisell Baillie, 1692–1733*, ed. by Robert Scott Moncrieff, Scottish History Society Publications, Series 2, vol. 1, Edinburgh, 1911.

Blencowe, Ann, *The Receipt Book of Mrs. Ann Blencowe, A.D. 1694*, with an intro. by George Saintsbury, London, 1925.

Essex, John, *The Young Ladies Conduct: Or, Rules for Education*, London, 1722.

Gaine, Hugh, *Catalogue of Books, Lately Imported*, New York, 1792.

—— *The Journals of Hugh Gaine*, ed. by Paul Leicester Ford, 3 vols., New York, 1902.

Garnett, Thomas, *Observations on a Tour Through the Highlands and Part of the Western Isles of Scotland*, London, 1800.

Lockhart, Martha, Lady Castlehill, *Lady Castlehill's Receipt Book*, [from a collection made in 1712], ed. by Hamish Whyte, Glasgow, 1976.

Macdonald, John, *Travels: 1745–1779; The Memoirs of an Eighteenth Century Footman*, with an intro. by John Beresford, London, 1927.

Newington, Thomas, *A Butler's Recipe Book, 1719*, ed. by Philip James, Cambridge, 1935.

Orlebar, Diana (*née* Astry), *Diana Astry's Recipe Book, c. 1700*, ed. by Bette Stitt, Bedfordshire Hist. Rec. Soc. pubn., No. 37, Streatley, 1957.

Raper, Elizabeth, *The Receipt Book of Elizabeth Raper, and a Portion of her Cipher Journal, 1756–1770*, London, 1924.

Robertson, Hannah, *The Life of Mrs. Robertson*, Edinburgh, 1792.

Simmons, Amelia, *American Cookery* [Facsimile edition], Oxford, 1958.

Smith, E[liza], *The Compleat Housewife: Or, Accomplish'd Gentlewoman's Companion* (15th ed., 1753) [Facsimile edition], with a foreword by Lord Montagu of Beaulieu, London, 1968.

Verral, William, *The Cook's Paradise* [Being William Verral's *Complete System of Cookery*, published in 1759. With Thomas Gray's Cookery Notes in Holograph], with an intro. by Rodolphe Louis Mégroz (and appendices), London, 1948.

C. *Works of Reference*

This section includes biographical dictionaries, catalogues, lists of books displayed at exhibitions, directories, and, above all, bibliographies, particularly those covering household and cookery books.

Abigail Books [Specialists in cookery books], of 31 Sackville Street, London, W1X 1DB. Book catalogues. Various dates (including those issued from the former address at Buckham Hill, Uckfield, Sussex).

American Antiquarian Society, Worcester, Massachusetts, *Dictionary-Catalog of American Books*, Boston, 1971.

—— *A Society's Chief Joys* [An exhibition from the collections of the American Antiquarian Society for the Grolier Club of New York], Worcester, Mass., 1969.

Amerine, Maynard (compiler), *A List of Bibliographies and a Selected List of Publications that Contain Bibliographies on Grapes, Wines and Related Subjects*, Berkeley, California, 1971.

Aresty, Esther B., *The Delectable Past* [Bibliographical Section], London, 1965.

Ash, Lee (compiler), *Subject Collections* [A guide to special book collections and subject emphases as reported by university, college, public, and special libraries and museums in the United States and Canada]. 4th edition. New York and London, 1974.

ASLIB Directory, ed. by Brian J. Wilson, *Information Sources in Science, Technology and Commerce*, vol. 1, London, 1968; vol. 2, London, 1970.

Axford, Lavonne B., *English Language Cookbooks*, 1600-1973, New York, 1976.

Baker, E. Allan, *Bibliography of Food*, London, 1958.

Beeleigh Abbey Books [The Antiquarian Book Dept. of W. & G. Foyle Limited], of Beeleigh Abbey, Maldon, Essex. Catalogue BA/20—*Agriculture and Botany, Medicine, Science and Technology*, [1975].

Besterman, Theodore, *A World Bibliography of Bibliographies, and of Bibliographical Catalogues, Calendars, Abstracts, Digests, Indexes, and the Like*, 4 vols., Lausanne, 1965-6.

Bethell, Richard Morland Tollemache, Lord Westbury, *A Handlist of Italian Cookery Books*, Firenze [Florence], 1963.

Birrell & Garnett Limited, of 30 Garrard Street, London, W.1. Catalogue No. 27, *Domestic Books of All Ages*, [c.1931].

—— Catalogue No. 37, *A Catalogue of Cookery Books from the Collection of J. E. Hodgkin, Esq., Dr. A. W. Oxford and other sources*, [c.1934].

Bitting, Katherine Golden, *Gastronomic Bibliography*, San Francisco, 1939; reprinted Ann Arbor, 1971.

Book Auction Records, vols. 1-72, London, 1902-75. [A priced and annotated annual record of international book auctions.]

Boston Public Library, *A List of Books on Domestic Science in the Public Library of the City of Boston*, Boston, Massachusetts, 1911.

British Museum General Catalogue of Printed Books, photolithographic edition to 1955, 263 vols., London, 1960-6.

Burke's Peerage and Baronetage, 105th edition, London, 1970.

Cahoon, Herbert, *Labels to Accompany the Grolier Club Exhibition Held at the Pierpont Morgan Library*, New York, 1960.

Carlson, Victoria, *A Bibliography for Cookery Investigation*, New York, 1927.

Christie's [Messrs. Christie, Manson & Woods], Auctioneers, London. Book Catalogues. Various dates.

Clarke, Janet, Antiquarian Cookery Bookseller, late of Manor House, Hunterston, Nantwich, Cheshire. Her series of cookery book Catalogues, Nos. 1–15. Various dates (including those issued from the new address at 3 Woodside Cottages, Freshford, Bath, Avon).

Cochrane, John George, *Catalogue of the Library at Abbotsford*, Edinburgh, 1836.

Cornell University, School of Hotel Administration Library, *A List of Selected Material from the Vehling Collection*, Ithaca, N.Y., n.d.

Crahan, Marcus E., *One Hundred Sixteen Uncommon Books on Food and Drink*, Berkeley, California, 1975. [Published by the Friends of the Bancroft Library.]

Dictionary of National Biography, ed. by Sir Leslie Stephen and Sir Sidney Lee, 21 vols., London, 1908–9.

Doeltz, Clara L., *Complete Catalog of the Clara L. Doeltz Collection of Rare and Modern Cookery Books*, Detroit, [c.1923].

Drexel, Theodor, *Catalog der Kochbücher-Sammlung von Theodor Drexel*, Frankfurt, 1885–91 [6 catalogues issued: 1885, 1887, 1888, and 1891].

Edinburgh: Edinburgh Bibliographical Society, *General Index to Publications I–XV*, compiled by Marryat Ross Dobie, Edinburgh, 1936.

Edinburgh: Faculty of Advocates, *A Catalogue of the Library of the Faculty of Advocates*, 3 vols., Edinburgh, 1742.

—— *A Catalogue of the Printed Books in the Library of the Faculty of Advocates*, 7 vols., Edinburgh, 1863–79.

Edinburgh: National Library of Scotland, *Catalogue of the Lauriston Castle Chapbooks*, Boston, 1964.

Edinburgh: Royal College of Physicians, *Catalogue of the Library of the Royal College of Physicians of Edinburgh*, compiled by J. Matheson Shaw, 2 vols., Edinburgh, 1898.

Edinburgh: Signet Library, *Catalogue of an Exhibition of 18th Century Scottish Books at the Signet Library, Edinburgh*, Scottish Committee of the Festival of Britain, Edinburgh, 1951.

Edinburgh: University of Edinburgh Library, *Catalogue of the Printed Books in the Library of the University of Edinburgh*, 3 vols., Edinburgh, 1918–23.

English Bibliographical Sources, Series 1: Periodical Lists of New Publications, ed. by David Fairweather Foxon; as follows:
    No. 1—*The Monthly Catalogue: 1714–17*, 1964.
    No. 2—*The Monthly Catalogue: 1723–30*, 2 vols., 1964.
    No. 3—*A Register of Books: 1728–32*, 1964.
    No. 4—*Bibliotheca Annua: 1699–1703*, 2 vols., 1964.
    No. 5—*The Annual Catalogue: 1736–37*, 1965.
    No. 6—*The Gentleman's Magazine: 1731–51*, 1966.
    No. 7—*The London Magazine: 1732–66*, 1966.
    No. 8—*The British Magazine: 1746–50*, 1965.

Evans, Charles, *American Bibliography: A Chronological Dictionary of all Books, Pamphlets and Periodical Publications Printed in the United States of America, 1639–1800*, 14 vols., Chicago, 1903–34.

Feret, Barbara L., *Gastronomical and Culinary Literature*, Metuchen, N.J., and London, 1979.

Foxon, David Fairweather, *Thoughts on the History and Future of Bibliographical Description*, Los Angeles and Berkeley, 1970.

Halkett, Samuel, and Laing, John, *Dictionary of Anonymous and Pseudonymous English Literature*, 9 vols., Edinburgh, 1926–62.

Hawkes, Arthur John, *Lancashire Printed Books*, Wigan, 1925. [A bibliography of all the books printed in Lancashire down to the year 1800.]

Hazlitt, William Carew, *Old Cookery Books and Ancient Cuisine*, London, 1886; 2nd edn., London, 1902.

Heltzel, Virgil Barney, *A Check List of Courtesy Books in the Newberry Library*, Chicago, 1942.

Henrey, Blanche, *British Botanical and Horticultural Literature before 1800*, 3 vols., Oxford, 1975.

Hofstra Library Associates, Hofstra University Library, New York, *Cook Books: A Special Collection. Drawn in its Entirety from the Collection of Lucille Fillin*, Hempstead, N.Y., 1976. [Prepared for an exhibition in the Filderman Gallery, Hofstra University, held from 22 June to 3 September 1976.]

Kitchiner, *Apicius Redivivus: The Cook's Oracle*, 4th edition, London, 1822. [Full name of author should read: Kitchiner, William.].

Lewer, Henry William (editor), *A Book of Simples*, London, 1908.

Lillywhite, Bryant, *London Coffee Houses: A Reference Book of the Coffee Houses of the Seventeenth, Eighteenth and Nineteenth Centuries*, London, 1963.

Lincoln, Waldo, *American Cookery Books, 1742-1860*, Worcester, Mass., 1929; reprinted 1954.

London: Library Committee of the Corporation of London, *The Guildhall Miscellany*, No. 9, London, 1958.

London: The London Library, *Catalogue of the London Library*, 5 vols., London, 1913-53.

—— *Subject Index of the London Library*, 4 vols., London, 1909-55.

London: The Patent Office Library, *Subject List of Works on Domestic Economy*, London, 1902.

Lowenstein, Eleanor, *Bibliography of American Cookery Books, 1742-1860*, Worcester, Mass., 1972 [based on Waldo Lincoln's *American Cookery Books, 1742-1860*—see earlier].

Lyle, John, Bookseller [Lyle and Davidson Limited], of Harpford, Sidmouth, Devon. Book Catalogue No. 3 [1976].

Maggs Bros. Limited, Antiquarian Booksellers, of 34/35 Conduit St., London, W.1. Catalogue No. 645, *Food and Drink through the Ages: 2500 B.C. to 1937 A.D.*, 1937.

Manchester Libraries Committee, *The Manchester Press before 1801*, Manchester, 1931.

Murphy, Claudia Quigley, *The Fine Collection of Cookery Books formed by Mrs. Claudia Quigley Murphy*, issued as Catalogue No. 2063 by The Anderson Galleries, Inc., of 489 Park Avenue, New York City, 1926.

Murrey, Thomas J., *The Murrey Collection of Cookery Books*, New York, [*c*.1895].

National Union Catalog Pre-1956 Imprints, 684 vols., London and Chicago, 1968–

New York Academy of Medicine, *Subject Catalog of Books held by the New York Academy of Medicine*, Boston, 1969 [and Supplement No. 1, Boston, 1974].

Noling, A. W., *Beverage Literature: A Bibliography*, Metuchen, New Jersey, 1971.

Nouvelle Biographie Générale, 44 tomes, Paris, 1855-66.

Osler, Sir William, *Bibliotheca Osleriana: A Catalogue of Books Illustrating the History of Medicine and Science, Collected, Enlarged and Annotated*, 2 vols., Oxford, 1929.

Oxford, Arnold Whitaker, *English Cookery Books to the Year 1850*, London, 1913; reprinted London, 1977.

—— *Notes from a Collector's Catalogue; with a Bibliography of English Cookery Books*, London, 1909.

Parke-Bernet Galleries Inc., of New York City. Book Catalogue, *Books on Cookery, XV-XX Centuries, Collected by Arnold Shircliffe*, New York, 1954.

Peddie, Robert Alexander, *Subject Index of Books Published before 1800, A-Z*, London, 1933.

Pennell, Elizabeth Robins, *My Cookery Books*, New York and Boston, 1903.

Petits Propos Culinaires, vols. 1-5, London, 1979-80.

Plomer, Henry Robert, *A Dictionary of the Printers and Booksellers who were at work in England, Scotland, and Ireland from 1688 to 1725*, Oxford, 1922.

Plomer, Henry Robert, *A Dictionary of the Printers and Booksellers who were at work in England, Scotland and Ireland from 1726 to 1775*, Oxford, 1932.

Robinson, F. J. G., and Wallis, Peter John, *Book Subscription List: A Revised Guide*, Newcastle, 1975.

Rosenthal, A., Limited, Booksellers, of 5 Turl Street, Oxford [now of 9/10 Broad Street, Oxford], Catalogue No. 56, *Food and Drink*, 1959.

Rudolph, G. A., *The Kansas State University Receipt Book and Household Manual*, Kansas State University Library Bibliography Series, No. 4, Manhattan, Kansas, 1968.

Schraemli, Harry, *A Resumé of the Great Herr Schraemli Collection*, Beverly Hills, California, 1963.

Simon, André Louis, *Bibliotheca Bacchica*, London, 1927; reprinted 1972.

—— *Bibliotheca Gastronomica*, London, 1953; reprinted 1978.

—— *Bibliotheca Vinaria*, London, 1913. [A bibliography of works dealing with viticulture, wine-making, distillation, etc.]

—— *An Exhibition of Rare Printed Books Assembled and Annotated by André Simon*, National Book League, London, 1961.

Sotheby's [formerly Sotheby & Co., now Sotheby Parke-Bernet & Co.], Auctioneers, London. Book Catalogues. Various dates.

Stark, Lewis M., *The Whitney Cookery Collection*, New York, 1946.

Swinton, Cordelia W., *A Bibliography of Cookbooks and Gastronomical Treatises in the Pennsylvania State University Collection*, University Park, Pennsylvania, 1972.

Times Bookshop Cookery Books 1500–1954, London, 1954.

Vicaire, Georges, *Bibliographie gastronomique*, Paris, 1890; reprinted London, 1954 and 1978.

Vinceus, S., *An Evaluation of the Vehling Collection*, Ithaca, New York, n.d.

Watt, Robert, *Bibliotheca Britannica; or a General Index to British and Foreign Literature*, 4 vols., Edinburgh, 1824.

Weiss, Harry B., *A Catalogue of the Chapbooks in the New York Public Library*, New York, 1936.

Welford, Richard, *Early Newcastle Typography: 1639–1800*, Newcastle upon Tyne, 1907.

Wellcome Institute, 183 Euston Road, London, NW1 2BP, *Catalogue of Printed Books in the Wellcome Historical Medical Library, 1641–1850*, London, 1966–76. [Vol. 2 (A–E), Vol. 3 (F–L)—to be continued.]

Wing, Donald (compiler), *Short-Title Catalogue of Books Printed in England, Scotland, Ireland, Wales, and British America, and of English Books Printed in other Countries: 1641–1700*, 3 vols., New York, 1945–51.

D. *Select Typescripts*

Robb-Smith, Alastair Hamish Tearlach, 'Hannah Glasse. Notes on Editions and Variants' [copy held by the National Library of Scotland was catalogued on 22 January 1962, with press-mark 6.98], 3 p.

University of Bristol, Department of Agriculture and Horticulture Research Station, Long Ashton, Bristol, 'Fruit and Cider' [A list of horticultural and cider classics and works of antiquarian interest in the Library of Long Ashton Research Station], 1963, 22 p.

University of British Columbia, Woodward Biomedical Library, Vancouver, British Columbia, 'Captions from the Cookery Book Exhibition held at the Woodward Biomedical Library in July 1976', 19 p.

University of Glasgow, Special Collections Department, 'Three Glasgow Book Collectors: William Euing, 1788–1874; John Ferguson, 1837–1916; David Murray, 1842–1928. An Exhibition of Books and Manuscripts held in the Hunterian Library, University of Glasgow, November 1969', 39 p.

University of Glasgow, Special Collections Department, 'Women and Books from the Sixteenth Century to the Suffragettes. An Exhibition held in the Hunterian Library, University of Glasgow, November 1971', 24 p.

University of Leeds, Brotherton Library, 'A List of Works in the Blanche Leigh Collection of Cookery Books', [c.1964], 36 p.

—————— 'A List of Works in the Preston Collection of English Cookery Books', 20 May 1963, 16 p.

2. SECONDARY SOURCES

A. *Books*

Ainsworth-Davis, James Richard, *Cooking through the Centuries*, London, 1931.

Aitken, George Atherton, *The Life and Works of John Arbuthnot*, Oxford, 1892.

Arnold, Walter, *The Life and Death of the Sublime Society of Beef Steaks*, London, 1871.

Askwith, George Ranken, *British Taverns: Their History and Laws*, London, 1928.

Aylett, Mary, and Ordish, Olive, *First Catch your Hare: A History of the Recipe-makers*, London, 1965.

Ayrton, Elisabeth, *The Cookery of England*, London, 1974.

Bayne-Powell, Rosamond, *House-keeping in the Eighteenth Century*, London, 1956.

Bell, Vicars, *To Meet Mr. Ellis*, London, 1956.

Blakelock, Mildred P., *Old English Cookery: 1775–1931*, London, [1932].

Boswell, James, *The Life of Samuel Johnson*, ed. by Frank Brady, London, 1968.

Brillat-Savarin, Jean-Anthelme, *The Philosopher in the Kitchen*, London, 1970. [First published as *Physiologie du Goût*, Paris, 1825.]

Buckland, Anne Walbank, *Our Viands: Whence They Come and How They are Cooked*, London, 1893.

Burnet, Regula, *Ann Cook and Friend*, London, 1936.

Burton, Elizabeth, *The Pageant of Georgian England*, New York, 1967.

Clair, Colin, *Kitchen and Table*, London, 1964.

Comrie, John Dixon, *History of Scottish Medicine*, 2nd edition, 2 vols., London, 1932.

Cooper, Ambrose, *The Complete Domestic Distiller*, London, 1826.

Cooper, Charles, *The English Table in History and Literature*, London, 1929.

Doran, John, *Table Traits, with Something on Them*, 2nd edition, London, 1854.

Drummond, Sir Jack Cecil, and Wilbraham, Anne [later Lady Drummond], *The Englishman's Food: A History of Five Centuries of English Diet*, revised by Dorothy Hollingsworth, London, 1957.

Dunbar, Dunbar E., *Social Life in Former Days, Chiefly in the Province of Moray*, Edinburgh, 1865.

Dutton, Thomas, *Food and Drink Rationally Discussed*, London, 1894.

Ellwanger, George Herman, *The Pleasures of the Table: An Account of Gastronomy from Ancient Days to Present Times*, London, 1902.

Ferguson, John, *Bibliographical Notes on Histories of Inventions and Books of Secrets*, London, 1959.

Flower, Barbara, and Rosenbaum, Elisabeth, *The Roman Cookery Book, a Critical Translation of The Art of Cooking by Apicius, for Use in the Study and the Kitchen*, London, 1958; reprinted 1961; reissued 1974. [Given the short-title on cover and spine of *Apicius: The Roman Cookery Book*.]

Franklin, Benjamin, *On the Art of Eating, Together with Rules of Health and Long Life*, ed. by Gilbert Chinard for the American Philosophical Society, [Princeton], 1958.

Furnivall, Frederick James, *Early English Meals and Manners*, Early English Text Society, Original Series, No. 32, London, 1931.

Fussell, George Edwin, *The Old English Farming Books from Fitzherbert to Tull, 1523-1730*, London, 1947.

—— *More Old English Farming Books from Tull to the Board of Agriculture, 1731-1793*, London, 1950.

—— and Fussell, Kathleen Rosemary, *The English Countrywoman. A Farmhouse Social History, A.D. 1500-1900*, London, 1953.

Gray, Sarah Virginia, *A History of the Publication of Cookbooks in the United States, 1796-1896*, Chapel Hill, North Carolina, 1964.

Hackwood, Frederick William, *Good Cheer. The Romance of Food and Feasting*, London, 1911.

Hampson, Charles Phillips, *Salford through the Ages*, Manchester, 1930.

Handley, James Edmund, *Scottish Farming in the Eighteenth Century*, London, 1953.

Hartley, Dorothy, *Food in England*, London, 1954.

Haywood, Abraham, *Art of Dining; or Gastronomy and Gastronomers*, London, 1852.

Hecht, J. Jean, *The Domestic Servant Class in Eighteenth-Century England*, London, 1956.

Henderson, Alexander, *The History of Ancient and Modern Wines*, London, 1824.

Herman, Judith, and Herman, Marguerite Shalett, *The Cornucopia*, New York, 1973.

Isaac, Peter Charles Gerald, *History of Printing in the North*, Newcastle upon Tyne, 1968.

Jeaffreson, John Cordy, *A Book about the Table*, 2 vols., London, 1875.

Kitchin, Arthur H., and Passmore, Reginald, *The Scotman's Food. An Historical Introduction to Modern Food Administration*, Edinburgh, 1949.

Law, Alexander, *Education in Edinburgh in the Eighteenth Century*, London, 1965.

Library Association, *Anglo-American Cataloguing Rules* (British Text), London, 1967.

Lochhead, Marion Cleland, *The Scots Household in the Eighteenth Century*, Edinburgh, 1948.

McDowall, William, *History of Dumfries*, Edinburgh, 1867.

Maclean, James Noël Mackenzie, *Reward is Secondary*, London, 1963.

Maclean, Virginia Elizabeth, *Much Entertainment*, London and New York, 1973.

McNeill, F[rances] Marian, *The Scots Kitchen*, 2nd edition, Edinburgh, 1963.

Marshall, Dorothy, *The English Poor in the Eighteenth Century*, London, 1926; reissued 1969.

Mitchell, Sir Arthur, *List of Travels and Tours in Scotland, 1296-1900*, Edinburgh, 1902.

Nichols, John, *Literary Anecdotes of the Eighteenth Century*, ed. by Colin Clair, Fontwell, Sussex, 1967.

Norman, Barbara, *Tales of the Table*, New York, 1972.

Phillips, Frank Taverner, *A Second History of the Worshipful Company of Cooks*, London, 1966.

Plant, Marjorie, *The Domestic Life of Scotland in the Eighteenth Century*, Edinburgh, 1952.

—— *The English Book Trade. An Economic History of the Making and Sale of Books*, 2nd edition, London, 1965.

Priestley, Mary, *The Female Spectator*, London, 1929.

Roscoe, Sydney, *John Newbery and Successors: 1740-1814*, London, 1973.

Salaman, Redcliffe Nathan, *The History and Social Influence of the Potato*, Cambridge, 1949.

Soyer, Alexis, *Pantropheon, or, History of Food and its Preparation from the Earliest States of the World*, London, 1853.

Stenton, Doris May, *The English Woman in History*, London, 1957.

Straus, Ralph, *Robert Dodsley*, London, 1910.

Stuart, Marie W., *Old Edinburgh Taverns*, London, 1952.

Tannahill, Reay, *Food in History*, London, 1973.

Tweed, John, *Popular Observations on Regimen and Diet*, London [*c*.1820].

Watson, J[ohn] Steven, *The Reign of George III* [The Oxford History of England series, ed. by Sir George Clark], Oxford, 1960.

Williams, Iolo A., *Seven XVIIIth Century Bibliographies*, London, 1924.

Wilson, C. Anne, *Food and Drink in Britain from the Stone Age to recent times*, London, 1973. Reissued in a paperback edition, 1976.

B. *Articles*

Blake, John B., 'The Compleat Housewife', *Bulletin of the History of Medicine*, Vol. 49, No. 1, Spring 1975, pp. 30–42.

Bonnet, Jean-Claude, 'Le réseau culinaire dans "L'Encyclopédie"', *Annales, économies, sociétés, civilisations*, Vol. 31, No. 6, November–December 1976, pp. 891–914.

Dodds, Madeleine Hope, 'The Rival Cooks: Hannah Glasse and Ann Cook', *Archaeologia Aeliana*, Series 4, Vol. 15, pp. 43–68.

Drake, T. G. H., 'Eighteenth Century Cookery: *The Art of Cookery Made Plain and Easy, by a Lady* (Hannah Glasse)', *Journal of the American Dietetic Association*, Vol. 28, 1952, pp. 422–4.

Hecht, J. Jean, 'Continental and Colonial Servants in Eighteenth-Century England', *Smith College Studies in History*, Vol. 40, pp. 1–61, 1954.

Herbert, A. Kenney, 'The Literature of Cookery', *National Review*, Vol. 24, September 1894–February 1895, pp. 676–84.

Gourley, James Edwin, 'An Annotated List of Bibliographies of Cookery Books', *Bulletin of the New York Public Library*, Vol. 41, 1937, pp. 696–700.

Guthrie, [Douglas James?] [Dr], 'The Lady Sedley's Receipt Book', *Proceedings of the Royal Society of Medicine*, 6th ed., Part 2, 1912–13, pp. 163–70.

Law, Alexander, 'Teachers in Edinburgh in the Eighteenth Century', *Book of the Old Edinburgh Club*, Vol. 32, 1966, pp. 113–55.

Maclean, Virginia Elizabeth, 'Dr. Johnson in Scotland', *Illustrated London News*, No. 6901, Vol. 261, August 1973, pp. 49–52.

O'Connor, John, 'The Man who Invented the Kitchen Range', *Catering Times*, 19 February 1976, pp. 5–6. [A biographical sketch of Sir Benjamin Thompson (*c*.1753–1814), later Count Rumford in the Holy Roman Empire, a leading authority on large-scale cookery and, in 1789, the inventor of the closed-top kitchen range.]

Robb-Smith, Alastair Hamish Tearlach, 'Doctors at Table', *Journal of the American Medical Association*, Vol. 224, No. 1, 2 April 1973, pp. 28–34.

Stark, Lewis M., 'The Whitney Cookery Collection', *Bulletin of the New York Public Library*, Vol. [50?], February 1946, pp. 1–26. [Reprinted with corrections as a separate booklet.]

Steer, Francis W[ilson?], 'A Housewife's Affairs', *Guildhall Miscellany*, No. 9, July 1958, pp. 43–51.

Wilson, C. Anne, 'The Preston Collection', *University of Leeds Review*, Vol. 9, 1964, pp. 58–70.

Wilson, Mary Tolford, 'Amelia Simmons Fills a Need: *American Cookery*, 1796', *William and Mary Quarterly*, 3rd Series, Vol. 14, 1957, pp. 16–30.

Yost, Genevieve, 'The Compleat Housewife or Accomplish'd Gentlewoman's Companion: A Bibliographical Study', *William and Mary Quarterly*, 2nd Series, Vol. 18, 1938, pp. 418–35.

Zeldin, Theodore, 'Fin, Très Fin, Extra Fin', *New Statesman*, 17 January 1975, pp. 86–7.

C. *Theses*

Chalmers, John Putnam, 'Bodleian Deposit Survivors of the First Sixteen Years of the Copyright Act of Queen Anne, 10 April 1710–25 March 1726', University of Oxford B.Litt. thesis, 1974.

Law, Alexander, 'Education in Edinburgh in the Eighteenth Century', University of Edinburgh Ph.D. thesis, 1959.

McDougall, Warren James, 'Gavin Hamilton, John Balfour and Patrick Neill; A Study of Publishing in Edinburgh in the 18th Century', University of Edinburgh Ph.D. thesis, 1975.

Parr, Elizabeth, 'Early Leeds Printers, Publishers and Booksellers; An Example of the Provincial Book Trade in the Eighteenth Century', University of Leeds M.Phil. thesis, 1973.

Robinson, F. J. G., 'Trends in Education in Northern England during the Eighteenth Century: A Biographical Study', 3 vols., University of Newcastle Ph.D. thesis, 1972.

CHRONOLOGICAL LIST OF
SHORT TITLES

This list gives, under each year, the shortest identifiable title of every *main entry* listed in the catalogue and the *main entry heading* under which it can be found. No *further editions* of any main entry are included. Approximate dates [*c.*] have been normalized.

1701

COMPLETE	The complete caterer
WHOLE	The whole duty of a woman: or a guide to the female sex

1702

COMPLEAT	The compleat servant maid
MASSIALOT, François	The court and country cook
TRYON, Thomas	The good house-wife made a doctor
TRYON, Thomas	The way to get wealth
UNIVERSAL	The universal family book

1703

GUIDE	A guide to gentlemen . . . for brewing
HOWARD, Henry	England's newest way in all sorts of cookery
MORE, Sir Jonas	Englands interest: or the gentleman and farmers friend

1704

ACCOMPLISH'D	The accomplish'd female instructor
LÉMERY, Louis	A treatise of foods
WORLIDGE, John	Dictionarium rusticum & urbanicum

1705

APICIUS	Apicii Coelii de opsoniis et condimentis
BEAUTIES	Beauties treasury: or, the ladies vade mecum
PASTRY-COOK	The pastry-cook's vade-mecum
SALMON, William	The family-dictionary

1706

ACCOMPLISHED	The accomplished ladies rich closet
ACCOMPLISH'D	The accomplish'd lady's delight in preserving
DUNCAN, Daniel	Wholesome advice against abuse of hot liquors
EVELYN, John	Acetaria. A discourse of sallets
HOUSE-KEEPER	The house-keeper's guide

1707

GREY, Elizabeth	A true gentlewoman's delight

1708

GREY, Elizabeth	A choice manuall
KING, William	The art of cookery. A poem
KING, William	The art of cookery, in imitation of Horace's [']Art of poetry[']

1709
HALL, T.   The queen's royal cookery

1710
COMPLEAT   The compleat cook
LAMB, Patrick   Royal cookery
QUEEN   The Queen's closet opened
TUSSER, Thomas   Tusser redivivus

1711
LÉMERY, Nicolas   Curiosa arcana

1712
UNIVERSAL   The universal library

1713
None

1714
KETTILBY, Mary   A collection of above three hundred receipts

1715
BRADLEY, Richard   A short historical account of coffee

1716
None

1717
None

1718
EALES, Mary   Mrs. Mary Eales's receipts

1719
None

1720
KIDDER, Edward   E. Kidder's receipts of pastry and cookery

1721
None

1722
BROADBENT, Humphrey   Domestick coffee man
ESSAY   An essay on the nature, use and abuse of tea

1723
NOTT, John   The cook's and confectioner's dictionary
SMITH, Robert   Court cookery

1724
GRINDAL, Martin   Warm beer, a treatise
QUÉLUS, D. de   The natural history of chocolate

1725

CHOMEL, Noel	Dictionnaire oeconomique
SEDGWICK, James	A new treatise on liquors
SMITH, George	A compleat body of distilling

1726

CAREY, Henry	A learned dissertation on dumpling
WAY	The way to health and long life

1727

BRADLEY, Richard	The country housewife and lady's director
SEDGWICK, James	Vinum Britannicum
SMITH, Eliza	The compleat housewife
SWITZER, Stephen	The practical kitchen gardiner

1728

None

1729

FAMILY	The family companion for health
HOWARD, Henry	The British cook's companion
SMITH, George	The nature of fermentation explain'd

1730

CARTER, Charles	The complete practical cook
SHORT, Thomas	A dissertation upon tea

1731

ARBUTHNOT, John	An essay concerning the nature of aliments
WHEATLAND, Thomas	A manual for servants

1732

BRADLEY, Richard	The country housewife and lady's director. Part II
CARTER, Charles	The compleat city and country cook
SERVANT	The servant's plea
TWO	Two new and curious essays

1733

EALES, Mary	The compleat confectioner
FEMALE	The female glossary
HARRISON, Sarah	The house-keeper's pocket book
LA CHAPELLE, Vincent	The modern cook

1734

ELLIS, William	The London and country brewer
MIDDLETON, John	Five hundred new receipts in cookery
PRACTICAL	The practical distiller
YOUNG	The young lady's companion in cookery

1735

CAMPBELL, Duncan	A poem upon tea
GENTLEMAN	The gentleman's companion
GODFREY, Boyle	Miscellanea vere utilia

1736

ACCOMPLISH'D The accomplish'd housewife, and house-keeper's pocket-companion
BAILEY, Nathan Dictionarium domesticum
COMPLETE The complete family-piece
COUNTRY The country magazine, or, the gentleman and lady's pocket companion
McLINTOCK, [Mrs] Mrs. McLintock's receipts for cookery

1737

DUNBAR, James The industrious country-man
WHOLE The whole duty of a woman: or, an infallible guide to the fair sex

1738

None

1739

None

1740

ARNAUD, Jasper An alarm to all persons
JOHNSTON, [Mrs] Mrs. Johnston's receipts
LAIRD The laird and farmer

1741

FAMILY The family magazine: in two parts
MOXON, Elizabeth English housewifry

1742

CURIOUS A curious collection of receipts in cookery
LESSIUS, Leonardus Hygiasticon: or, a treatise of . . . health
NEW A new and complete book of cookery

1743

HAYWOOD, Eliza Fowler A present for a servant-maid

1744

ADAM Adam's luxury, and Eve's cookery
ARMSTRONG, John The art of preserving health: a poem
LAMBERT, Edward The art of confectionary

1745

ACCOMPLISH'D The accomplish'd housewife; or, the gentlewoman's companion
COCCHI, Antonio C. The Pythagorean diet, of vegetables only
MASON, Simon The good and bad effects of tea consider'd
SWIFT, Jonathan Directions to servants

1746

DOUGLASS, C. The summer's amusements
MOUFET, Thomas Health's improvement
PAULI, Simon A treatise on tobacco, tea, coffee and chocolate
SUMMER The summer's amusement[s]

1747

GLASSE, Hannah The art of cookery, made plain and easy
JOHNSTON, Eliza The accomplish'd servant-maid

1748

BEST	The best and easiest method of preserving uninterrupted health to extreme old age
OLD	The old man's guide to health
PENKETHMAN, John	A collection of several authentick accounts of the history and price of wheat

1749

BRADSHAW, Penelope	Bradshaw's valuable family jewel
BUTLER	The butler's assistant
CARTER, Charles	The London and country cook

1750

ARMSTRONG, John	The muncher's and guzler's diary
BATTAM, Anne	A collection of scarce and valuable receipts
BEST	The best and most approved method of curing white-herrings
CLIFTON, Elizabeth	The cookmaid's assistant
COLLECTION	A collection of the most approved receipts
ELLIS, William	The country housewife's family companion
FISHER, Lydia	The prudent housewife: or, compleat English cook
GRAHAM, William	The art of making wines
HEALTH	Health's preservative
HILL, John	The old man's guide to health
SHORT, Thomas	Discourses on tea, sugar, milk . . . etc.

1751

EXPLANATION	An explanation and translation of a modern bill of fare
MODERN	A modern bill of fare

1752

DODD, James Solas	An essay towards a natural history of the herring

1753

BRADSHAW, Penelope	Bradshaw's family companion
COMPLEAT	The compleat family companion
COOK, Ann	The new system of cookery
FAIRFAX, Arabella	The family's best friend: or the whole art of cookery
JOHNSON, Mary	The young woman's companion; or the servant maid's assistant
NELSON, James	An essay on the government of children
ROZEA, Jassintour	The gift of Comus; or, practical cookery
SERVANT	The servant-maid's assistant
STAFFORD, Hugh	A treatise on cyder-making

1754

BRADSHAW, Penelope	The family jewel
BRITISH	The British legacy
BRUES, John	The servant's sure guide
CELLAR	The cellar book, or the butler's assistant
COOK, Ann	Professed cookery
FAMILY	The family magazine, or accomplish'd housewife and house-keeper's pocket-companion
HILL, John	The useful family herbal
JACKSON, Sarah	Complete family cook; or young woman's best companion
JACKSON, Sarah	The director: or, young woman's best companion
JOHNSON, Mary	Madam Johnson's present

1755
CLELAND, Elizabeth   A new and easy method of cookery
COOKERY   Cookery reformed: or the lady's assistant

1756
COOK   The cook's pocket companion
HONEYWOOD, Lydia   The cook's pocket-companion
LADIES   The ladies companion; or, the housekeeper's guide
ROZEA, Jassintour   The compleat cook

1757
CHAPMAN, Thomas   The cyder-maker's instructor
COOPER, Ambrose   The complete distiller
FAMILY   The family chronicle
MASON, Simon   Practical observations in physick
POISON   Poison detected
WILKINSON, [Mrs]   The compleat servant maid

1758
JACKSON, H.   An essay on bread
MACKENZIE, James   The history of health
PHILLIPS, Sarah   The ladies handmaid
SMITH, Alice   The art of cookery: or, the compleat house-wife
THACKER, John   The art of cookery
TREATISE   A treatise on . . . the steward's table

1759
VERRAL, William   A complete system of cookery

1760
BRADLEY, Martha   The British housewife
BUTLER, Caroline   The new London and country cook
GLASSE, Hannah   The compleat confectioner
GLASSE, Hannah   The servant's directory
HOUDLSTON, Thomas   A new method of cookery
LADIES   The ladies companion
MODERN   The modern method of regulating . . . a table
PRICE, Elizabeth   The new book of cookery
PRICE, Elizabeth   The new, universal and complete confectioner

1761
COUNTRY   The country gentleman
HOFFMAN, Frederick   A treatise on the nature of aliments

1762
BARKER, Anne   The complete servant maid: or young woman's best companion
BROOKS, Catharine   The complete English cook
GELLEROY, William   The London cook, or the whole art of cookery

1763
COUNTRY   The country magazine

1764
YOUNG   The young wifes guide

1765

CARTER, Susannah   The frugal housewife, or, complete woman cook

1766

COMPLEAT   The compleat family cook
DIRECTIONS   Directions to lords and ladies
FAMILY   The family œconomist or complete cook
LOCKE, John   Observations upon . . . vines and olives
ROBERTSON, Hannah   The young ladies school of arts
WARD, Maria   The complete cook-maid, or housewife's assistant

1767

EDMONDS, W.   A new and easy way of making wines
JOHNSON, Robert W.   Some friendly cautions to the heads of families
MENON, [——]   The art of modern cookery displayed
PECKHAM, Ann   The complete English cook; or, prudent housewife
PRIMITIVE   Primitive cookery
SHACKLEFORD, Ann   The modern art of cookery improved

1768

CHILD, Samuel   Everyman his own brewer; or a compendium of the English brewery
JENKS, James   The complete cook
MONTAGUE, Peregrine   The family pocket-book
PAHUD DE VALANGIN,   A treatise on diet, or the management of human life
     François Joseph

1769

BRITISH   The British jewel; or complete housewife's best companion
BUCHAN, William   Domestic medicine
COMPLEAT   The compleat English family companion
RAFFALD, Elizabeth   The experienced English house-keeper
SKEAT, J.   The art of cookery
TAYLOR, E.   The lady's, housewife's, and cookmaid's assistant: or, the art of cookery

1770

BORELLA, [——] [Mr]   The court and country confectioner
DOSSIE, Robert   An essay on spirituous liquors
LADIES   The ladies annual journal
LADIES   The ladies delight, or cook-maid's best instructor
PERCY, Henry Algernon   The regulations and establishment of the houshold [sic]
STONE, James   The complete baker
WILSON, Mary   The ladies complete cookery

1771

HAYWOOD, Eliza Fowler   A new present for a servant-maid
POWELL, [——]   The guide to preferment: or, Powell's complete book of cookery

1772

BUC'HOZ, Pierre Joseph   The toilet of Flora
LETTSOM, John Coakley   The natural history of the tea-tree
MOORE, Isabella   The useful and entertaining family miscellany
SMITH, Mary   The complete housekeeper and professed cook
WIMPEY, Joseph   An essay on the present high price of provisions

1773
Easy	An easy way to prolong life
Heasel, Anthony	The servant's book of knowledge
Maciver, Susanna	Cookery and pastry
Maciver, Susanna	A new and experimental treatise on cookery
Mason, Charlotte	The lady's assistant for regulating . . . her table
Pownall, Thomas	The great advantage of eating pure and genuine bread
Townshend, John	The universal cook; or, lady's complete assistant

1774
Collection	A collection of 137 approved receipts in pastry and cookery
Economist	The economist
Ellis, John	An historical account of coffee
Pennington, [Mrs]	The royal cook

1775
Barry, Sir Edward	Observations . . . on the wines of the ancients
Choice	A choice collection of cookery receipts
Valuable	Valuable secrets concerning arts and trades

1766
Farmer	The farmer's magazine
House-keeper	The house-keeper's pocket book, and compleat family cook
Smith, William	A sure guide in sickness and health, in the choice of food

1777
Essay	An essay on tea, sugar, white bread
Marshall, Elizabeth	The young ladies' guide in the art of cookery

1778
Falconer, William	Observations . . . on diet and regimen
Frugal	The frugal house-keeper, or, the complete cook

1779
None

1780
Accomplished	The accomplished lady's delight in cookery
Bath	The Bath cookery book
Farmer	The farmer's wife; or the complete country housewife
Kellet, Susanna, etc.	A complete collection of cookery receipts
Partridge, Ann	The new and complete universal cook; or, young woman's best guide
Pegge, Samuel	The forme of cury
Town	The town and country cook; or, young woman's best guide

1781
Dalrymple, George	The practice of modern cookery
Robertson, Joseph	An essay on culinary poisons
Saunders, Sarah	The fountain of knowledge; or, complete family guide
Smith, A., [Mrs]	A new book of cookery; or, every woman a perfect cook
Wilmer, Bradford	Observations on . . . poisonous vegetables

1782
None

1783
FARLEY, John   The London art of cookery, and housekeeper's complete assistant
PARMENTIER, Antoine A.   Observations on . . . nutritive vegetables
POOLE, T.   A treatise on strong beer, ale, etc.

1784
SPENCER, E.   The modern cook; and frugal housewife's compleat guide
TWAMLEY, Josiah   Dairying exemplified

1785
MOSELEY, Benjamin   Observations on the properties . . . of coffee

1786
BRAIDLEY, A.   The complete English cook

1787
CONCISE   Concise observations on the nature of our common food
CROFT, John   A treatise on the wines of Portugal
NEW   A new collection of . . . methods of preparing baths, essences, pomatums

1788
BRIGGS, Richard   The English art of cookery
COLE, Mary   The lady's complete guide; or, cookery and confectionary in all its branches
TRUSLER, John   The honours of the table

1789
CARTWRIGHT, Charlotte   The lady's best companion; or, a complete treasure for the fair sex
COMPLETE   The complete family brewer
NUTT, Frederic   The complete confectioner; or, the whole art of confectionary

1790
ABBOT, Robert   The housekeeper's valuable present
[BREWER, Samuel Child   Everyman his own brewer. A small treatise]
CHILD, Samuel   Everyman his own brewer. A small treatise
COLLECTION   A collection of ordinances and regulations
HENDERSON, William A.   The housekeeper's instructor; or, universal family cook
NEW   The new handmaid to arts
PERKINS, John   The ladies library

1791
FRAZER, [Mrs]   The practice of cookery
USEFUL   Useful hints on a variety of subjects
WARNER, Richard   Antiquitates culinariæ

1792
COLLINGWOOD, Francis,   The universal cook, and city and country housekeeper
and WOOLLAMS, John

1793
ART   The art of cheese-making
COMPLETE   The complete distiller
MACBRIDE, Duncan   General instructions for the choice of wines and spirituous liquors
MENON, [——]   The French family cook

1794

ENGLISH	The English pocket gardener; or, country gentleman's vade mecum
FAUST, Bernard C.	Catechism of health
HAZLEMORE, Maximilian	Domestic economy
PRENTISS, John	The compleat toilet, or ladies companion

1795

CARTER, [Mrs]	The British jewel or art of cookery made perfectly easy
HINTS	Hints for the relief of the poor
McVITIE, William	Whisky: a poem
MARTIN, Sarah	The new experienced English-housekeeper
USEFUL	Useful suggestions favourable to the comfort of the labouring people
WRIGHT, John	An essay on wines

1796

ENUMERATION	An enumeration of the principal vegetables
KIRKPATRICK, H.	An account of the manner in which potatoes are cultivated
SIMMONS, Amelia	American cookery

1797

ACCOUNT	An account of a meat and soup charity
BATTAM, Anne	The new and complete cook
BUCHAN, William	Observations concerning the diet of common people
GARNETT, Thomas	A lecture on the preservation of health
GLASSE, A.	The accomplished female cook
JONE[s], [Mrs]	The cottage cook; or, Mrs. Jone's [sic] cheap dishes
LONDON	The London complete art of cookery
WILLIAMS, T.	The accomplished housekeeper, and universal cook

1798

MELROE, Eliza	An economical, and new method of cookery

1799

ECONOMY	The economy of an institution
WILLICH, Anthony Florian Madinger	Lectures on diet and regimen

1800

CARRUTH, P.	Domestic economy; or, general recipe book
CHAMBERS, Amelia	The ladies best companion; or, a golden treasure for the fair sex
DOMESTIC	Domestic management
FARLEY, [Mr]	The guide to preferment; or, complete art of cookery
HOLLAND, Mary	The complete British cook
MACDONALD, Duncan	The new London family cook; or, town and country housekeeper's guide
RUSSELL, Elizabeth	The complete family cook
SUGGESTIONS	Suggestions offered to the consideration of the public

SELECTIVE SUBJECT INDEX

This list is designed to give the reader a guide to the contents of the various main entries in the catalogue. If the contents are extremely varied the entry will appear under Household Compendiums and Dictionaries. Further editions have not been included, and the shortest identifiable title has been used. The following headings have been included:

ADULTERATION

ARNAUD, J.	An alarm to all persons
CONCISE	Concise observations on the nature of our common food
FARLEY, J.	The London art of cookery
JACKSON, H.	An essay on bread
POISON	Poison detected
POWNALL, T.	The great advantage of eating pure and genuine bread
ROBERTSON, J.	An essay on culinary poisons

APIARY

BAILEY, N.	Dictionarium domesticum
FARMER	The farmer's wife
MORE, SIR J.	England's interest: or the . . . farmers friend

BILLS OF FARE AND TABLE SETTINGS

BRADLEY, M.	The British housewife
BRADSHAW, P.	The family jewel
BRIGGS, R.	The English art of cookery
CARTER, C.	The compleat city and country cook
CARTER, C.	The complete practical cook
CARTER, C.	The London and country cook
CARTER, S.	The frugal housewife
CLIFTON, E.	The cookmaids assistant
COLLINGWOOD, F., and WOOLLAMS, J.	The universal cook

COMPLEAT   The compleat family cook
EXPLANATION   An explanation and translation of a modern bill of fare
FARLEY, [——]   The guide to preferment
FARLEY, J.   The London art of cookery
FRAZER, Mrs   The practice of cookery
GELLEROY, W.   The London cook
HARRISON, S.   The house-keeper's pocket book
HENDERSON, W.   The housekeeper's instructor
JENKS, J.   The complete cook
LADIES   The ladies annual journal
LAMB, P.   Royal cookery
MASON, C.   The lady's assistant
MENON, [——]   The French family cook
MODERN   A modern bill of fare for seven
MODERN   The modern method of regulating and forming a table
NOTT, J.   The cook's and confectioner's dictionary
PECKHAM, A.   The complete English cook
PENNINGTON, Mrs   The royal cook
PHILLIPS, S.   The ladies handmaid
RUSSELL, E.   The complete family cook
SKEAT, J.   The art of cookery
THACKER, J.   The art of cookery
VERRAL, W.   A complete system of cookery
WILLIAMS, T.   The accomplished housekeeper

BREWING

BAILEY, N.   Dictionarium domesticum
BRADLEY, R.   The country housewife and lady's director
BRADSHAW, P.   Bradshaw's valuable family jewel
CARTWRIGHT, C.   The lady's best companion
CELLAR   The cellar book
CHAMBERS, A.   The ladies best companion
CHILD, S.   Everyman his own brewer
CHILD, S.   Everyman his own brewer [second entry]
CLELAND, E.   A new and easy method of cookery
COLE, M.   The lady's complete guide
COMPLEAT   The compleat family cook
COMPLETE   The complete distiller
COMPLETE   The complete family brewer
CURIOUS   A curious collection of receipts in cookery
EALES, M.   The compleat confectioner
ELLIS, W.   The country housewife's family companion
ELLIS, W.   The London and country brewer
ESSAY   An essay on tea
FRUGAL   The frugal house-keeper
GRINDAL, M.   Warm beer
GUIDE   A guide ... for brewing malt liquors
HAZLEMORE, M.   Domestic economy
HENDERSON, W.   The housekeeper's instructor
LADIES   The ladies companion
LONDON   The London complete art of cookery
MACDONALD, D.   The new London family cook
MORE, SIR J.   Englands interest: or the farmers friend
PENNINGTON, Mrs   The royal cook
POOLE, T.   A treatise on strong beer
SEDGWICK, J.   A new treatise on liquors
SEDGWICK, J.   Vinum Brittanicum

COOKERY

COSMETICS AND BEAUTY

CHAMBERS, A.   The ladies best companion
COLLECTION   A collection of 137 approved receipts
FRUGAL   The frugal house-keeper
HALL, T.   The queen's royal cookery
HOWARD, H.   England's newest way in all sorts of cookery
LADIES   The ladies annual journal
LADIES   The ladies companion
LÉMERY, N.   Curiosa arcana
MACDONALD, D.   The new London family cook
NEW   A new collection . . . with receipts for cosmetics
PRENTISS, J.   The compleat toilet
PRICE, E.   The new book of cookery
SALMON, W.   The family-dictionary
UNIVERSAL   The universal family book
WHOLE   The whole duty of a woman

CYDER-MAKING

CHAPMAN, C.   The cyder-maker's instructor
EDMONDS, W.   A new and easy way of making wines
MORE, SIR J.   Englands interest: or the . . . farmers friend
STAFFORD, H.   A treatise on cyder-making
WHOLE   The whole duty of a woman

DAIRYING AND POULTRY

ART   The art of cheese-making
BAILEY, N.   Dictionarium domesticum
BARKER, A.   The complete servant maid
BRADLEY, R.   The country housewife and lady's director
ELLIS, W.   The country housewife's family companion
ESSAY   An essay on tea
HEALTH   Health's preservative
MACDONALD, D.   The new London family cook
ROZEA, J.   The compleat cook
TWAMLEY, J.   Dairying exemplified
WIMPEY, J.   An essay on the present high price of provisions

DIET AND REGIMEN

ACCOUNT   An account of a meat and soup charity
ARBUTHNOT, J.   An essay concerning the nature of aliments
ARNAUD, J.   An alarm to all persons
BEST   The best and easiest method of preserving uninterrupted health
BRADLEY, M.   The British housewife
BRITISH   The British legacy
BUCHAN, W.   Domestic medicine
BUCHAN, W.   Observations concerning the diet of common people
CARTWRIGHT, C.   The lady's best companion
COCCHI, A.   The Pythagorean diet
COMPLEAT   The compleat family cook
ELLIS, J.   An historical account of coffee
ENUMERATION   An enumeration of the principal vegetables
ESSAY   An essay on the nature . . . of tea
FAIRFAX, A.   The family's best-friend
FALCONER, W.   Observations . . . on diet and regimen
FAMILY   The family companion for health
FAUST, B.   Catechism of health

HERBS AND SPICES

HOUSEHOLD COMPENDIUMS AND DICTIONARIES

ICE CREAM

KITCHEN GARDEN

MARKETING AND PROVISIONS

MEDICAL RECEIPTS AND MATTERS

NON-ALCOHOLIC BEVERAGES

OLD AGE

PICKLING, PRESERVING, AND CURING

BAILEY, N.	Dictionarium domesticum
BATH	The Bath cookery book
BATTAM, A.	A collection of scarce and valuable receipts
BEST	The best . . . method of curing white herrings
BRADLEY, R.	The country housewife and lady's director
BRADSHAW, P.	Bradshaw's valuable family jewel
CARTER, S.	The frugal housewife
CARTWRIGHT, C.	The lady's best companion
CHAMBERS, A.	The ladies best companion
CHOMEL, N.	Dictionnaire oeconomique
CLELAND, E.	A new and easy method of cookery
COMPLEAT	The compleat cook
CURIOUS	A curious collection of receipts in cookery
EALES, M.	The compleat confectioner
ENGLISH	The English pocket gardener
FAMILY	The family magazine
FRAZER, Mrs	The practice of cookery
FRUGAL	The frugal house-keeper
GREY, E.	A choice manuall
GREY, E.	A true gentlewoman's delight
HAYWOOD, E.	A new present for a servant-maid
HENDERSON, W.	The housekeeper's instructor
JOHNSTON, Mrs	Mrs Johnston's receipts
LADIES	The ladies companion
LADIES	The ladies companion [second entry]
LAMBERT, E.	The art of confectionary
LOCKE, J.	Observations . . . upon the growth of vines
MASSIALOT, F.	The court and country cook
PENNINGTON, Mrs	The royal cook
QUEEN	The Queen's closet opened
ROBERTSON, H.	The young ladies school of arts
SIMMONS, A.	American cookery
SMITH, E.	The compleat housewife
SPENCER, E.	The modern cook
YOUNG	The young ladies companion in cookery

POEMS AND SATIRES

ARMSTRONG, J.	The art of preserving health
ARMSTRONG, J.	The muncher's and guzler's diary
CAMPBELL, D.	A poem upon tea
CAREY, H.	A learned dissertation on dumpling
KING, W.	The art of cookery. A poem
KING, W.	The art of cookery
McVITIE, W.	Whisky: a poem

SERVANTS AND HOUSEHOLD DUTIES

ACCOMPLISHED	The accomplished ladies rich closet
ACCOMPLISHED	The accomplished lady's delight in cookery
BARKER, A.	The complete servant maid
BORELLA, [——]	The court and country confectioner
BRUES, J.	The servant's sure guide to favour and fortune
BUTLER	The butler's assistant
CELLAR	The cellar book
CHAPMAN, T.	The cyder-maker's instructor
COLLECTION	A collection of ordinances
COMPLEAT	The compleat English family companion

WELFARE OF THE POOR

WINES, FERMENTATION, AND DISTILLATION

VEGETARIAN AND VEGETABLE DISHES

SHORT-TITLE INDEX

NOTES